SUSAN BARNES

JOSEANN HELMES DEWITT

DAWNA MARTICH

GOLDEN TRADEWELL

STUDY GUIDE FOR

FUNDAMENTALS OF NURSING

Concepts, Process, and Practice

SEVENTH EDITION

KOZIER ■ ERB
BERMAN ■ SNYDER

Upper Saddle River, New Jersey

Notice: Care has been taken to confirm the accuracy of information presented in this book. The authors, editors, and the publisher, however, cannot accept any responsibility for errors or omissions or for consequences from application of the information in this book and make no warranty, express or implied, with respect to its contents. The authors and publisher have exerted every effort to ensure that drug selections and dosages set forth in this text are in accord with current recommendations and practice at time of publication. However, in view of ongoing research, changes in government regulations, and the constant flow of information relating to drug therapy and drug reactions, the reader is urged to check the package inserts of all drugs for any change in indications of dosage and for added warnings and precautions. This is particularly important when the recommended agent is a new and/or infrequently employed drug.

Pearson Education LTD.
Pearson Education Australia PTY, Limited
Pearson Education Singapore, Pte. Ltd
Pearson Education North Asia Ltd
Pearson Education Canada, Ltd.
Pearson Educación de Mexico, S.A. de C.V.
Pearson Education—Japan
Pearson Education Malaysia, Pte. Ltd
Pearson Education, Upper Saddle River, NJ

10 9 8 7 6 5 4
ISBN 0-13-049300-7

Contents

PREFACE

A career in nursing is filled with opportunities for lifelong learning. Nurses today must be able to grow and evolve in a rapidly changing environment. This concise study guide has been developed to help you learn and apply key concepts and procedures and master critical thinking skills based upon ***Fundamentals of Nursing: Concepts, Process, and Practice, Seventh Edition*** by Kozier, et al. The content addresses the concepts of contemporary nursing care, and has been updated to reflect the latest nursing research and increasing emphasis upon aging, wellness, and home-and-community based care.

At the beginning of each chapter in this study guide, you will find a MediaLink box. Just as in the main textbook, this box identifies for you, the student, all the specific media resources and activities available for each chapter on the Student CD-ROM found in the main textbook and on the Companion Website at www.prenhall.com/kozier. You will find reference to video clips and animations from the Student CD-ROM to help you visualize and comprehend difficult concepts. On the Companion Website, you will find a variety of activities, such as Case Studies and MediaLink Applications, to help you apply these concepts in clinical scenarios.

In addition, each chapter of this Study Guide provides a variety of questions and activities that help you comprehend difficult concepts and reinforce basic knowledge gained from textbook reading assignments. Following is the list of features included in this edition that will enhance your learning experience:

- The **Overview** summarizes material presented in each chapter of the text.
- **Learning Outcomes** and **Key Topics** highlight the key concepts that are reinforced by completing the study guide exercises.
- **Lecture Outline** helps you to follow lectures and organize your notes.
- **Focused Study Tips** help you recall the important nursing concepts from each chapter.
- **NCLEX Test Questions** provide you with additional review of key nursing topics.
- **Case Studies** provide clinical settings for critical thinking and the application of learned processes and procedures.
- **Care Plan Critical Thinking Activities** apply concepts from the textbook to real nursing scenarios and asks you to identify the steps of the nursing processes.
- An **Answer Key** with rationales for NCLEX test questions is provided in the back of the study guide.

We hope that you will benefit from using this study guide and that it will help prepare you to provide quality-nursing care based on knowledge and clinical judgment.

CHAPTER 1

HISTORICAL AND CONTEMPORARY NURSING PRACTICE

OVERVIEW

This chapter provides a concise summary of the state of professional nursing. It identifies the main historical figures and forces that have helped shape nursing and discusses your role as an evolving professional. The chapter also explains and outlines professional organizations that are active in shaping your profession.

LEARNING OUTCOMES

After completing this chapter, the student will be able to:

- Discuss historical and contemporary factors influencing the development of nursing
- Identify the essential aspects of nursing
- Identify four major areas within the scope of nursing practice
- Identify the purposes of nurse practice acts and standards for nursing practice
- Describe the roles of nurses
- Describe the expanded career roles and their functions
- Discuss the criteria of a profession and the professionalization of nursing
- Discuss Benner's levels of nursing proficiency
- Relate essential nursing values with attitudes, personal qualities, and professional behaviors
- Explain the functions of the national and international nurses associations

www.prenhall.com/kozier

Additional resources for this chapter can be found on the Student CD-ROM accompanying this textbook, and on the Companion Website at www.prenhall.com/kozier. Click on Chapter 1 to select the activities for this chapter.

CD-ROM
- Audio Glossary
- NCLEX Review

Companion Website
- Additional NCLEX Review
- Case Study: Evolution of Nursing
- MediaLink Applications:
  - Florence Nightingale
  - American Association of Colleges of Nursing
  - Sigma Theta Tau
- Links to Resources

KEY TOPICS

This study guide chapter reinforces the following terms/topics discussed in the textbook chapter:

- caregiver
- case manager
- change agent
- Clara Barton
- client
- client advocate
- communicator
- consumer
- counseling
- demography
- diagnostic-related groups (DRGs)
- Fabiola
- Florence Nightingale
- governance
- Harriet Tubman
- Knights of Saint Lazarus
- Lavinia L. Dock
- leader
- Lillian Wald
- manager
- Margaret Sanger
- Mary Breckinridge
- patient
- Patient Self-Determination Act (PSDA)
- profession
- professionalism
- professionalization
- Sairy Gamp
- socialization
- Sojourner Truth
- standards of clinical nursing practice
- teacher
- telecommunications

LECTURE OUTLINE

I. Historical perspectives
   A. Women's roles
   B. Religion
   C. War
   D. Societal attitudes
   E. Nursing leaders
      1. Nightingale (1820–1910)
      2. Barton (1812–1912)
      3. Wald (1867–1940)
      4. Dock (1858–1956)
      5. Sanger (1879–1966)
      6. Breckinridge (1881–1965)

II. Contemporary nursing practice
   A. Definitions of nursing
   B. Recipients of nursing
   C. Scope of nursing
      1. Promoting health and wellness
      2. Preventing illness
      3. Restoring health
      4. Care for the dying
   D. Settings for nursing
   E. Nurse practice acts
   F. Standards of clinical nursing practice

III. Roles and functions of the nurse
   A. Care giver
   B. Communicator
   C. Teacher
   D. Client advocate
   E. Counselor
   F. Change agent
   G. Leader
   H. Manager
   I. Case manager
   J. Research consumer
   K. Expanded career roles

IV. Criteria of a profession
   A. Specialized education
   B. Body of knowledge
   C. Service orientation
   D. Ongoing research
   E. Code of ethics
   F. Autonomy
   G. Professional organization

V. Socialization to nursing
   A. Critical values of nursing

VI. Factors influencing contemporary nursing practice
   A. Economics
   B. Consumer demands
   C. Family structure
   D. Science and technology
   E. Information and telecommunications
   F. Legislation
   G. Demography
   H. The new nursing shortage
   I. Collective bargaining
   J. Nursing associations

FOCUSED STUDY TIPS

1. Compare and contrast the American Nurses Association with the Canadian Nurses Association.
2. Discuss the contributions made by each of the following nursing leaders:
   Clara Barton
   Florence Nightingale
   Lavinia Dock
   Lillian Wald
   Margaret Sanger
   Mary Breckinridge
3. Define the different types of nursing professionals:
   clinical specialist
   nurse anesthetist
   nurse midwife
   nurse researcher
   nurse administrator
   nurse entrepreneur
   nurse practitioner
4. List the different types of nursing images that have influenced the way society views nursing.
5. Describe different areas of focus that are involved in nursing practice.
6. Marta is a nursing student enrolled in her first clinical course. At which level of nursing practice might she be functioning?
7. At which level of nursing practice would a new graduate nurse be practicing? Why?
8. What is the difference between a competent practitioner and an expert?
9. Describe the purpose and functions of each of the following organizations:
   American Nurses Association
   National Student Nurses Association
   National League for Nursing
   Sigma Theta Tau

CASE STUDY

8:00 A.M. Monday: Home health nurse Eduardo Salazar is reviewing his caseload for the day. He has five clients to visit. The home health agency is holding a staff meeting this morning. In order to attend the meeting, Eduardo plans to see two clients before lunch and the remaining three in the afternoon.

Eduardo schedules his first visit with Jason Essex. Jason is terminally ill with AIDS. His partner cares for him at home. Jason is failing rapidly. His weight has dropped 25 pounds in 3 months, and his activity level is severely diminished. Jason is receiving parenteral antibiotics. Eduardo will need to inspect the IV site and administer the medication. He will begin teaching Richard, Jason's partner, how to administer the medication. During the time the medication is infusing, Eduardo plans to assess the need for additional home services and to provide emotional support for Jason and Richard.

Only four blocks from Jason's home, Eduardo will visit Bridget Coan. Bridget is a 58-year-old woman with severe cognitive impairment secondary to Alzheimer's disease. Eduardo needs to meet with Bridget's family to discuss ongoing care. Bridget has begun to wander, and her family fears for her safety. A family conference has been scheduled for 11 A.M. to discuss Bridget's ongoing care.

1. *What role is Eduardo fulfilling when he inspects Jason's IV site and administers the medication?*
2. *What role is Eduardo fulfilling when he assesses the need for additional home services for Jason?*
3. *What role is Eduardo fulfilling when he provides emotional support for Jason and Richard?*
4. *What role is Eduardo fulfilling when he coordinates a conference with the Coan family?*

NCLEX TEST QUESTIONS

1. A new nursing graduate began working in a local hospital. The nurse understands that the scope of nursing practice includes:
   a. ordering medications for the client.
   b. suturing wounds on the client.
   c. restoring a client's health.
   d. ordering laboratory tests for the client.
2. On a busy day on a clinical floor, the nurse began delegating certain tasks to licensed and unlicensed assistive personnel. This demonstrated that the nurse:
   a. did not want to be responsible for certain duties.
   b. understood the necessity of establishing priorities.
   c. understood the importance of being accessible to doctors.
   d. understood that the licensed and unlicensed assistive personnel could effectively provide nursing care.
3. The charge nurse is required to evaluate professional behavior of the nurses working on the floor. To do this, the nurse must utilize which of the following criteria?
   a. Standards of Clinical Practice
   b. Standards of Hospice Care
   c. Standards of Home Care
   d. Standards of Nurse Practitioners
4. As a nurse with baccalaureate education, one would expect the nurse to have knowledge of which of the following roles?
   a. midwife
   b. administrator
   c. clinical nurse specialist
   d. client advocate
5. A group of nursing students developed an educational program for the fourth- and fifth-graders at a local elementary school. This is a form of:
   a. restoring health.
   b. promoting health and wellness.
   c. care of the dying.
   d. rehabilitation.
6. The physician's order states, "Examine feces for occult blood." The nurse obtains a stool culture. This is a form of:
   a. restoring health.
   b. promoting health and wellness.
   c. preventing illness.
   d. rehabilitation.
7. A hospitalized client told the nurse that he had a living will. The nurse documented this information on the chart and then notified:
   a. a lawyer.
   b. the physician.
   c. the pharmacist.
   d. the family.
8. Relaying the client's wishes to the physician and the rest of the health care team is a form of:
   a. counseling.
   b. change agent.
   c. client advocate.
   d. teacher.
9. In helping unlicensed assistive personnel, the nurse demonstrated techniques to transfer clients from bed to wheelchair. This is a form of:
   a. counseling.
   b. change agent.
   c. client advocate.
   d. teacher.
10. Which of the following guidelines must a nurse adhere to?
    a. American Medical Association
    b. State Board of Nurses
    c. National League for Nursing
    d. International Council of Nurses

CHAPTER 2

NURSING EDUCATION AND RESEARCH

OVERVIEW

This chapter offers a concise view of the pathways to nursing practice, as well as the importance of nursing research to the practice and refinement of nursing. The chapter presents the importance of continuing education and the nurse's role in research.

LEARNING OUTCOMES

After completing this chapter, the student will be able to:

- Describe the different types of educational nursing programs
- Discuss aspects of entry to professional nursing practice
- Explain the importance of continuing nursing education
- Identify ways the nurse can participate in research activities in practice
- Differentiate the quantitative approach from the qualitative approach in nursing research
- Describe the nurse's role in protecting the rights of human subjects in research
- Identify the steps of the research process

MediaLink

www.prenhall.com/kozier

Additional resources for this chapter can be found on the Student CD-ROM accompanying this textbook, and on the Companion Website at www.prenhall.com/kozier. Click on Chapter 2 to select the activities for this chapter.

CD-ROM
- Audio Glossary
- NCLEX Review

Companion Website
- Additional NCLEX Review
- Case Study: Nursing Profession
- MediaLink Applications: Entry into Practice
- Links to Resources

KEY TOPICS

This study guide chapter reinforces the following terms/topics discussed in the textbook chapter:

- confidentiality
- continuing education (CE)
- dependent variable
- descriptive statistics
- empirical data
- ethnography
- feasibility
- full disclosure
- grounded theory
- independent variable
- in-service education
- mean
- measures of central tendency
- measures of variability

- median
- mode
- operational definitions
- phenomenology
- population
- range
- reliability
- researchability
- right of self-determination
- risk of harm
- sample
- significance
- standard deviation
- statistically significant
- validity
- variance

LECTURE OUTLINE

I. Nursing education
II. Types of educational programs
   A. Licensed practical (vocational) nursing programs
   B. Registered nursing programs
      1. Diploma programs
      2. Community college/associate degree programs
      3. Baccalaureate degree programs
   C. Graduate nursing education
      1. Master's programs
      2. Doctoral programs
   D. Entry to practice
   E. Continuing education
   F. In-service education
III. Nursing research
   A. Approaches to nursing research
      1. Quantitative research
      2. Qualitative research
   B. Protecting the rights of human subjects
      1. Right not to be harmed
      2. Right to full disclosure
      3. Right of self-determination
      4. Right of privacy and confidentiality
   C. The quantitative research process
      1. State a research question or problem
      2. Define the study's purpose or rationale
      3. Review the related literature
      4. Formulate hypotheses and define variables
      5. Select a research design to test the hypothesis
      6. Select the population, sample, and setting
      7. Conduct a pilot study
      8. Collect the data
      9. Analyze the data
      10. Communicate conclusions and implications
   D. The qualitative research process
   E. Critiquing research reports

FOCUSED STUDY TIPS

1. Define the following:
   feasibility
   research design
   validity
   reliability
   significance
2. What is the role of licensed practical or vocational nurses (LPNs or LVNs)?
3. What are some characteristics that describe the different levels of entry into practice as a registered nurse?
4. What is graduate education in nursing? Why is it important?
5. Why is continuing education for nurses important?
6. Which patient right is defined as safeguarding the human subject?
7. What is the purpose of nursing research?
8. What criteria should be considered when a research problem is being formulated?
9. All clients must be informed about the consequences of participating in a research study. The nurse must serve as a client advocate in safeguarding the subject's rights. What rights does a research subject have?
10. Which step of the research process is missing from the following list?
    State a research question or problem.
    Define the study's purpose or rationale.
    Review the related literature.
    Formulate hypotheses and define variables.
    Select the population, sample, and setting.
    Conduct a pilot study.
    Collect the data.
    Analyze the data.
    Communicate conclusions and implications.

CASE STUDY

Mary Thomas, the community health nurse, has been seeing an increasing number of children developing pneumonia after the "common cold." She has decided to conduct a study in efforts to find out why.

1. *What would be a problem statement for this health care issue?*
2. *What criteria could Mary use to establish the hypothesis and variables?*
3. *How many children would be an adequate sample size for Mary to study?*
4. *How might Mary report the findings of the study?*

NCLEX TEST QUESTIONS

1. An 80-year-old client was facing decisions about life support and dying. The nurse on the floor was not familiar with end-of-life issues. What action could the nurse take to become more familiar with end-of-life issues?
   a. Ask the client for more information.
   b. Notify the physician that the client has unresolved issues.
   c. Explore the Internet for nursing articles related to end-of-life issues.
   d. Ask the family for more information.
2. The major goal of nursing research is to:
   a. gain medical knowledge.
   b. improve client care.
   c. promote nurses into becoming physicians.
   d. promote nurses into becoming scientists.
3. A nurse on the floor can delegate which of the following functions to the licensed practical nurse?
   a. assessing client's condition
   b. developing client care plan
   c. evaluating the effectiveness of the care provided
   d. providing basic direct care to client
4. The major emphasis of a baccalaureate degree in nursing is to:
   a. prepare a generalist.
   b. prepare a researcher.
   c. prepare a nurse educator.
   d. prepare a nurse administrator.
5. The major emphasis of an associate degree in nursing is to:
   a. prepare a researcher.
   b. prepare a nurse educator.
   c. prepare a nurse administrator.
   d. prepare a bedside nurse.
6. The major emphasis of a master's degree in nursing is to:
   a. prepare a bedside nurse.
   b. prepare a generalist.
   c. prepare a technician.
   d. prepare an advanced role in nursing practice.
7. Keeping within the guidelines for relicensure, a nurse must attend continuing education programs. Which of the following is considered a continuing education program?
   a. A program sponsored by the hospital on the new intravenous pumps
   b. talking to a pharmaceutical representative about a new drug
   c. watching videos on fire safety and body mechanics
   d. receiving a certificate of completion for a workshop on bioterroism
8. A nursing student was asked to participate in a doctoral study. The researcher planned to interview the student using a structured, open-ended format. This best fits what type of research study?
   a. longitudinal study
   b. quantitative study
   c. mixed methodology
   d. qualitative study
9. A survey with clients who were being admitted to hospice is used to assess religious and spiritual influences on health. This best fits what type of research study?
   a. longitudinal study
   b. quantitative study
   c. mixed methodology
   d. qualitative study
10. A client is admitted to a chemical dependency unit. The physician on this unit is using new evidence-based behavioral interventions. Because this is a federally funded program, the nurse must ensure:
    a. that the client not be informed of alternative behavioral interventions.
    b. that the client be allowed to withdraw from the study at any time.
    c. that the client's history be made public information.
    d. that the client may be exposed to financial risk.

CHAPTER 3

NURSING THEORIES AND CONCEPTUAL FRAMEWORKS

OVERVIEW

This chapter examines the beliefs and philosophies of the most influential nursing theorists. It exposes you to the thoughts that have guided the development of modern nursing.

LEARNING OUTCOMES

After completing this chapter, the student will be able to:

- Differentiate the terms *concept, conceptual framework, theory, paradigm, metaparadigm for nursing*
- Identify the purposes of nursing theory in nursing education, research, and clinical practice
- Identify the components of the metaparadigm for nursing
- Describe the major purpose of theory in the natural sciences
- Describe the major purpose of theory in the social sciences and practice disciplines
- Identify one positive and one negative effect of using theory to understand clinical practice

www.prenhall.com/kozier

Additional resources for this chapter can be found on the Student CD-ROM accompanying this textbook, and on the Companion Website at www.prenhall.com/kozier. Click on Chapter 3 to select the activities for this chapter.

CD-ROM
- Audio Glossary
- NCLEX Review

Companion Website
- Additional NCLEX Review
- Case Study: Theories
- MediaLink Applications:
  - Nursing Theory Growth
  - Shaping Watson's Theory
- Links to Resources

KEY TOPICS

This study guide chapter reinforces the following terms/topics discussed in the textbook chapter:

- client
- concepts
- conceptual framework
- conceptual model
- critical theory
- environment
- grand theories
- health
- metaparadigm
- midlevel theories
- nursing
- paradigm
- philosophy
- practice disciplines
- theory

LECTURE OUTLINE

I. Introduction to theories in other disciplines
   A. Context for theory development in American universities
   B. Defining terms
II. The "metaparadigm" for nursing
III. Purposes of nursing theory
   A. In education
   B. In research
   C. In clinical practice
IV. Overview of selected nursing theories
   A. Nightingale's environmental theory
   B. Peplau's interpersonal relations model
   C. Henderson's definition of nursing
   D. Rogers's science of unitary human beings
   E. Orem's general theory of nursing
   F. King's goal attainment theory
   G. Neuman's systems model
   H. Roy's adaptation model
   I. Leininger's cultural care diversity and universality theory
   J. Watson's human caring theory
   K. Parse's human becoming theory
V. Critique of nursing theory

FOCUSED STUDY TIPS

1. Define the following:
   concept
   conceptual model
   hypothesis
   theory
   conceptual framework
   construct
   proposition
2. Identify characteristics for the theories associated with each of the following nurse theorists:
   Henderson
   Leininger
   Nightingale
   Parse
   Rogers
   Watson
   King
   Neuman
   Orem
   Peplau
   Roy
3. Why are nursing theories important?
4. List the four major concepts of nursing.
5. What three elements are included in a nursing theory?
6. Which nursing model(s) guide your nursing education program?
7. Which nursing model(s) do you most identify with? Why?
8. Explain the relationship between nursing theory and research.

CASE STUDY

Jennifer Hayes, a fourth year nursing student, is drafting a scholarly paper on a nurse theorist. The problem Jennifer has noticed is the lack of motivation seen in patients with chronic illnesses. The patients seem to "not care" about their health and are very depressed.

1. *Which nurse theorists might help Jennifer when drafting her scholarly paper?*
2. *What are the elements of these theories?*

NCLEX TEST QUESTIONS

1. In caring for an adolescent, the nurse would use which of the following theories to plan a nursing care plan?
   a. Freud's theory of the unconscious
   b. Darwin's theory of evolution
   c. Einstein's theory of relativity
   d. Erickson's theory of development
2. Caring for clients during their end-of-life experiences requires following whose nursing theories?
   a. Imogene King
   b. Callista Roy
   c. Dorothea Orem
   d. Jean Watson

3. During an initial assessment, a client experiencing depression said, "I am so glad you are here. I know that you will be able to help me." Using Peplau's theory, the psychiatric nurse understands that the client and nurse are developing which phase of the therapeutic relationship?
   a. orientation phase
   b. identification phase
   c. exploration phase
   d. resolution phase
4. Virginia Henderson believed that nurses needed to be more than caregivers, they needed to be both educators and advocates. A nurse must help an individual fulfill which fundamental need?
   a. refraining from expressing their emotions
   b. dependence on health care providers
   c. seeking help from health care providers
   d. working in such a way that one feels a sense of accomplishment
5. In helping a hospice client cope with intense pain, the nurse decided to use principles of noncontact therapeutic touch. This nurse is using whose nursing model?
   a. Virginia Henderson
   b. Hildegard Peplau
   c. Jean Watson
   d. Martha Rogers
6. Home care focuses on restoring the client to a homeostatic balance. In doing so, the nurse must teach self-care activities. Whose theory most supports self-care concepts?
   a. Virginia Henderson
   b. Martha Rogers
   c. Dorothea Orem
   d. Jean Watson
7. In dealing with childbearing women and their families, whose theories would a nurse most likely use?
   a. Virginia Henderson
   b. Martha Rogers
   c. Jean Watson
   d. Imogene King
8. In using Betty Neuman's theory, which of the following is an example of an intrapersonal stressor?
   a. unrealistic role expectations
   b. financial concerns
   c. community resources
   d. infections
9. To provide culturally competent care, which theorist's models can be used?
   a. Sister Callista Roy
   b. Jean Watson
   c. Imogene King
   d. Madeleine Leininger
10. Primary prevention is best achieved when clients choose to accept responsibility for their own personal health. Which of the following models emphasizes that clients are the authority figures and decision makers for their personal health?
    a. Roy's Adaptation Model
    b. Watson's Human Caring Theory
    c. Parse's Human Becoming Theory
    d. Orem's General Theory Model

CHAPTER 4

LEGAL ASPECTS OF NURSING

OVERVIEW

This chapter provides a vast amount of information on legal aspects that affect your role as a student nurse and your future role as a licensed nurse. The emphasis is on application in the clinical setting and your responsibility for providing safe care.

www.prenhall.com/kozier

Additional resources for this chapter can be found on the Student CD-ROM accompanying this textbook, and on the Companion Website at www.prenhall.com/kozier. Click on Chapter 4 to select the activities for this chapter.

CD-ROM
- Audio Glossary
- NCLEX Review

Companion Website
- Additional NCLEX Review
- Case Study: Obstetrics
- MediaLink Applications:
  - Nurse Practice Act
  - Collective Bargaining
  - Liability

LEARNING OUTCOMES

After completing this chapter, the student will be able to:

- List sources of law and types of law
- Describe ways nurse practice acts, standards of care, and agency policies and procedures affect the scope of nursing practice
- Compare and contrast the state-based licensure model and the mutual recognition model for multi-state licensure
- Describe the purpose and essential elements of informed consent
- Describe the purpose of the following legislated acts: the Good Samaritan acts and Americans with Disabilities Act
- Discuss the impaired nurse and available diversion or peer assistance programs
- Recognize the nurse's legal responsibilities with selected aspects of nursing practice
- Differentiate crimes from torts, and give examples in nursing
- Discriminate between negligence and malpractice
- Delineate the elements of malpractice
- Compare and contrast intentional torts (assault/battery, false imprisonment, invasion of privacy, defamation) and unintentional torts (negligence, malpractice)
- Describe the purpose of professional liability insurance
- List information that needs to be included in an incident report
- Identify ways nurses and nursing students can minimize their chances of liability

KEY TOPICS

This study guide chapter reinforces the following terms/topics discussed in the textbook chapter:

- answer
- assault
- battery
- breach of duty
- burden of proof
- causation
- civil action
- civil law
- common law
- complaint
- contract
- contract law
- contractual obligations
- contractual relationships
- credentialing
- crime
- criminal action
- criminal law
- damages
- decision
- defamation
- defendant
- delegation
- discovery
- duty
- expert witness
- express consent
- false imprisonment
- felony
- foreseeability
- gross negligence
- harm
- impaired nurse
- implied consent
- implied contract
- informed consent
- injury
- interstate compact
- invasion of privacy
- law
- liability
- libel
- license
- litigation
- malpractice
- mandated reporters
- manslaughter
- misdemeanor
- mutual recognition model
- negligence
- plaintiff
- private law
- public law
- *res ipsa loquitur*
- *respondeat superior*
- right
- responsibility
- slander
- standards of care
- statutory law
- strike
- tort
- tort law
- trial
- unprofessional conduct
- verdict

LECTURE OUTLINE

I. General legal concepts
   A. Functions of the law in nursing
   B. Sources of law
      1. Constitutional law
      2. Legislation (statutory law)
      3. Administrative law
      4. Common law
   C. Types of laws
   D. Kinds of legal actions
   E. The civil judicial process
   F. Nurses as witnesses

II. Regulation of nursing practice
   A. Nurse practice acts
   B. Credentialing
      1. Licensure
      2. Mutual recognition model
      3. Interstate compacts
      4. Certification
      5. Accreditation/approval of basic nursing education programs
   C. Standards of care

- III. Contractual arrangements in nursing
  - A. Legal roles of nurses
    1. Provider of service
    2. Employee or contractor for service
    3. Citizen
  - B. Collective bargaining
- IV. Selected legal aspects of nursing practice
  - A. Informed consent
    1. Exceptions
    2. Nurse's role
  - B. Delegation
  - C. Violence, abuse and neglect
  - D. The Americans with Disabilities Act
  - E. Controlled substances
  - F. The impaired nurse
  - G. Sexual harassment
  - H. Abortions
  - I. Death and related issues
- V. Areas of potential liability in nursing
  - A. Crimes and torts
    1. Unintentional torts
    2. Intentional torts
  - B. Loss of client property
  - C. Unprofessional conduct
- VI. Legal protections in nursing practice
  - A. Good Samaritan acts
  - B. Professional liability insurance
  - C. Carrying out a physician's orders
  - D. Providing competent nursing care
  - E. Record keeping
  - F. The incident report
- VII. Reporting crimes, torts, and unsafe practices
- VIII. Legal responsibilities of student

FOCUSED STUDY TIPS

1. Define the following laws:
   civil law
   contract law
   public law
   tort law
   common law
   criminal law
   statutory law
2. Define the following terms:
   battery
   invasion of privacy
   malpractice
   slander
   false imprisonment
   libel
   sexual harassment
   unprofessional conduct
3. You are a nurse assigned to provide care for a client recovering from knee replacement surgery. The client is alert and oriented and able to bathe and feed himself. After breakfast you place his bed in the lowest position (relative to the floor), raise all four side rails, provide him with the call bell, and instruct him to call for help before getting out of bed. An hour later, when you enter the room to administer his medications, you find him trying to climb out of bed over the side rails. He states that he wants to use the bathroom and did not want to bother you because he knows you are busy. On examination, there is no evidence of injury. The physician who is making rounds agrees with your assessment and reminds the client that he needs assistance getting out of bed. Later in the day, the client's wife threatens to sue you for malpractice, claiming that you have inadequately protected her husband. What should you do?
4. What is the purpose of the Nurse Practice Act?
5. How does the Good Samaritan Act protect health care providers?
6. What is an incident report?
7. The nurse has many day-to-day roles, including caregiver, client advocate, and researcher, among others. From a legal perspective, list the three roles of the nurse.
8. What is collective bargaining?
9. Etta Nichols is a 79-year-old woman recently admitted to the surgical unit with a fractured hip. She has a history of Alzheimer's disease associated with severe cognitive impairment. Can Etta give informed consent for the surgical repair of her hip? Explain your answer.
10. Jason Pulaski is a 42-year-old airline pilot who suffered a 10-cm laceration of the right lower leg while playing rugby with friends. He drove himself to the urgent care clinic. The nurse practitioner determined that the laceration required suturing. Could Jason give informed consent for the laceration repair? Explain your answer.
11. Four-year-old Scott Branch has been seen repeatedly in the pediatric clinic for tonsillitis. The pediatrician recommends tonsillectomy. Can Scott give consent for the tonsillectomy? Explain your answer.
12. Your client's family asks you to serve as a witness to a will. What should you do? Why?

13. The physician orders Demerol 1,000 mg IM q4h PRN pain. The nurse examines the order and notes that the dosage is 10 times the dose he anticipated. What should he do?
14. How do you feel about nurses participating in collective bargaining?
15. Imagine that a nursing strike is called at the hospital you are scheduled to use for your next clinical experience. The nurses at the facility are on strike demanding better staffing ratios. They believe that the safety of client care has been compromised by recent staff layoffs. Management contends that layoffs were necessary due to the facility's financial situation. Your nursing instructor has asked you to cross the picket line to report for your clinical experience. The striking nurses believe that the school is undermining their position by staffing the hospital while they are out on strike. Would you cross the picket line to continue to attend clinical? Explain your answer.
16. What are the four elements of proof for nursing negligence and malpractice?
17. Identify at least five situations in which a nurse may be charged with malpractice.
18. Identify the three elements that must be present for informed consent to occur.
19. Imagine that you are caring for a 14-year-old boy who was hit by a truck while riding his bicycle home from school. The physician has determined that the boy has a flat EEG and is "brain dead." Would you be comfortable approaching the family with an organ donation request? Describe how you would handle this situation.
20. Does your state have right-to-die and living will statutes?
21. Identify and describe the three types of advanced medical directives.
22. Does your school provide liability insurance? If so, what is the extent of coverage? Is it advisable for you to have your own personal coverage?

CASE STUDY

Sheryl is a fellow student in your clinical group. While you are both preparing pain medications for administration, you observe that Sheryl signs out two tablets of Percodan but places one tablet in the medicine cup and the other in her pocket. Later in the day, you overhear her telling the physician that the client is not getting relief from his pain medication. She reports that she has administered two tablets of Percodan every 3 hours but that the client is still complaining of severe pain. Sheryl asks the physician to prescribe an injectable opioid for pain relief.

1. *What would you do in this circumstance?*

NCLEX TEST QUESTIONS

1. A client undergoing an exploratory laporoscopy was asked to sign the informed consent. The client asked the nurse, "What is a laporoscopy?" Which action should the nurse take?
   a. Inform the client what the procedure is.
   b. Inform the physician that the client does not understand the procedure.
   c. Demand the client sign the informed consent.
   d. Request the family to sign the informed consent.
2. Which of the following cannot provide consents?
   a. a 40-year-old female undergoing surgery
   b. a 60-year-old male undergoing surgery
   c. a 6-year-old undergoing surgery
   d. an 18-year-old undergoing surgery
3. The nurse witnesses a client's signature on the informed consent. The nurse's signature indicates:
   a. the nurse explained the procedure to the client.
   b. the client did not give her consent willingly.
   c. the client's signature is authentic.
   d. the client has appointed the nurse as the power of attorney.
4. A nurse was explaining the risks associated with a surgical procedure. What action should the nurse take to ensure the client understood the informed consent?
   a. Have the family sign the consent.
   b. Have the client sign the consent.
   c. Have the client report in her own words what she has been told.
   d. Have family members repeat in their own words what they have been told.
5. A nurse on the 3–11 shift was passing medications. She noticed that a client who was

not in her section was using a call-light. What action should the nurse take?

a. Ignore the call-light and continue passing medications.
b. Have a housekeeping staff answer the call light.
c. Wait until a family member comes to visit the client.
d. Answer the call light.

6. Understanding about medications being administered to a client is an example of what nursing role?
   a. educator
   b. counselor
   c. advocate
   d. caregiver
7. While supervising a clinical unit, the nurse noticed one of the new nurses on the floor had a history of working a lot of overtime. Other noticeable behaviors included frequent bathroom breaks, mood swings, and volunteering to medicate other nurses' clients. These behaviors are indicative of:
   a. alcoholism.
   b. drug addiction.
   c. schizophrenia.
   d. depression.
8. An adult female client, who has been deaf secondary to antibiotic therapy, was admitted to the surgical unit. The physician has written an order for the client to sign the surgical consent form. What is the appropriate action to take?
   a. Have her husband sign the consent.
   b. The nurse will sign the client's name.
   c. Have the client read the consent and sign it.
   d. Have the client appoint the nurse as the power of attorney.
9. A client was discharged after having a baby. The nurse failed to give the client her discharge instructions. This can result in:
   a. assault.
   b. battery.
   c. negligence.
   d. malpractice.
10. In providing culturally competent care, a nurse was caring for a Korean woman. Which of the following actions should the nurse take?
    a. Explain the procedure to the client.
    b. Provide a translator if the client wishes.
    c. Inform the physician that the woman does not understand anything.
    d. Just have the client make an "X" on the informed consent.

CHAPTER 5

VALUES, ETHICS, AND ADVOCACY

OVERVIEW

This chapter examines the roles of values, ethics, and advocacy as they relate to client care. It presents several frameworks for moral decision making and explores the correlations between your views as a nurse and those of the clients to whom you provide care. Numerous clinical examples illustrate the relevance of ethical decision making to nursing practice.

www.prenhall.com/kozier

Additional resources for this chapter can be found on the Student CD-ROM accompanying this textbook, and on the Companion Website at www.prenhall.com/kozier. Click on Chapter 5 to select the activities for this chapter.

CD-ROM
- Audio Glossary
- NCLEX Review

Companion Website
- Additional NCLEX Review
- Case Study: Ethics Committee
- MediaLink Applications:
  - AIDS Resource
  - Privacy
- Links to Resources

LEARNING OUTCOMES

After completing this chapter, the student will be able to:

- Explain how cognitive development, values, moral frameworks, and codes of ethics affect moral decisions
- Explain how nurses use knowledge of values transmission and values clarification to make ethical decisions and facilitate ethical decision making of clients
- Identify the moral issues and principles involved in a given ethical situation
- Explain the uses and limitations of professional codes of ethics
- Discuss common ethical issues currently facing health care professionals
- Describe ways in which nurses can enhance their ethical decision making and practice
- Discuss the advocacy role of the nurse

KEY TOPICS

This study guide chapter reinforces the following terms/topics discussed in the textbook chapter.

- accountability
- active euthanasia
- advocate
- assisted suicide
- attitudes
- autonomy

- beliefs
- beneficence
- bioethics
- client advocate
- code of ethics
- consequence-based (teleological) theories
- ethics
- fidelity
- justice
- moral development
- moral rules
- morality
- nonmaleficence
- nursing ethics
- passive euthanasia
- personal values
- principles-based (deontological) theories
- professional values
- relationships-based (caring) theories
- responsibility
- utilitarianism
- utility
- value set
- value system
- values
- values clarification
- veracity

LECTURE OUTLINE

I. Values
   A. Values transmission
      1. Personal values
      2. Professional values
   B. Values clarification
      1. Clarifying the nurse's values
      2. Clarifying client values
II. Morality and ethics
   A. Moral development
   B. Moral frameworks
   C. Moral principles
III. Nursing ethics
   A. Nursing codes of ethics
   B. Origins of ethical problems in nursing
      1. Social and technologic changes
      2. Conflicting loyalties and obligations
   C. Making ethical decisions
   D. Strategies to enhance ethical decisions and practice
IV. Specific ethical issues
   A. Acquired Immune Deficiency Syndrome (AIDS)
   B. Abortion
   C. Organ transplantation
   D. End-of-life issues
      1. Advance directives
      2. Euthanasia and assisted suicide
      3. Termination of life-sustaining treatment
      4. Withdrawing or withholding food and fluids
   E. Allocation of scarce health resources
   F. Management of computerized information
V. Advocacy
   A. The advocate's role
      1. Advocacy in home care
      2. Professional and public advocacy

FOCUSED STUDY TIPS

1. What word/words could describe a freely chosen, enduring belief or attitude about the worth of a person, object, idea, or action?
2. What would be viewed as a reflection of the moral values of a society?
3. What term is used to connote a mental position or feeling about a person, object, or idea?
4. What would be considered a method of inquiry that helps people understand the morality of human behavior?
5. Define the following:
   autonomy
   caring-based ethics
   fidelity
   nonmaleficence
   utility
   beneficence
   deontology
   justice
   teleology
   veracity
6. What is the role of the nurse in relation to moral issues?
7. What does it mean when a nurse acts as a client advocate?
8. What is the relationship between nurses and ethical decision making?

9. List four important professional values for nursing according to Watson.
10. Does your clinical facility have an ethics committee? Who belongs to the ethics committee? How often does the committee meet? Are you allowed to attend a meeting?
11. Catherine Pardee is a 22-year-old college student who presents to the OB/GYN clinic requesting pregnancy testing and an abortion if she is pregnant. As the nurse working in the clinic, you obtain a nursing history from Catherine. Catherine informs you that she has had four prior pregnancies. Each of the prior pregnancies has been terminated by an abortion. During the interview she tells you, "I'm terrible about birth control. I just can't remember it, and besides, if I get pregnant I can always have an abortion."

    How do you feel about Catherine's views and clinic presentation? Would your views affect your ability to provide care to Catherine?
12. Nan Motto is a 35-year-old mother of three children, ages 4, 7, and 9. Her younger sister has developed renal failure and is being considered for renal transplantation. Nan's sister has asked her to be the kidney donor. You are the nurse coordinator for the renal transplant program. Nan arrives at the clinic for an appointment with you to evaluate her status as a potential donor. In your discussion, Nan admits that she is very uncomfortable about her decision. Using the seven-step values clarification process, describe how you would help Nan work through her decision-making process.

CASE STUDY

Jedi Annihi is a 37-year-old man who has undergone a craniotomy and debulking procedure (removal of mass) for a malignant brain tumor. During his initial hospitalization, he is informed by the neurosurgeon that the tumor is a vigorously growing carcinoma. Treatment options are presented. However, the surgeon tells Jedi that he will probably only live another 12 to 18 months. Jedi opts for minimal treatment. During his hospitalization, he prepares a living will with the assistance of a friend who is an attorney. You are a witness to this event. Jedi asks to be discharged home as soon as possible. He plans to take a vacation with his family and to enjoy the remainder of his life.

Approximately 9 months later, Jedi is brought to the emergency department by his family. He is markedly thinner and confused. An MRI scan demonstrates that the tumor has advanced rapidly. Jedi's family insists that he be admitted and that "Everything should be done," including surgery. The family believes that this is what Jedi would want. The family denies the existence of a living will.

1. *Is this a decision-focused problem or an action-focused problem?*
2. *Where does the conflict lie?*
3. *Apply one of the ethical decision-making models to the situation. Choose several plans of action and follow the outcome using the multistep process.*

NCLEX TEST QUESTIONS

1. Which of the following statements implies that the nursing student is operating from his value system?
    a. "I believe if I study hard, I will get a good grade."
    b. "I believe that if I smoke, I will get cancer."
    c. "No one cares about me."
    d. "My health is important to me. I must eat right and exercise frequently."
2. Which of the following is an example of a nurse's professional value?
    a. to get a job
    b. to be dependent on doctor's orders
    c. believes in the dignity and worth of each person
    d. noncommittal to service of others
3. The nurse was developing a plan of care for an 80 year-old undergoing cataract surgery. In order

to help the client clarify his values, the nurse would say:

a. "I think you need the surgery."
b. "What do you think you will gain from the surgery?"
c. "Does it matter to you that you do not have any other choice?"
d. "Do you care that your family does not want you to have this surgery?"

4. In following the rule "Do not lie," a nurse believes she should tell the truth to a dying patient, even though the physician has given instructions not to do so. From what moral framework is the nurse operating?
   a. consequences-based
   b. principles-based
   c. relationships-based
   d. caring-based
5. While catching a client who is falling, the nurse grips the client tightly enough to cause bruises to the client's arm. This is an example of:
   a. autonomy.
   b. nonmaleficence.
   c. beneficence.
   d. justice.
6. Nurses are governed by which of the following?
   a. American Medical Association
   b. American Practical Nurse Association
   c. Code of Ethics for Nurses
   d. Patient's Bill of Rights
7. One strategy a nurse can use to enhance her ethical decisions is:
   a. be aware of client's values.
   b. be familiar with nursing codes of ethics.
   c. be familiar with the Patient's Bill of Rights.
   d. be aware of state laws.
8. Which of the following ethical problems would a nurse most frequently encounter?
   a. a client receiving dialysis three times a week
   b. a woman who has just delivered a full term healthy infant
   c. a heart transplant client
   d. a client who has chosen to have an abortion
9. A home health nurse found a client tearful and depressed. She knows that she could help by staying for 30 minutes to talk. However, that would take time from her next client, who is a diabetic needing a great deal of teaching. What moral principle would guide this nurse's decision?
   a. nonmaleficence or "do no harm"
   b. beneficence or "doing good"
   c. justice or "fairness"
   d. autonomy or "independence"
10. When a nurse promises a client she will find out more about his medication, she is practicing:
    a. autonomy.
    b. justice.
    c. fidelity.
    d. veracity.

CHAPTER 6

HEALTH CARE DELIVERY SYSTEMS

OVERVIEW

This chapter provides an orientation to the health care delivery system. It explains the roles and responsibilities of other health care professionals and gives an overview of various levels of care.

LEARNING OUTCOMES

After completing this chapter, the student will be able to:

- Differentiate primary, secondary, and tertiary health care services
- Describe the functions and purposes of the health care agencies outlined in this chapter
- Identify the roles of various health care professionals
- Describe the factors that affect health care delivery
- Compare various systems of payment for health care services

KEY TOPICS

This study guide chapter reinforces the following terms/topics discussed in the textbook:

- case management
- coinsurance
- critical pathways
- diagnosis-related groups (DRGs)
- health care system
- health maintenance organization (HMO)
- independent practice association (IPA)
- integrated delivery system (IDS)
- licensed vocational (practical) nurse (LVN/LPN)
- managed care
- Medicaid
- Medicare
- patient-focused care
- preferred provider arrangement (PPA)
- preferred provider organization (PPO)
- Supplemental Security Income (SSI)
- team nursing

www.prenhall.com/kozier

Additional resources for this chapter can be found on the Student CD-ROM accompanying this textbook, and on the Companion Website at www.prenhall.com/kozier. Click on Chapter 6 to select the activities for this chapter.

CD-ROM
- Audio Glossary
- NCLEX Review

Companion Website
- Additional NCLEX Review
- Case Study: Delivery Systems
- MediaLink Applications:
  - Where Do Elders Live?
  - Issues Plaguing Women and Children
  - Health Care and the Homeless and Poor
  - The Competent Case Manager
- Links to Resources

LECTURE OUTLINE

I. Types of health care services
  A. Health promotion and illness prevention
  B. Diagnosis and treatment
  C. Rehabilitation, health restoration, and palliative care
II. Types of health care agencies and services
  A. Public health
  B. Physicians' offices
  C. Ambulatory care centers
  D. Occupational health clinics
  E. Hospitals
  F. Extended-care (long-term care) facilities
  G. Retirement and assisted-living centers
  H. Rehabilitation centers
  I. Home health care agencies
  J. Day-care centers
  K. Rural care
  L. Hospice services
  M. Crisis centers
  N. Mutual support and self-help groups
III. Providers of health care
  A. Nurse
  B. Alternative health provider
  C. Case manager
  D. Dentist
  E. Dietician or nutritionist
  F. Occupational therapist
  G. Paramedical technologist
  H. Pharmacist
  I. Physician
  J. Physician assistant
  K. Physical therapist
  L. Podiatrists
  M. Respiratory therapist
  N. Social worker
  O. Spiritual support person
  P. Unlicensed assistive personnel
IV. Factors affecting health care delivery
  A. Increasing number of elderly
  B. Advances in technology
  C. Economics
  D. Women's health
  E. Uneven distribution of services
  F. Access to health care
  G. The homeless and the poor
  H. Demographic changes
V. Frameworks for care
  A. Managed care
  B. Case management
  C. Patient-focused care
  D. Differentiated practice
  E. Shared governance
  F. Case method
  G. Functional method
  H. Team nursing
  I. Primary nursing
VI. Financing health care
  A. Payment sources in the United States
    1. Medicare and Medicaid
    2. Supplemental Security Income
    3. Prospective payment system
  A. Payment sources in Canada
  B. Insurance plans
    1. Private insurance
    2. Group plans
      a. Health Maintenance Organizations
      b. Preferred Provider Organizations
      c. Preferred Provider Arrangements
      d. Independent Practice Associations
      e. Physician/Hospital Organizations

FOCUSED STUDY TIPS

1. Define the roles for each of the following providers of health care:
   alternative provider
   case manager
   dentist
   dietitian
   licensed vocational nurse (LVN)
   occupational therapist (OT)
   paramedical technologist
   pharmacist
   physical therapist (PT)
   physician (MD)
   physician's assistant (PA)
   registered nurse (RN)
   respiratory therapist (RT)
   social worker
   unlicensed assistive personnel
2. Describe today's health care system.
3. The Patient's Bill of Rights was developed out of the movement for clients' rights. This need for protection resulted largely from the vulnerability of the client during illness and the complexity of the health care system. Which right is not protected by the Patient's Bill of Rights?
4. List factors that have influenced the reshaping of health care services.
5. In what way has the use of critical pathways changed nursing care?

6. Health care services can be grouped by the type of service they provide. Give two examples of each type of the following services:
   Health promotion and illness prevention — Diagnosis and treatment
   Rehabilitation and health restoration
7. What is the difference between Medicare and Medicaid?
8. What is the most striking difference between the Canadian and Australian health care systems and the U.S. health care system?
9. Identify the model(s) of nursing in place at the health facilities used for your clinical rotations.

CASE STUDY

While completing the admission assessment of an elderly female, you learn that she has been on Medicare for several years. What type of health care coverage is included with Medicare?

During the course of routine care with this client, she mentions to you that she has seen a chiropractor and an herbalist to help with a variety of health care issues. What roles do these alternative healthcare providers play with your current plan of care?

After a few days your client is being discharged to home. During the review of discharge instructions, your client states that she does not intend to have any of her prescriptions filled and can't wait to get back to see her chiropractor and herbalist. What should you do with this information?

NCLEX TEST QUESTIONS

1. At a local community clinic, a group of nurses volunteered to screen clients for hypertension. The purpose of this screening is to:
   a. treat high blood pressure.
   b. detect high blood pressure early.
   c. restore the client to wellness.
   d. provide comfort for the client with hypertension.
2. Immunizing children against Hepatitis B is a form of:
   a. health promotion.
   b. palliative care.
   c. secondary prevention.
   d. health restoration.
3. A client was admitted to cardiac rehabilitation following a heart attack. This is a form of:
   a. health promotion.
   b. palliative care.
   c. secondary prevention.
   d. health restoration.
4. A client was admitted to an outpatient surgi-center for a colonoscopy. This is a form of:
   a. health promotion.
   b. palliative care.
   c. secondary prevention.
   d. health restoration.
5. Employee health has been recognized as an important link to employee productivity. What is the major concern of occupational nurses?
   a. annual employee health screening
   b. counseling
   c. worker safety
   d. major surgical procedures
6. A 70-year-old client was admitted to the behavioral care unit in a local hospital for 3 weeks. This hospital is classified as:
   a. acute care.
   b. medical care.
   c. long-term care.
   d. outpatient.
7. A client was to be discharged from the medical-surgical unit. After interviewing the client, the nurse realized that the client would have no caregiver at home. The nurse recommended assisted living for this client. What facility would best fit for this client?
   a. acute care
   b. medical care
   c. extended care
   d. retirement home
8. The local police department brought a young man into the emergency department. After a drug

test, the client agreed to enter into a psychiatric unit in the hospital. What is the level of care?

a. retirement center
b. extended care
c. rehabilitation
d. day care

9. Which of the following is considered an alternative care provider?
   a. registered nurse
   b. advanced practice nurse
   c. licensed vocational nurse
   d. chiropractor

10. A stroke client was receiving home health services. For the client to gain the skills to perform activities of daily living, the physician ordered which of the following practitioners?
    a. dietitian
    b. occupational therapist
    c. registered nurse
    d. social worker

CHAPTER 7

COMMUNITY-BASED NURSING AND CARE CONTINUITY

OVERVIEW

This chapter introduces you to the ideas, policies, and forces that are moving health care into the community. A variety of recommendations and competencies that facilitate community-based nursing care are discussed.

www.prenhall.com/kozier

Additional resources for this chapter can be found on the Student CD-ROM accompanying this textbook, and on the Companion Website at www.prenhall.com/kozier. Click on Chapter 7 to select the activities for this chapter.

CD-ROM
- Audio Glossary
- NCLEX Review

Companion Website
- Additional NCLEX Review
- Case Study: Community Health Nursing
- MediaLink Applications:
  - Community Nursing Standards
  - Government Services
- Link to Resources

LEARNING OUTCOMES

After completing this chapter, the student will be able to:

- Discuss factors influencing health care reform
- Describe community-based health care, including the Pew Health Professions Commission recommendations for health care systems
- Describe various community-based frameworks, including integrated health care systems, community initiatives and conditions, and case management
- Differentiate community-based health care settings from traditional settings
- Differentiate community-based nursing from traditional institutional-based nursing
- Discuss competencies community-based nurses need for practice
- Explain essential aspects of collaborative health care: definitions, objectives, benefits, and the nurse's role
- Describe the role of the nurse in providing continuity of care

KEY TOPICS

This study guide chapter reinforces the following terms/topics discussed in the textbook:

- collaboration
- community-based health care (CBHC)
- community-based nursing (CBN)
- community nursing centers
- continuity of care
- integrated health care system
- primary care (PC)
- primary health care (PHC)

LECTURE OUTLINE

I. Health care reform
II. Community-based health care
  A. Community-based frameworks
  B. Community-based settings
    1. Community nursing centers
    2. Parish nursing
    3. Telehealth
III. Community-based nursing
  A. Competencies required for community-based care
  B. Collaborative health care
    1. The nurse as a collaborator
    2. Competencies basic to collaboration
IV. Continuity of care
  A. Discharge planning
  B. Preparing clients to go home
  C. Home health care teaching
  D. Referrals

FOCUSED STUDY TIPS

1. Define the following terms:
   case management
   community initiatives
   community-based health care
   community-based nursing
   continuity of care
   discharge planning
   integrated health care system
2. Primary care and primary health care are two distinct aspects of health care delivery. How do they differ?
3. List the essential elements of a community-based health care system.
4. What are some predictions about the future of health care?
5. Collaboration is an important nursing skill. What might be needed to enhance your ability to practice collaboration?
6. Identify the competencies required for successful practice in a community-based integrated health care system.
7. Identify the persons/groups with whom nurses should aim to collaborate.
8. Identify three nursing activities that ensure continuity of care.

CASE STUDY

Melena Roberts, 80 years old, slips and falls on an icy sidewalk while retrieving her mail from her curbside mailbox. Her neighbor summons an ambulance, and Ms. Roberts is brought to ABC Medical Center for evaluation. In the emergency department, she is diagnosed with a fracture of the right femur. She is admitted and spends 5 days on the orthopedic unit after successfully undergoing an open reduction and internal fixation of the fracture.

1. *Identify the areas that must be assessed by the nurse prior to sending Ms. Roberts home.*
2. *What type of information will Ms. Roberts require before discharge?*

NCLEX TEST QUESTIONS

1. The difference between traditional health care and integrated health care is:
   a. traditional health care is in clients' homes, whereas integrated health care is found in hospitals.
   b. traditional health care is community-based.
   c. integrated health care is in the hospital.
   d. integrated health care is community-based.
2. The increase of advanced practice nurses has resulted in which of the following groups of clients receiving primary care?
   a. rich
   b. school-age children
   c. homeless
   d. institutionalized
3. A principle of primary health care is:
   a. use of technology.
   b. community participation.
   c. personal health services.
   d. inequitable distribution.
4. One of the roles of a parish nurse is to:
   a. establish an abuse program.
   b. serve as an outreach coordinator.
   c. serve as a faith healer.
   d. serve as a personal health counselor.

5. A key element for collaboration includes:
   a. independent decision making.
   b. effective communication.
   c. distrust of other members of the team.
   d. decreased authority.
6. A client is admitted to labor and delivery. During the initial interview, the nurse focuses on continuity of care. To provide this continuity of care, the nurse needs to:
   a. involve the physician in plan of care.
   b. involve unlicensed assistive personnel in plan of care.
   c. initiate discharge planning.
   d. instruct grandparents on how to feed the baby.
7. A client was admitted to the surgical unit after undergoing extensive surgery following a motorcycle accident. During the night, the client's condition deteriorated and the patient had to be transferred to the ICU. What action must the nurse on the surgical unit take?
   a. Readmit client to the hospital.
   b. Discharge client to a nursing home.
   c. Discharge client from surgical unit and readmit to ICU.
   d. Discharge from the hospital.
8. On the first home health visit, the nurse assesses:
   a. the mileage to and from the client's home.
   b. environmental features in the client's home.
   c. the need for housekeeping.
   d. the need for palliative care.
9. Essential information before discharge includes:
   a. environmental features.
   b. transportation needs for family.
   c. the need for palliative care.
   d. plans to ensure the client's and caregiver's needs are met.
10. A common nursing diagnosis for a client receiving care in the home is:
   a. alteration in comfort.
   b. risk for injury.
   c. inadequate oxygenation.
   d. impaired sensory perception.

CHAPTER 8

HEALTH PROMOTION

OVERVIEW

This chapter discusses goals, models, strategies, and your role in health promotion of individuals, families, and communities. Numerous health promotion assessment tools and programs are discussed.

LEARNING OUTCOMES

After completing this chapter, the student will be able to:

- Describe how the *Healthy People 2010* Leading Health Indicators can help improve the health of a community
- Differentiate health promotion from health protection or illness prevention
- Discuss essential components of health promotion
- Identify various types and sites of health-promotion programs
- Discuss the Health-Promotion Model
- Explain the stages of health behavior change as proposed by Prochaska, Norcross, and DiClemente
- Discuss the nurse's role in health promotion
- Assess the health of individuals
- Develop, implement, and evaluate plans for health promotion

MediaLink

www.prenhall.com/kozier

Additional resources for this chapter can be found on the Student CD-ROM accompanying this textbook, and on the Companion Website at www.prenhall.com/kozier. Click on Chapter 8 to select the activities for this chapter.

CD-ROM
- Audio Glossary
- NCLEX Review

Companion Website
- Additional NCLEX Review
- Case Study: Health Promotion Program
- MediaLink Applications:
  - Health Belief Model
  - Community Services
- Links to Resources

KEY TOPICS

This study guide chapter reinforces the following terms/topics discussed in the textbook chapter:

- action stage
- contemplation stage
- health promotion
- health protection
- health risk assessment
- maintenance stage
- precontemplation stage
- preparation stage
- primary prevention
- secondary prevention
- termination stage
- tertiary prevention
- wellness diagnosis

LECTURE OUTLINE

I. *Healthy People 2010*
II. Defining health promotion
III. Sites for health-promotion activities
IV. Health-Promotion Model
  A. Individual characteristics and experiences
  B. Behavior-specific cognitions and affect
  C. Commitment to a plan of action
  D. Immediate competing demands and preferences
  E. Behavioral outcome
V. Stages of health behavior change
  A. Precontemplation
  B. Contemplation
  C. Preparation
  D. Action
  E. Maintenance
  F. Termination
VI. The nurse's role in health promotion
VII. The nursing process and health promotion
  A. Assessing the health of individuals
    1. Health history and physical examination
    2. Physical fitness assessment
    3. Lifestyle assessment
    4. Spiritual health assessment
    5. Social support systems review
    6. Health risk assessment
    7. Health beliefs review
    8. Life-stress review
    9. Validating assessment data
  B. Diagnosing
  C. Planning
    1. Steps in planning
    2. Exploring available resources
  D. Implementing
    1. Providing and facilitating support
      a. Individual counseling
      b. Telephone counseling
      c. Group support
      d. Facilitating social support
    2. Providing health education
    3. Enhancing behavior change
    4. Modeling
  E. Evaluating

FOCUSED STUDY TIPS

1. Define the following:
   health promotion
   health protection
   primary prevention
   secondary prevention
   tertiary prevention
2. A 32-year-old female client has a family history of heart disease. To decrease her risk of developing heart disease, she regularly participates in a program of aerobic activity that includes mountain biking, race walking, and light weight lifting. What role does aerobic exercise serve for this client?
3. Define Pender's health promotion model.
4. Your client has hypertension. The physician has prescribed a low-sodium diet. The client discusses the new diet with you and takes a pamphlet home to share with his wife. In which stage of health behavior change is this client?
5. What is the primary role of the nurse in health promotion?
6. Provide at least one example of each of the following types of health promotion programs in your community:
   information dissemination program
   health appraisal and wellness assessment program
   lifestyle and behavior change program
   environmental control program
7. Evaluate your own risk for health problems using the lifestyle assessment tool found in the text.
   Describe the results of your assessment.

Based on your self-evaluation, determine how you might improve your health. Follow the nursing process as outlined in the text, and identify at least one health promotion activity to improve your health status.

Identify at least one support service to help you achieve your goal.

CASE STUDY

Jack Cooke is 62 years old and very physically fit. He reports to your clinic for a yearly checkup. Jack states that he runs an average of 35 miles per week and does a light weight-training workout three times per week. His vital signs are: BP 98/56, P 52, RR 12, T 97.2F. He is currently taking no medications, does not smoke, and has a low serum cho-

lesterol level. Jack states that he occasionally has a glass of wine with dinner. He estimates that this occurs approximately one or two times per week.

1. *What is your assessment of Jack's health?*
2. *Write a nursing diagnosis for Jack.*
3. *Identify at least two ways that you can work with Jack to enhance or promote his health.*

NCLEX TEST QUESTIONS

1. One of the main goals of Healthy People 2010: Understanding and Improving Health (USDHHS, 2000) is to:
   a. increase consumption of over the counter medication.
   b. decrease exercise to once a week to improve heart muscle.
   c. eliminate health disparities among the population.
   d. decrease quality of life in the aging process.
2. What is one way to link individual health to community health?
   a. Educate businesses.
   b. Form partnerships between the individual and the community.
   c. Restore the individual's health.
   d. Prevent the individual's aging process.
3. Which of the following is an example of primary prevention?
   a. a client undergoing cardiac rehab
   b. a client undergoing dialysis treatments
   c. a client receiving nebulizer treatments for COPD
   d. a dialysis nurse being immunized for Hepatitis B
4. Which of the following is an example of a community-based site for health promotion activities for the public?
   a. an outpatient surgical clinic
   b. a local industry
   c. a local fire department
   d. an outpatient dentist office
5. The rationale for school-health promotion programs is to:
   a. reduce infection rates.
   b. reduce absenteeism.
   c. gain knowledge of community resources.
   d. gain knowledge about personal hygiene.
6. A diabetic client told the nurse that it was difficult to balance her eating and exercise because her job required frequent out-of-town trips. Using a health promotion model, the nurse recognized that which of the following behavior-specific cognitions had occurred?
   a. perceived benefits of action
   b. perceived barriers to action
   c. perceived self-efficacy
   d. activity-related effect
7. In the stages of health behavior change, which of the following is an example of the preparation stage?
   a. Client denies there is a problem.
   b. Client gathers information about changing a specific behavior.
   c. Client begins making small behavioral changes.
   d. Client integrates newly adopted behavioral patterns.
8. Which of the following is an example of a NANDA wellness diagnosis?
   a. high risk for injury
   b. alteration in health maintenance
   c. readiness for enhanced weight loss
   d. alteration in communication
9. In health promotion plans, who develops the care plan?
   a. nurse
   b. family
   c. client
   d. physician
10. Which of the following would benefit from Pender's health promotion model?
    a. an active 18-year-old who does not smoke or drink and plays tennis daily
    b. A 40-year-old who exercises four times a week
    c. an overweight 50-year-old who smokes
    d. a 25-year-old who is serving his country in the armed services

CHAPTER 9

HOME CARE

OVERVIEW

This chapter introduces you to the important trend of delivering health care in the home. As a nursing student, you will find the discussion of the home visit and safety and infection control in the home setting very helpful for planning care.

LEARNING OUTCOMES

After completing this chapter, the student will be able to:

- Define home health care
- Compare the characteristics of home health nursing with those of institutional nursing care
- Describe the types of home health agencies, including reimbursement and referral sources
- Describe the roles of the home health nurse
- Identify the essential aspects of the home visit
- Discuss the safety and infection control dimensions applicable to the home care setting
- Identify ways the nurse can recognize and minimize caregiver role strain
- Apply the nursing process to care of the client in the home

www.prenhall.com/kozier

Additional resources for this chapter can be found on the Student CD-ROM accompanying this textbook, and on the Companion Website at www.prenhall.com/kozier. Click on Chapter 9 to select the activities for this chapter.

CD-ROM
- Audio Glossary
- NCLEX Review

Companion Website
- Additional NCLEX Review
- Case Study: Home Care Nurse
- MediaLink Applications:
  - Hospice Nursing
  - Nurse Assistant
- Links to Resources

KEY TOPICS

This study guide chapter reinforces the following terms/topics discussed in the textbook chapter:

- caregiver role strain
- durable medical equipment company (DME)
- home care
- home care nursing
- home health clinical specialists
- home health nursing
- hospice nursing
- visiting nursing

LECTURE OUTLINE

I. Home health nursing
   A. Definitions of home nursing
   B. Unique aspects of home health nursing
II. The home health care system
   A. Referral process
   B. Home health agencies
   C. Private duty agencies
   D. Durable medical equipment companies
   E. Reimbursement
III. Roles of the home health nurse
   A. Advocate
   B. Caregiver
   C. Educator
   D. Case manager or coordinator
IV. Perspectives of home care clients
V. Selected dimensions of home health nursing
   A. Client safety
   B. Nurse safety
   C. Infection control
   D. Caregiver support
VI. Applying the nursing process in the home
VII. The future of home health care

FOCUSED STUDY TIPS

1. Define the following terms/phrases:
   caregiver role strain
   homebound
   hospice nursing
   Vial of Life program
2. How do home health nursing and community nursing differ?
3. Although home health care offers numerous advantages, it also has disadvantages. What is the chief disadvantage to home health care?
4. Home care agencies provide a number of services to meet the needs of clients in the home. List some of these services.
5. Identify at least three advantages to delivering care in the home.
6. Identify the major nursing roles the home health nurse may practice.

CASE STUDY

Diane Hanford is a 30-year-old client recently referred to your home health agency. She has a two-year-old at home and triplets who were born 10 weeks premature. Due to their health care needs, the triplets remained in the nursery for 1 month. They are scheduled for discharge from the hospital tomorrow. Diane's physician has ordered home care follow-up of the infants.

1. *Describe your process for initiating home care.*
2. *Describe your main tasks while in Diane's home.*
3. *Diane lives in a neighborhood in which you feel unsafe. Identify several ways in which you may protect yourself on this visit.*
4. *Once in the home, you realize that Diane is overwhelmed by the addition of triplets and is simultaneously caring for an immunocompromised parent receiving chemotherapy and radiation. Identify your role in infection control and in providing support for Diane.*

NCLEX TEST QUESTIONS

1. The trend for home care has been:
   a. an extension of the hospital stay.
   b. to avoid hospitalization.
   c. to provide preventive care.
   d. to provide private duty in the home.
2. One factor that has contributed to the growth of home health care is:
   a. consumers who prefer hospitalization over home care.
   b. an increase in the younger population.
   c. third-party reimbursers favor hospitalization over home health care.
   d. the ability to provide high technology in the home.
3. The main consumers for home health nursing are:
   a. individuals.
   b. groups.

c. families.
d. individuals and families.

4. A family member called a local home care agency about services for her aged parent living in her home. The home health nurse answered the family member with these words:
   a. "We must obtain a physician's order before we can make an evaluation."
   b. "You must call the attending physician and ask for a referral."
   c. "We will send a nurse to your home immediately."
   d. "If you think your aged parent needs this service, you must place her in the hospital first."
5. The local hospital has a home care department within the organizational structure. What is this type of home health agency?
   a. voluntary not-for-profit
   b. private not-for-profit
   c. proprietary for-profit
   d. institution-based
6. The family member questioned the nurse about obtaining a hospital bed. What is the nurse's best response?
   a. "You will have to pay for the equipment."
   b. "Your parent does not qualify for equipment."
   c. "Is your parent covered by Medicare?"
   d. "Do you think the physician will order a hospital bed?"
7. On the initial visit, the home health nurse informed the client about her advanced directives. The nurse was acting in the role of:
   a. caregiver.
   b. case manager.
   c. educator.
   d. advocate.
8. During a home health visit, the nurse assisted the client and family member by:
   a. placing the medications in a locked box.
   b. posting a list of emergency phone numbers by the telephone.
   c. disposing all needles in the trash can.
   d. bringing personal belongings in the house rather than leaving them in the car.
9. Signs of caregiver overload include which of the following?
   a. performing routine tasks for the client
   b. feelings of peace and joy
   c. well-cleaned house
   d. declining physical energy
10. An important part of the nurse's implementing role includes:
    a. obtaining informed consents.
    b. financial assessment including insurance verification.
    c. assessment of client's ability to perform self-care.
    d. teaching the client and caregiver the skills for self-care.

CHAPTER 10

NURSING INFORMATICS

OVERVIEW

This chapter discusses the growing use of computers in nursing education, practice, and research. The basic overview of computer equipment, terminology, and uses will be helpful to the computer novice. The discussion on the expanding use of computers by nurses and other health care providers offers insight into the expanding world of informatics.

LEARNING OUTCOMES

After completing this chapter, the student will be able to:

- Define the terms used to describe the common components of desktop computers
- Recognize the uses of word processing, databases, spreadsheets, and communications software in nursing
- Describe the uses of computers in nursing education
- Discuss the advantages of and concerns about computerized patient documentation systems
- Identify computer applications used in direct client monitoring and diagnosis
- List ways computers may be used by nurse-administrators in the areas of personnel, facilities management, finance, quality assurance, and accreditation
- Identify the role of computers in each step of the research process

MediaLink

www.prenhall.com/kozier

Additional resources for this chapter can be found on the Student CD-ROM accompanying this textbook, and on the Companion Website at www.prenhall.com/kozier. Click on Chapter 10 to select the activities for this chapter.

CD-ROM
- Audio Glossary
- NCLEX Review

Companion Website
- Additional NCLEX Review
- Case Study: Computerizing Clinical Documentation
- MediaLink Applications:
  - Confidentiality Laws
  - Informatics Certification Exam
- Links to Resources

KEY TOPICS

This study guide chapter reinforces the following terms/topics discussed in the textbook chapter:

- central processing unit (CPU)
- compact disc (CD)
- computer-based patient record (CPRs)
- data warehousing
- database
- digital video disc (DVD)

- distance learning
- electronic medical records (EMRs)
- hardware
- hospital information system (HIS)
- Internet
- local area network (LAN)
- management information system (MIS)
- network
- nurse informaticist
- nursing informatics
- online
- peripherals
- personal computers (PCs)
- random access memory (RAM)
- read-only memory (ROM)
- spreadsheet
- telemedicine
- wide area network (WAN)
- world wide web (www)

LECTURE OUTLINE

I. General concepts
  A. Computer hardware
    1. The Central Processing Unit
    2. Computer memory and storage
    3. Input devices
    4. Output devices
    5. Communications devices
    6. Presentation graphics programs
  B. Computer software
    1. Word processing
    2. Databases
    3. Spreadsheets
    4. Communications
  C. Computer systems
    1. Management information systems
    2. Hospital information systems
    3. World Wide Web and the Internet
II. Computers in nursing education
  A. Teaching and learning
    1. Literature access and retrieval
    2. Computer-assisted instruction
    3. Classroom technology
    4. Distance learning
  B. Testing
  C. Student and course record management
III. Computers in nursing practice
  A. Documentation of client status and medical record keeping
    1. Bedside data entry
    2. Computer-based Patient Records (CPR)
    3. Tracking client status
    4. Data standardization and classifications
      a. Electronic access to patient data
    5. Client monitoring and computerized diagnostics
    6. Telemedicine/telehealth
  B. Practice management
  C. Specific applications of computers in nursing practice
    1. Community and home health
    2. Case management
IV. Computers in nursing administration
  A. Human resources
  B. Medical records management
  C. Facilities management
  D. Budget and finance
  E. Quality assurance and utilization review
  F. Accreditation
V. Computers in nursing research
  A. Problem identification
  B. Literature review
  C. Research design
  D. Data collection and analysis
  E. Research dissemination
  F. Research grants

FOCUSED STUDY TIPS

1. Define the following:
   distance learning
   nursing informatics
   software
   telenursing
   hardware
   online
   telemedicine
2. Use of computers throughout the world has increased dramatically. Health care has been no exception. To maximize use of computers in the health arena, each user needs to have access to which three computer elements?
3. Computer-assisted instruction (CAI) and computerized distance learning are tools used by nurses to further their education. How do they differ?

4. Novice and experienced nurse researchers use computers in their work. In which phase of the research process are computers most widely used?
5. Identify a client situation or clinical issue of interest to you and/or your class. How would you research this topic using computerized literature access and retrieval systems?
6. Investigate the variety of clinical facilities used as educational sites by your nursing program. Do any of them use bedside data entry or computer-based client records? If so, what advantages and disadvantages of these systems have been identified by other students, faculty, and staff?
7. Visit a ward/unit at your local hospital. Identify at least 10 ways in which computers are used to assist client care.

CASE STUDY

Mary Lynn Crush, a registered nurse on a general medical-surgical care unit, must document patient care in the computer system. What will this nurse need to gain access to the system?

Once Mary Lynn accesses a patient's chart, she needs to answer a call bell. What should she do with the information on the computer screen?

After returning to continue documenting, Mary Lynn makes a data entry error. What should she do about the error?

Later in the day, Mary Lynn phones a patient at home to see how she's been doing since being discharged from the hospital 3 days ago. What type of patient care is Mary Lynn demonstrating?

NCLEX TEST QUESTIONS

1. One way in which nurses in hospitals have used computers is:
   a. to develop software.
   b. to develop computers.
   c. to assess and document client's health conditions.
   d. to develop newer models.
2. How would a nurse seek information about the dosage and side effects of medications a client is taking?
   a. hospital database
   b. computerized telephone log
   c. hospital chart
   d. pharmacy database
3. As the nurse manager on your unit, what computer information would help develop a staff schedule?
   a. pharmacy database
   b. business office file
   c. spreadsheets
   d. word processing
4. What linkage would a nurse use to gain access to the National Institute of Nursing Research?
   a. edu
   b. com
   c. gov
   d. org
5. What is one way nurse educators have utilized computers in the academic field?
   a. hospital information system
   b. computer based patient records
   c. management information systems
   d. distance learning
6. How does using an electronic medical record improve health care?
   a. It helps nurses document their daily activities.
   b. It helps nurses enter data at the bedside.
   c. It helps clients share in knowledge and activities that influence their health.
   d. It helps nurses to manage client scheduling.
7. Which of the following computerized systems helps to transmit electronic data about clients to persons at a distant location?
   a. computer-based patient records
   b. telemedicine
   c. distance learning
   d. data standardization
8. As a nursing administrator, how would you use computers?
   a. case management
   b. research grants
   c. client monitoring
   d. budget and finance

9. According to the American Nurses' Association, what is the role of nursing in maintaining privacy and confidentiality related to access to electronic data?
   a. Nurses monitor their clients' health status.
   b. Nurses update their clients' health histories.
   c. Clients retain the right to decide whom and under what circumstances their health information will be disclosed.
   d. Health care providers choose how much health information can be released.

10. In conducting nursing research, a nurse will use a computer to:
    a. examine trends and resources available.
    b. locate current literature about the problem and related concepts.
    c. transmit data to a hospital's main office.
    d. reduce costs by limiting clerical services tasks.

CHAPTER 11

HEALTH, WELLNESS, AND ILLNESS

OVERVIEW

This chapter explores a variety of definitions and meanings of health, wellness, illness, and disease. You are exposed to different ways of thinking about health. Your role in promoting health is emphasized.

www.prenhall.com/kozier

Additional resources for this chapter can be found on the Student CD-ROM accompanying this textbook, and on the Companion Website at www.prenhall.com/kozier. Click on Chapter 11 to select the activities for this chapter.

CD-ROM
- Audio Glossary
- NCLEX Review

Companion Website
- Additional NCLEX Review
- Case Study: Nonadherent Diabetic Client
- MediaLink Application: Health Beliefs
- Links to Resources

LEARNING OUTCOMES

After completing this chapter, the student will be able to:

- Differentiate health, wellness, and well-being
- Describe five dimensions of wellness
- Compare various models of health outlined in this chapter
- Identify factors affecting health status, beliefs, and practices
- Describe factors affecting health care adherence
- Differentiate illness from disease, and acute illness from chronic illness
- Identify Parsons' four aspects of the sick role
- Explain Suchman's stages of illness
- Describe effects of illness on individuals and family members' roles and functions

KEY TOPICS

This study guide chapter reinforces the following terms/topics discussed in the textbook chapter:

- acute illness
- adherence
- autonomy
- chronic illness
- disease
- etiology
- exacerbation
- health
- health behaviors
- health beliefs
- health status
- illness

- illness behavior
- lifestyle
- locus of control
- remission
- risk factors
- well-being
- wellness

LECTURE OUTLINE

I. Concepts of health and well-being
   A. Health
   B. Personal definitions of health
   C. Wellness and well-being
II. Models of health and wellness
   A. Clinical model
   B. Role performance model
   C. Adaptive model
   D. Eudemonistic model
   E. Agent–host environmental model
   F. Health–illness continua
      1. Dunn's high-level wellness grid
      2. Travis's illness–wellness continuum
III. Variables influencing health status, beliefs, and practices
   A. Internal variables
      1. Biologic dimension
      2. Psychologic dimension
      3. Cognitive dimension
   B. External variables
      1. Environment
      2. Standards of living
      3. Family and cultural beliefs
      4. Social support networks
IV. Health belief models
   A. Health locus of control model
   B. Rosenstock's and Becker's health belief models
      1. Individual perceptions
      2. Modifying factors
      3. Likelihood of action
V. Health care adherence
VI. Illness and disease
   A. Illness behaviors
      1. Stage 1 Symptom experiences
      2. Stage 2 Assumption of the sick role
      3. Stage 3 Medical care contact
      4. Stage 4 Dependent client role
      5. Stage 5 Recovery or rehabilitation
   B. Effects of illness
      1. Impact on the client
      2. Impact on the family

FOCUSED STUDY TIPS

1. Define the following models of health:
   adaptive model
   clinical model
   ecological model
   eudaemonistic model
   role performance model
2. Define wellness.
3. What are the external factors that affect health status and beliefs?
4. Your client tells you that he believes diet, exercise, and medications have limited ability to control his high blood pressure and chest pain. He believes that he has been cursed and must suffer the consequences. Explain this client's thinking.
5. Adherence to prescribed therapy is influenced by many factors. List some of these factors.
6. How do you define health? Evaluate your health status based on your own definition.
7. Using Dunn's health grid (see the textbook), rate yourself on the health/wellness continuum. Draw a grid below, plot yourself, and label your status based on the interaction of health with environment.
8. Identify four measures that the nurse should evaluate to improve client compliance with therapy.
9. Jorge Magallanes is a new client at the primary care clinic where you work. On his initial visit, it was determined that he had moderate hypertension. He began a diuretic as part of step 1 therapy for hypertension. On his follow-up visit, an additional agent was added because his blood pressure remained elevated. He is at the clinic today for another follow-up visit. Following your instruction, he has brought all his medications. When you examine the medications, you note that the containers are almost full. Based on the date the prescription was filled, if he has been following the prescribed regimen, the bottles should be almost empty. You suspect nonadherence with the treatment plan. What steps would you take to encourage adherence?
10. Examine the aspects of the sick role as presented by Parsons. Reflect back on your personal experience with illness and on your experience with delivering client care as a nursing student. Do you agree with these aspects of the sick role? Do you believe that clients agree with these aspects?

CASE STUDY

Nikki Mack is a 27-year-old paralegal who has been hospitalized for evaluation of pre-term labor. She is 27 weeks pregnant (normal term is 40 weeks) but having frequent contractions. Niki has one other child, Scott, age 3. Her husband travels frequently for his job. Evaluate the effect this hospitalization will have on Niki and her family.

Once Nikki is discharged, she will have to change her lifestyle to incorporate periods of rest. How will this affect the current home situation? List the types of assistance Nikki will need and who might be available to help.

NCLEX TEST QUESTIONS

1. Which of the following is an example of *health* as defined by the American Nurses' Association?
   a. absence of disease
   b. living in an environment without water and electricity
   c. a single mother undergoing chemotherapy treatments for breast cancer
   d. a paralyzed war veteran using his wheelchair to travel across the country
2. A middle-aged client has been jogging for the last 2 years to help reduce stress. The client has been participating in what part of wellness?
   a. physical and social
   b. physical and emotional
   c. social and emotional
   d. intellectual and emotional
3. A man who works at his job all day as expected is considered healthy even though an x-ray film of his lungs indicates a tumor. This is an example of what type of health model?
   a. clinical model
   b. adaptive model
   c. role performance model
   d. agent-host-environment model
4. A career woman has been told by her physician to lose weight. Because she travels frequently on her job, she has found it difficult to fit in an exercise program. According to Dunn's High-Level Wellness Model, this woman is displaying what type of wellness?
   a. high-level wellness in a favorable environment
   b. emergent high-level wellness in an unfavorable environment
   c. protected poor health in a favorable environment
   d. poor health in an unfavorable environment
5. Which of the following is an example of an internal variable that influences health practices?
   a. getting sunburned at the beach
   b. working at the local petroleum industry
   c. living in poverty
   d. religious convictions opposing blood transfusions
6. A client with hypertension decided it was time to reduce his blood pressure by exercising and reducing salt intake. The client had no family history of hypertension. Which health belief model would the nurse use to help this client?
   a. Health Locus of Control Model
   b. Rosenstock's Health Belief Model
   c. Becker's Health Belief Model
   d. Pender's Health Belief Model
7. Diabetes mellitus is an example of:
   a. acute illness.
   b. adherence.
   c. chronic illness.
   d. exacerbation.
8. An elderly client began having symptoms of nausea, vomiting, and diarrhea. The elderly adult called her daughter and explained the symptoms. The elderly adult is in what stage of illness?
   a. Stage 1: Symptoms Experience
   b. Stage 2: Assumption of the Sick Role
   c. Stage 3: Medical Care Contact
   d. Stage 4: Dependent Client Role
9. What kind of impact does illness have on a client?
   a. Client becomes independent on others.
   b. Client's role in family changes.
   c. Client becomes more autonomous.
   d. Client's self-esteem becomes enhanced.
10. Which of the following causes of nonadherence are specific to teenagers?
   a. alternative/complementary therapies
   b. forgetfulness
   c. dementia
   d. don't consider the consequences of their actions

CHAPTER 12

INDIVIDUAL, FAMILY, AND COMMUNITY HEALTH

OVERVIEW

This chapter examines your role in caring for the individual, the family, and the community. It presents a discussion of personal, family, and community needs along with application of the nursing process to these groups. You are exposed to the expanding role of the community health nurse and the movement toward family-centered nursing care.

LEARNING OUTCOMES

After completing this chapter, the student will be able to:

- Explain the relationships of individuality and holism to nursing practice
- Give four main characteristics of homeostatic mechanisms
- Describe the roles and functions of the family
- Describe different types of families
- Identify the components of a family health assessment
- Identify common risk factors regarding family health
- Develop nursing diagnoses, outcomes, and interventions pertaining to family functioning
- Develop outcome criteria for specific nursing diagnoses related to family functioning
- Identify theoretical frameworks used in individual and family health promotion
- Identify Maslow's characteristics of the self-actualized person
- Identify various types of communities
- Describe the use of the nursing process in the community setting

www.prenhall.com/kozier

Additional resources for this chapter can be found on the Student CD-ROM accompanying this textbook, and on the Companion Website at www.prenhall.com/kozier. Click on Chapter 12 to select the activities for this chapter.

CD-ROM
- Audio Glossary
- NCLEX Review

Companion Website
- Additional NCLEX Review
- Case Study: The Amish
- MediaLink Application: Health Care Resources
- Links to Resources

KEY TOPICS

This study guide chapter reinforces the following terms/topics discussed in the textbook chapter:

- boundary
- closed system
- community
- community health nursing
- compensatory
- equilibrium
- extended family
- family
- family-centered nursing
- feedback
- holism
- homeostasis
- input
- negative feedback
- nuclear family
- open system
- output
- positive feedback
- psychologic homeostasis
- self-regulation
- subsystems
- suprasystem
- system
- throughput

LECTURE OUTLINE

I. Individual health
   A. Concept of individuality
   B. Concept of holism
   C. Concept of homeostasis
      1. Physiologic homeostasis
      2. Psychologic homeostasis
   D. Assessing the health of individuals
II. Family health
III. Functions of the family
IV. Types of families in today's society
      1. Traditional family
      2. Two-career family
      3. Single-parent family
      4. Adolescent family
      5. Foster family
      6. Blended family
      7. Intra-generational family
      8. Cohabitating family
      9. Gay or lesbian family
      10. Single adults living alone
   A. Assessing the health of families
      1. Health beliefs
      2. Family communication patterns
      3. Family coping mechanisms
      4. Risk for health problems
         a. Maturity factors
         b. Hereditary factors
         c. Sex or race
         d. Sociologic factors
         e. Lifestyle factors
V. Applying theoretical frameworks to individuals and families
   A. Needs theories
      1. Kalish's hierarchy of needs
      2. Characteristics of basic needs
   B. Developmental stage theories
   C. Systems theories
   D. Structural-functional theories
VI. Community health

FOCUSED STUDY TIPS

1. Define and give an example of the following terms/phrases:
   holism
   negative feedback
   positive feedback
   self-regulation
   homeostasis
   perception homeostasis
   self-identity
2. List the major homeostatic regulators of the body.
3. What are human needs? What role do they play in homeostasis?
4. A family assessment includes an examination of family function, interactions, strengths, and weaknesses. Why should the nurse conduct an overall family assessment?
5. What is a community? What are the dimensions of individuality?
6. Identify the major prerequisites for achieving psychological homeostasis.
7. Identify at least two ways in which knowledge of human needs helps the nurse in practice.

8. Label the hierarchy of human needs according to Maslow.
9. Describe your own family.
   a. Which one of the eight types of families does your family most resemble?
   b. Is your current family different from your family of origin? If so, describe your family of origin.
10. Provide your own definition of family and analyze how much your personal experience has affected your definition.
11. Analyze your own family for risk factors, developmental factors, hereditary factors, lifestyle factors, and sociological factors that may influence its health and well-being.
12. Use Major Aspects of a Community Assessment in the chapter to examine your community. Identify the major problems, issues, or opportunities in your own community. Write a nursing diagnosis for your community and identify resources that may help you address your issue.

CASE STUDY

Marybeth Smithton, a 35-year-old female, is in a same-sex relationship. She tells the community health nurse, during a routine clinic visit, that her partner is pushing her for a commitment. Marybeth wants to have more freedom but doesn't want her partner to leave. What type of support can the community health nurse provide for this client?

Marybeth returns to the clinic in 3 weeks and tells the nurse that her partner has left. Marybeth is very emotional and her health is suffering. What can the community health nurse do to help this client?

Four months pass, and Marybeth returns to the clinic. She seems happier than during the last visit and hasn't been experiencing any changes in her health status. What could contribute to this change in Marybeth?

NCLEX TEST QUESTIONS

1. When a community is the client, what does the nurse assess?
   a. family functioning
   b. family interaction patterns
   c. family strengths and weaknesses
   d. environmental problems
2. Which of the following is an example of holism?
   a. A nurse is advising the mother of a preschooler to understand that the child desiring to explore his world is in a developmental stage.
   b. In helping a man who is grieving over the death of his spouse, the nurse explores the impact of the loss on the whole person.
   c. A nurse assesses environmental problems for a family.
   d. A nurse assesses a preschooler who has been diagnosed with attention deficit hyperactivity disorder.
3. In assessing a family, it is important for the nurse to assess:
   a. different personalities in the family.
   b. environmental problems.
   c. family interaction patterns.
   d. where the family lives.
4. Parents placing limits on their teenagers are an example of:
   a. input.
   b. output.
   c. feedback.
   d. closed system.
5. A young woman brought in a 3-year-old child to the emergency department. In assessing the child, the nurse asked the woman if she was the mother. The young mother explained that the child was her stepchild. The nurse assessed the family structure as:
   a. traditional.
   b. extended.
   c. blended.
   d. single-parent.
6. A nurse was working with a young couple who had lost their infant to SIDS (sudden infant death syndrome). To assess their coping mechanism, which of the following is an example of internal resources?
   a. social support systems
   b. religious affiliations
   c. compassionate friends support group
   d. a sense of mutuality within the family

7. Which of the following is at risk for health problems?
   a. a child who has annual dental checkups
   b. an unwed teenage mother
   c. an 80-year-old who walks in the mall three times a week
   d. a young career woman who just received a job promotion
8. Data gathered during a family assessment may lead to which of the following nursing diagnoses?
   a. alteration in comfort
   b. readiness for effective parenting
   c. interrupted family processes
   d. readiness for effective communication
9. Which of the following is an example of Maslow's needs?
   a. a grief support group
   b. a child exploring the environment
   c. a college student learning how to hang glide
   d. an obese woman eating chocolate after a difficult day at work
10. Which of the following is an example of community health?
    a. developmental stages
    b. self-esteem needs
    c. stimulation needs
    d. safety and transportation

CHAPTER 13

CULTURE AND HERITAGE

OVERVIEW

This chapter discusses the role of culture in health care beliefs and use of health services. You learn how to perform a cultural assessment and plan culturally competent care. Important tips address communicating with clients from other cultures.

LEARNING OUTCOMES

After completing this chapter, the student will be able to:

- Describe the rationale for the National Standards for Culturally and Linguistically Appropriate Services in Health Care
- Discuss the components of CulturalCare nursing, heritage consistency, and HEALTH traditions
- Identify methods of heritage assessment
- Differentiate folk healing from biomedical care
- Identify factors related to communication with culturally diverse patients and colleagues
- Describe examples the different health views of culturally diverse people
- Plan culturally sensitive, appropriate, and competent nursing interventions

www.prenhall.com/kozier

Additional resources for this chapter can be found on the Student CD-ROM accompanying this textbook, and on the Companion Website at www.prenhall.com/kozier. Click on Chapter 13 to select the activities for this chapter.

CD-ROM
- Audio Glossary
- NCLEX Review

Companion Website
- Additional NCLEX Review
- Case Study: Conveying Cultural Sensitivity
- MediaLink Application: Chinese Childbearing Beliefs
- Links to Resources

KEY TOPICS

This study guide chapter reinforces the following terms/topics discussed in the textbook chapter:

- acculturation
- assimilation
- bicultural
- biomedical health belief
- CulturalCare
- culturally appropriate
- culturally competent
- culturally sensitive
- culture
- culture shock
- discrimination
- diversity

- ethnic
- folk medicine
- Health
- health belief view
- heritage consistency
- heritage inconsistency
- holistic health belief
- interpreter
- magico-religious
- modern
- prejudice
- race
- religion
- scientific health belief
- socialization
- stereotyping
- subculture
- traditional
- translator

LECTURE OUTLINE

I. National Standards for Culturally and Linguistically Appropriate Services in Health Care
   A. Demographic change
   B. Immigration
II. Culturalcare nursing
III. Concepts related to CulturalCare nursing
   A. Subculture
   B. Biculture
   C. Diversity
   D. Acculturation
   E. Assimilation
   F. Race
   G. Prejudice
   H. Stereotyping
   I. Discrimination
   J. Culture shock
IV. Heritage consistency
   A. Culture
   B. Ethnicity
   C. Religion
   D. Socialization
V. Heritage assessment tool
   A. Example of heritage consistency
   B. Heritage assessment
VI. Health traditions
   A. Interrelated aspects
   B. Symbolic examples
VII. Selected parameters for CulturalCare nursing
   A. Health beliefs and practices
   B. Family patterns
   C. Communication style
      1. Verbal communication
      2. Nonverbal communication
   D. Space orientation
   E. Time orientation
   F. Nutritional patterns
VIII. Providing CulturalCare

FOCUSED STUDY TIPS

1. Define the following terms/phrases:
   cultural awareness
   cultural competence
   cultural shock
   culture
   diversity
   ethnic group
   ethnic identity
   race
2. Nurses must be aware of how individuals and cultures view the use of space. List some characteristics of *space.*
3. What does the magico-religious health belief view mean?
4. Discuss the scientific or biomedical health belief view.
5. What are the six characteristics of culture?
6. Identify your orientation to time. Are you oriented toward the past, present, or future?
7. Identify a classmate, neighbor, friend, family member, or acquaintance from a different culture. Utilize the sample questions and discussion areas presented in the chapter to conduct a cultural assessment. Next, imagine that this person is a client undergoing surgery in your facility. How would this knowledge affect your nursing care?
8. Evaluate your knowledge of cultural sensitivity (see the chapter discussion entitled Conveying Cultural Sensitivity). Evaluate your current cultural sensitivity. Which suggestions do you currently follow? Which items will require behavior changes on your part?

CASE STUDY

The nurse is providing care to a client from a non-American culture. During the course of the admission assessment, the client becomes very angry and demands to be seen immediately by the doctor. What can the nurse do in this situation?

1. *What should the nurse include in the assessment of this client? How is this information helpful?*

NCLEX TEST QUESTIONS

1. When a nurse develops a plan of care for a Hispanic family, she must be aware of the family's view of health. What method of care is the nurse using?
   a. heritage care
   b. ethical care
   c. philosophical care
   d. cultural care
2. In working with a Cajun family, the nurse must be aware of nontraditional remedies. This is an example of:
   a. culturally competent.
   b. culturally sensitive.
   c. culturally appropriate.
   d. culturally inappropriate.
3. A young Vietnamese family was in need of health care. Family members attended a local nurse-managed community clinic. This was being ____________ into the United States values.
   a. subculturated
   b. diversified
   c. acculturated
   d. assimilated
4. While caring for an Italian client, the nurse expected the client to verbally express his pain loudly. This is an example of:
   a. racism.
   b. prejudice.
   c. discrimination.
   d. stereotyping.
5. Which of the following is an example of heritage consistency?
   a. Jewish grandparents pay for their grandchild to attend a local Jewish school.
   b. An Italian family lives in a predominantly Jewish neighborhood.
   c. A Vietnamese adolescent changes his name to an American name.
   d. A Hispanic woman tried to hide her Spanish heritage.
6. Which of the following is an example of spiritual health for a Catholic client?
   a. thousand-year eggs
   b. a thunderbird
   c. rosary beads
   d. Tiger Balm
7. A client with cancer told the nurse, "If it is God's will, I will recover." What type of health belief view is the client revealing?
   a. scientific
   b. magico-religious
   c. holistic
   d. folk medicine
8. In caring for a client whose language is not the same as that of the health care provider, the nurse must obtain a(an):
   a. translator.
   b. interpreter.
   c. family member.
   d. representative.
9. Which nonverbal behavior is acceptable while working with Asian clients?
   a. using a firm handshake
   b. kissing as a public greeting
   c. touching a client's head with permission
   d. using continuous direct eye contact
10. Which of the following is an example of a conflict between a cultural belief and the dominant U.S. health care system?
    a. a Jewish family requesting that its male child be circumcised
    b. a Jehovah's Witness refusing a blood transfusion
    c. a Native American diabetic woman complying with diet
    d. a Hispanic family choosing hospice for its dying family member

CHAPTER 14

COMPLEMENTARY AND ALTERNATIVE HEALING MODALITIES

OVERVIEW

This chapter introduces you to the important trends of holistic health care and alternative medical therapies. It offers a concise overview of many holistic healing modalities that will assist you in your care of clients and yourself.

www.prenhall.com/kozier

Additional resources for this chapter can be found on the Student CD-ROM accompanying this textbook, and on the Companion Website at www.prenhall.com/kozier. Click on Chapter 14 to select the activities for this chapter.

CD-ROM
- Audio Glossary
- NCLEX Review

Companion Website
- Additional NCLEX Review
- Case Study: Complementary Alternative Medicine
- MediaLink Application: Support for Alternative Therapies
- Links to Resources

LEARNING OUTCOMES

After completing this chapter, the student will be able to:

- Explain the Office of Alternative Medicine's definition of complementary and alternative (CAM) medicine as a social process
- Describe the evidence suggesting a role for nurses in promoting better communication between physicians and patients using CAM
- Explain the concepts of holism and the goal of holistic nursing
- Identify three common forms of touch therapy
- Describe what happens during a biofeedback session
- Describe the goals that yoga and meditative practices have in common
- Differentiate between the purposes and the effects of meditation
- Define disease from the perspective of Traditional Chinese Medicine (TCM)
- Define health from the perspective of Chiropractic
- Discuss the strengths and weaknesses of the homeopathic theory "like cures like"

KEY TOPICS

This study guide chapter reinforces the following terms/topics discussed in the textbook chapter:

- acupressure
- alternative medicine
- biofeedback
- chiropractic
- clinical aromatherapy
- complementary and alternative medicine (CAM)
- complementary therapies
- holism
- holistic health
- holistic health care
- holistic nursing
- homeopathy
- imagery
- information transduction
- intercessory prayer
- meditation
- mind–body
- mind modulation
- music therapy
- naturopathy
- neuropeptides
- psychoneuroimmunology
- qi
- reflexology
- Reiki
- therapeutic touch (TT)
- Traditional Chinese Medicine (TCM)
- yoga

LECTURE OUTLINE

I. Culture and the evolution of terms
II. Cam use in the United States
III. Concepts of holism and holistic nursing
IV. Concepts of healing
    A. Dossey's eras of medicine
    B. The bodymind or minded body
V. Healing modalities
    A. Touch therapies
        1. Massage
        2. Foot reflexology
        3. Acupressure
        4. Reiki
    B. Mind-body therapies
        1. Progressive relaxation
        2. Biofeedback
        3. Imagery
        4. Yoga
        5. Meditation
        6. Prayer
        7. Music therapy
        8. Humor and laughter
        9. Hypnosis
    C. Aromatherapy
    D. Transpersonal therapies
        1. Noncontact therapeutic touch
        2. Intercessory prayer
VI. Alternative medical therapies
    A. Acupuncture and Oriental medicine
    B. Chiropractic
    C. Herbal medicine
    D. Homeopathy
    E. Naturopathy

FOCUSED STUDY TIPS

1. Describe the following:
   acupressure
   aromatherapy
   chiropractic
   homeopathy
   imagery
   music therapy
   reflexology
   yoga
   acupuncture
   biofeedback
   herbal medicine
   hypnosis
   massage
   prayer
   therapeutic touch
2. Mainstream medicine is now broadening its view of holistic or nontraditional health care practices. According to the Office on Alternative Medicine, what era are we currently in? Why?
3. Mind–body refers to a state of integration that includes body, mind, and spirit. According to this belief system, where is the mind located?

4. What are two responsibilities that the nurse has as a healer?
5. Review the holistic health modalities in the chapter. Identify any modalities with which you have personal experience. What is your opinion of the usefulness of these modalities?
6. Review the self-healing methods for nurses described in the text. Identify the areas in which you must continue to improve.

CASE STUDY

A 45-year-old female client comes into the physician's office for a routine follow-up examination after spinal surgery. The nurse learns that the client has stopped taking all prescribed medications and is ingesting large quantities of vitamins, herbs, and minerals. What should the nurse do with this information?

After the physician's examination, the client states that she intends to return to using a chiropractor for routine adjustments to her spinal cord. What information can the nurse provide to assist the client to think through this health care decision?

Three weeks later, the client phones the physician to say she is experiencing extreme pain at the surgical site. She admits seeing a chiropractor one time; however, the surgical site was not addressed or touched. What information can the nurse provide to help this client at this time?

NCLEX TEST QUESTIONS

1. Receiving chemotherapy treatments for breast cancer is a form of practice for what era of medicine?
   a. Era I: Physical Medicine
   b. Era II: Mind-Body Medicine
   c. Era III: Transpersonal Medicine
   d. Era IV: Complementary Medicine
2. Which of the following therapies can be used to reduce anxiety for a surgical client?
   a. postpone surgery
   b. radiation
   c. biofeedback
   d. morphine
3. The nurse referred a client diagnosed with kidney disease to a clinic that specialized in various touch therapies. Which of the following is an example of a touch therapy?
   a. guided imagery
   b. progressive relaxation
   c. biofeedback
   d. reflexology
4. The nurse was teaching meditation techniques to women in a prenatal class. What kind of instructions would the nurse give the pregnant women?
   a. Massage your feet.
   b. Tense and then relax successive muscle groups.
   c. Focus attention completely on your breathing.
   d. Use prayer to communicate with God.
5. One technique used in long-term care facilities has been very helpful for aging clients. This technique is:
   a. music therapy.
   b. meditation.
   c. hypnosis.
   d. reflexology.
6. In teaching pregnant women about ways to relax, the nurse cautioned these women to be careful when using which technique to reduce stress?
   a. humor and laughter
   b. hypnosis
   c. aromatherapy
   d. music therapy
7. A young and pregnant Korean woman was experiencing severe nausea and vomiting. She requested which of the following CAM techniques?
   a. prayer
   b. progressive relaxation
   c. music therapy
   d. acupuncture
8. Upon discharge for back pain, the client told the nurse he would seek out an alternative therapy to relieve his lower back pain. What type of alternative therapy is most used to reduce lower back pain?
   a. chiropractic
   b. music therapy
   c. intercessory prayer
   d. reflexology

9. Which questions would the nurse ask the client during the initial assessment interview?
   a. "Do you like music?"
   b. "Would you like to read comics?"
   c. "Do you take any form of herbal supplement?"
   d. "Do you want information about intercessory prayer?"

10. A nursing outcome of using progressive relaxation technique is:
    a. to observe for signs of vasoconstriction.
    b. that the client's papillary response will increase.
    c. that the client's heart rate will slow down.
    d. to check vital signs frequently.

CHAPTER 15

CRITICAL THINKING AND THE NURSING PROCESS

OVERVIEW

This chapter introduces the importance of critical thinking, problem solving, and decision making in nursing practice. It defines and differentiates each of these areas. You are presented with an opportunity to evaluate your own strengths and limitations as a critical thinker.

www.prenhall.com/kozier

Additional resources for this chapter can be found on the Student CD-ROM accompanying this textbook, and on the Companion Website at www.prenhall.com/kozier. Click on Chapter 15 to select the activities for this chapter.

CD-ROM
- Audio Glossary
- NCLEX Review

Companion Website
- Additional NCLEX Review
- Case Study: Increased Pressure Ulcers
- MediaLink Application: Practice Critical Thinking
- Links to Resources

LEARNING OUTCOMES

After completing this chapter, the student will be able to:

- Discuss skills and attitudes of critical thinking
- Identify the elements of critical thinking
- Discuss the relationships among the nursing process, critical thinking, the problem-solving process, and the decision-making process
- Explore ways of demonstrating critical thinking

KEY TOPICS

This study guide chapter reinforces the following terms/topics discussed in the textbook chapter:

- creativity
- critical analysis
- critical thinking
- decision making
- deductive reasoning
- inductive reasoning
- intuition
- nursing process
- problem solving
- Socratic questioning

LECTURE OUTLINE

I. Critical thinking
II. Skills in critical thinking
III. Attitudes that foster critical thinking
   A. Independence of thought
   B. Fair-mindedness
   C. Insight into egocentricity and sociocentricity
   D. Intellectual humility and suspension of judgment
   E. Intellectual courage
   F. Integrity
   G. Perseverance
   H. Confidence in reason
   I. Interest in exploring both thoughts and feelings
   J. Curiosity
IV. Standards and elements of critical thinking
V. Applying critical thinking to nursing practice
   A. Problem solving
      1. Trial and error
      2. Intuition
      3. Research process and scientific/modified scientific method
   B. Decision making
VI. Developing critical-thinking attitudes and skills
   A. Self-assessment
   B. Tolerating dissonance and ambiguity
   C. Seeking situations where good thinking is practiced
   D. Creating environments that support critical thinking

FOCUSED STUDY TIPS

1. Define the following:
   cognitive dissonance
   critical thinking
   deductive reasoning
   problem solving
   creative thinking
   decision making
   inductive reasoning
   Socratic questioning
2. When in nursing practice is critical thinking demonstrated? List examples of situations.
3. Creativity is a major element of critical thinking. What are the four stages of creative thinking?
4. What are the conditions that must exist with decision making?
5. What does decision making involve?
6. List at least five attributes of critical thinking.
7. Name five commonly used problem-solving methods.
8. What are the differences between the scientific method and the modified scientific method?
9. Utilize the information contained in the text and Standards for Critical Thinkers to evaluate your own critical thinking skills. Are you a critical thinker? What are your strengths in this area? In what areas are you less adept?

CASE STUDY

The nurse is trying to determine why a client with an abdominal wound developed an infection at the site. All of the nurses' notes are reviewed, and every nurse is observed providing care to the wound. What additional information can this nurse collect to help her make a decision about the wound?

1. *Which nurse theorists might help Jennifer when drafting her scholarly paper?*

NCLEX TEST QUESTIONS

1. When unexpected situations arise, critical thinking enables the nurse to:
   a. delay in responding.
   b. overreact.
   c. meet the nurse's needs.
   d. recognize important cues.
2. While planning an educational program for diabetic clients, the nurse incorporated a bingo game to help teach diabetic management. This is an example of:
   a. critical thinking.
   b. creativity.
   c. scientific method.
   d. modified scientific method.
3. The emergency department nurse observed that a client had dry skin, poor skin turgor, sunken

eyes, and dark amber urine. The nurse reasoned that the client was dehydrated. This is an example of:

a. critical analysis.
b. inductive reasoning.
c. deductive reasoning.
d. creativity.

4. Postoperatively, a client's blood pressure began dropping. The nurse concluded that the client's blood volume had decreased. This is an example of:
   a. fact.
   b. inference.
   c. judgment.
   d. opinion.
5. During the initial interview, the client stated, "I think I have a tumor." Which response is the most appropriate response by the nurse?
   a. "Why do you think that?"
   b. "Have you told your family?"
   c. "Define the word *tumor*."
   d. "Have you asked your physician?"
6. A wound care nurse attended a national conference. At this conference, the nurse learned new techniques for wound care, which she began applying when she returned to the local hospital. Which of the following best describes the nurse's decision making about changing techniques for wound care?
   a. independence of thought
   b. fairmindedness
   c. intellectual humility
   d. intellectual courage
7. While working with an acutely ill client, the nurse stayed in the client's room, assessing him frequently. When questioned about her actions, the nurse said, "I just have a feeling that something is wrong." This is an example of:
   a. trial and error.
   b. intuition.
   c. research process.
   d. scientific method.
8. In developing a plan of care, the nurse will use which of the following methods?
   a. research process
   b. scientific process
   c. modified scientific method
   d. nursing process
9. Nurses use decision making in many areas of nursing. Which of the following is an example of decision making?
   a. bathing the client during visiting hours
   b. taking time to feed the client
   c. delegating to unlicensed personnel to feed the client
   d. discussing the client's condition with family members
10. A group of nurse managers decided to take 1 hour a week to discuss problems on their units. This is an example of:
    a. self-assessment.
    b. creating an environment to support critical thinking.
    c. seeking information about the problem.
    d. insight into egocentricity and sociocentricity.

CHAPTER 16

ASSESSING

OVERVIEW

This chapter introduces the nursing process and discusses assessing, the first step of the nursing process. You will gain a greater understanding of types of data collection, including observing, interviewing, and examining.

LEARNING OUTCOMES

After completing this chapter, the student will be able to:

- Describe the phases of the nursing process
- Identify the major characteristics of the nursing process
- Identify the four major activities associated with the assessment process
- Identify the purpose of assessing
- Differentiate objective and subjective data and primary and secondary data
- Identify three methods of data collection, and give examples of how each is useful
- Compare directive and nondirective approaches to interviewing
- Compare closed and open-ended questions, providing examples and listing advantages and disadvantages of each
- Describe important aspects of the interview setting
- Contrast various frameworks used for nursing assessment

www.prenhall.com/kozier

Additional resources for this chapter can be found on the Student CD-ROM accompanying this textbook, and on the Companion Website at www.prenhall.com/kozier. Click on Chapter 16 to select the activities for this chapter.

CD-ROM

- Audio Glossary
- NCLEX Review
- Animations:
  - Anatomical Landmarks
  - Introduction to Body Systems
  - Lymphatic Systems
  - A & P Review:
    - Anterior View
    - Posterior View
    - Body Cavity
    - Lymphatic System
    - Body Organization

Companion Website

- Additional NCLEX Review
- Case Study: Down's Syndrome Client
- MediaLink Application:
  - Researching Community Resources
- Links to Resources

KEY TOPICS

This study guide chapter reinforces the following terms/topics discussed in the textbook chapter:

- assessing
- cephalocaudal
- closed questions
- covert data
- cues
- data

- database
- directive interview
- inferences
- interview
- leading question
- neutral question
- nondirective interview
- objective data
- open-ended questions
- overt data
- rapport
- review of systems
- screening examination
- signs
- subjective data
- symptoms
- validation

LECTURE OUTLINE

I. Overview of the nursing process
  A. Phases of the nursing process
  B. Characteristics of the nursing process
II. Assessing
III. Collecting data
  A. Types of data
  B. Sources of data
    1. Client
    2. Support people
    3. Client records
    4. Health care professionals
    5. Literature
  C. Data collection methods
    1. Observing
    2. Interviewing
      a. Kinds of interview questions
      b. Planning the interview and setting
        1. Time
        2. Place
        3. Seating arrangement
        4. Distance
        5. Language
      c. Stages of an interview
        1. The opening
        2. The body
        3. The closing
  D. Examining
IV. Organizing data
  A. Nursing conceptual models
  B. Wellness models
  C. Non-nursing models
    1. Body systems model
    2. Maslow's hierarchy of needs
    3. Developmental theories
V. Validating data
VI. Documenting data

FOCUSED STUDY TIPS

1. Describe the placement of assessment within the nursing process.
2. What is the nursing process?
3. How do nursing assessments differ from medical assessments?
4. What is the purpose of assessment?
5. A reddened area on a client's coccyx is an example of what type of data?
6. What is the role of observation?
7. Physical examination of the client is a systematic data collection tool. What should you do when performing a physical examination?
8. What should you do when planning an interview?
9. At the beginning of each shift, the nurse performs an assessment on each of the assigned clients. What type of assessment is this?
10. What are the two purposes of the opening phase of an interview?
11. What is the purpose of the body of an interview?
12. What are the main goals in the closing phase of an interview?
13. Examine the data collection tool used on your clinical unit. What conceptual model(s) does this tool follow?

CASE STUDY

Abah Singh is a 47-year-old Indian male being admitted to the hospital for management of Congestive Heart Failure (CHF). On arrival to the floor, he is short of breath and appears fatigued. Admission vital signs are: BP 158/98, P 104 irregular, RR 26, T 97.9F oral. While you are taking his vital signs, Mr. Singh tells his wife, "I am dying. Let me rest. I will sleep and die." Mrs. Singh is teary-eyed and asks if she can speak with you. Outside the room she tells you, "My husband had a heart attack four months ago. Over the last month it has been harder and harder for him to breathe. He is so short of breath he sleeps sitting up in a chair."

1. *What are the objective data?*
2. *What are the subjective data?*
3. *What factors will you need to consider when planning your admission interview and physical assessment?*
4. *Identify potential sources of data for your assessment.*

NCLEX TEST QUESTIONS

1. The purpose of the nursing process is to:
   a. develop a scientific database.
   b. meet the nurse's needs.
   c. identify a client's health status.
   d. provide an infrastructure to the health care provider.
2. How is the nursing process different from the medical process?
   a. The medical process gathers data, whereas the nursing process does not.
   b. The medical process focuses on physiological systems and the disease process, whereas the nursing process is directed toward a client's response to disease and illness.
   c. The medical process develops a treatment plan, whereas the nursing process develops an intervention.
   d. The medical process focuses on symptom management, whereas the nursing process evaluates and revises the plan of care.
3. After a chart audit was done at a local clinic, the nurse decided to confirm her findings by telephoning the diabetic clients. This is an example of:
   a. assessing.
   b. diagnosing.
   c. planning.
   d. implementing.
4. Which of the following is a critical thinking activity in the planning phase of the nursing process?
   a. organizing data
   b. validating data
   c. comparing patterns with the norm
   d. prioritizing client problems
5. After completing the chart audit and telephone follow-up, the nurse identified gaps in the data. This is an example of:
   a. assessing.
   b. diagnosing.
   c. planning.
   d. evaluating.
6. A nurse was observing a stroke client hold his utensils during the breakfast meal. This is what type of assessment?
   a. initial assessment
   b. problem-focused assessment
   c. emergency assessment
   d. time-lapsed assessment
7. During the home health visit, the client stated, "I feel hot." Which of the following is the nurse's most appropriate response?
   a. "Tell me what you mean by 'I feel hot.'"
   b. Check the client's fluid intake.
   c. Check the client's body temperature.
   d. Check the client's blood pressure.
8. While obtaining a health history, the nurse asked open-ended questions. One advantage of asking open-ended questions is that:
   a. they take more time.
   b. brief answers may be given.
   c. responses are difficult to document.
   d. the client does most of the talking.
9. In which part of the nursing process does the nurse determine whether to continue, modify, or terminate the plan of care?
   a. assessing
   b. planning
   c. implementing
   d. evaluating
10. One of the advantages of closed questions is:
    a. interest and trust are conveyed.
    b. that it requires less effort from client.
    c. that it takes more time.
    d. that it provides more information.

CHAPTER 17

DIAGNOSING

OVERVIEW

This chapter introduces diagnosing, the second step of the nursing process. As a nursing student, you will find the discussion of the appropriate use and formulation of a nursing diagnostic statement very helpful on the clinical unit.

LEARNING OUTCOMES

After completing this chapter, the student will be able to:

- Differentiate various types of nursing diagnoses
- Identify the components of a nursing diagnosis
- Compare nursing diagnoses, medical diagnoses, and collaborative problems
- Identify basic steps in the diagnostic process
- Describe various formats for writing nursing diagnoses
- Describe the characteristics of a nursing diagnosis
- List common errors in writing diagnostic statements
- Describe the evolution of the nursing diagnosis movement, including work currently in progress
- List advantages of a taxonomy of nursing diagnoses

www.prenhall.com/kozier

Additional resources for this chapter can be found on the Student CD-ROM accompanying this textbook, and on the Companion Website at www.prenhall.com/kozier. Click on Chapter 17 to select the activities for this chapter.

CD-ROM

- Audio Glossary
- NCLEX Review

Companion Website

- Additional NCLEX Review
- Case Study: Selecting Nursing Diagnoses for Client with Pneumonia
- MediaLink Application: Resources for a Chronically Ill Child
- Links to Resources

KEY TOPICS

This study guide chapter reinforces the following terms/topics discussed in the textbook chapter:

- defining characteristics
- dependent functions
- diagnosis
- diagnostic label
- etiology
- independent functions
- norm
- nursing diagnosis
- PES format
- possible nursing diagnosis

- qualifiers
- risk factors
- risk nursing diagnosis
- standard
- syndrome diagnosis
- taxonomy
- wellness diagnosis

LECTURE OUTLINE

I. NANDA Nursing Diagnoses
   A. Definitions
   B. Types of nursing diagnoses
   C. Components of a NANDA nursing diagnosis
      1. Problem (diagnostic label)
      2. Etiology (related factors and risk factors)
      3. Defining characteristics
      4. Differentiating nursing diagnoses from medical diagnoses
      5. Differentiating nursing diagnoses from collaborative problems

II. The diagnostic process
   A. Analyzing data
      1. Comparing data with standards
      2. Clustering cues
      3. Identifying gaps and inconsistencies in data
   B. Identifying health problems, risks, and strengths
      1. Determining problems and risks
      2. Determining strengths
   C. Formulating diagnostic statements
      1. Basic two-part statements
      2. Basic three-part statements
      3. One-part statements
      4. Variations of basic formats
      5. Collaborative problems
      6. Evaluating the quality of the diagnostic statement
   D. Avoiding errors in diagnostic reasoning

III. Ongoing development of nursing objectives

FOCUSED STUDY TIPS

1. What is a nursing diagnosis?
2. What components does a correctly written nursing diagnosis contain?
3. What is the purpose of a validated nursing diagnosis taxonomy?
4. Define the following nursing diagnosis terms:
   defining characteristic(s)
   etiology
   problem statement
5. A medical diagnosis refers to a disease process that a physician may treat. How is it different from a nursing diagnosis?
6. Identify the following as a nursing diagnosis, a medical diagnosis, or a collaborative problem.
   diabetes mellitus
   health-seeking behaviors
   ineffective airway clearance related to C-5 paralysis as evidenced by crackles and rhonchi or gurgles on auscultation
   pneumonia
   potential complication of diabetes mellitus: altered wound healing
   potential complication of mastectomy surgery: lymphedema
7. Compare and contrast the terms *analysis* and *synthesis.*
8. Why is critical thinking important when planning client care?
9. List nursing diagnoses for a client with frequent coughing without secretions.
10. What does it mean when data are analyzed?
11. Identify at least three methods to avoid diagnostic errors.

CASE STUDY

Natalie Egan is a 47-year-old woman who reports to your outpatient surgery department at 6:30 A.M. She is scheduled for an 8:30 A.M. surgery. Natalie detected a lump in her breast approximately 3 weeks ago. She underwent a mammo-

gram and, on the advice of her surgeon, is in today for a right breast biopsy and possible radical mastectomy. Natalie informs you that she and her husband are certain that this is benign and that "This whole silly business will be over shortly." She giggles nervously after making the statement.

During your intake interview you assess the following:

BP 162/94 (elevated)

P 112 (elevated)

RR 22 (elevated)

T 97.8F oral

skin, cool and dry

height, 64 inches

weight, 118 pounds

Write at least two nursing diagnoses for Natalie.

Natalie is admitted to the hospital after undergoing a radical mastectomy for carcinoma. As the nurse caring for her on the surgical unit, you assess her upon arrival to the unit. Natalie reports that she is in "tremendous pain." She requests that her family be allowed to see her right away. She also tells you she wants to "get on top of this right away. I want to know everything I can do to get back up to speed and beat this cancer." Natalie's dressing is dry and intact. Her vital signs are:

BP 138/84

P 110 (elevated)

RR 20

T 98.9F oral

Generate additional nursing diagnoses based on this information.

NCLEX TEST QUESTIONS

1. The purpose of a nursing diagnosis is to:
   a. define a taxonomy of nursing language.
   b. promote a taxonomy of nursing language.
   c. identify a client's problem plus etiology.
   d. establish a set of principles.
2. To develop a care plan for a client in an ambulatory care center, the nurse uses which of the following references?
   a. *Physician's Desk Reference*
   b. *Joint Commission for Accreditation of Healthcare Organizations Guidelines*
   c. *American Medical Association Guidelines*
   d. *North American Nursing Diagnosis Association Guidelines*
3. An elderly female with symptoms of fever and burning upon urination was admitted to the hospital from a local nursing home. The client was bed bound and had bilateral extremity contractures. The nursing diagnosis most appropriate for this client is:
   a. alteration in nutrition.
   b. risk for activity intolerance.
   c. readiness for enhanced mobility.
   d. disuse syndrome.
4. In caring for a client with a nursing diagnosis of pain, the nurse instructed the client how to splint the incision. This is an example of:
   a. independent nursing intervention.
   b. dependent nursing intervention.
   c. collaborative nursing intervention.
   d. medical intervention.
5. The pediatric nurse screened a 9-month-old infant using the Denver Developmental Screening Tool. What part of the diagnostic process was the nurse performing?
   a. comparing data against standards
   b. generating hypotheses
   c. identifying inconsistencies in data
   d. identifying health problems

6. Which of the following nursing diagnostic statement is correct?
   a. fluid replacement related to fever
   b. impaired skin integrity related to immobility
   c. impaired skin integrity related to ulceration of sacral area
   d. pain related to severe headache
7. To write a nursing diagnosis for a collaborative problem, the nurse begins with which diagnostic label?
   a. readiness for
   b. alteration of
   c. potential complication
   d. impaired
8. To write a nursing diagnosis for a wellness problem, the nurse begins with which diagnostic label?
   a. readiness for
   b. alteration of
   c. potential complication
   d. impaired
9. The PES format for writing nursing diagnosis statements is used for which of the following?
   a. actual nursing diagnoses
   b. potential nursing diagnoses
   c. risk for nursing diagnoses
   d. wellness diagnoses
10. Which type of nursing diagnosis is to be developed as one-part statements, according to NANDA?
   a. actual nursing diagnoses
   b. potential nursing diagnoses
   c. risk for nursing diagnoses
   d. wellness diagnoses

CHAPTER 18

PLANNING

OVERVIEW

This chapter introduces planning, the third step of the nursing process. You learn to write expected outcomes/goals, nursing orders, and nursing care plans. You are introduced to priority setting and independent, dependent, and collaborative nursing strategies.

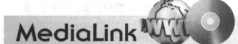

www.prenhall.com/kozier

Additional resources for this chapter can be found on the Student CD-ROM accompanying this textbook, and on the Companion Website at www.prenhall.com/kozier. Click on Chapter 18 to select the activities for this chapter.

CD-ROM

- Audio Glossary
- NCLEX Review

Companion Website

- Additional NCLEX Review
- Case Study: Client Who had a Bicycle Accident
- MediaLink Application: Client with Peptic Ulcer

LEARNING OUTCOMES

After completing this chapter, the student will be able to:

- Compare and contrast initial planning, ongoing planning, and discharge planning
- Identify activities that occur in the planning process
- Explain how standards of care and preprinted care plans can be individualized and used in creating a comprehensive nursing care plan
- Identify essential guidelines for writing nursing care plans
- Identify factors that the nurse must consider when setting priorities
- State the purposes of establishing client goals and desired outcomes
- Describe the relationship of goals and desired outcomes to the nursing diagnoses
- Identify guidelines for writing goals and desired outcomes
- Discuss the *Nursing Outcomes Classification*, including an explanation of how to use the outcomes and indicators in care planning

KEY TOPICS

This study guide chapter reinforces the following terms/topics discussed in the textbook chapter:

- assignment
- collaborative care plan
- collaborative interventions
- critical pathway
- delegation
- dependent interventions
- discharge planning
- formal nursing care plan

- goals/desired outcomes
- independent interventions
- indicator
- individualized care plan
- informal plan
- multidisciplinary care plan
- nursing intervention
- Nursing Interventions Classification (NIC)
- nursing orders
- Nursing Outcomes Classification (NOC)
- policies
- priority setting
- procedures
- protocols
- rationale
- standardized care plan
- standards of care
- standing order

LECTURE OUTLINE

I. Types of planning
  A. Initial planning
  B. Ongoing planning
  C. Discharge planning
II. Developing nursing care plans
  A. Standardized approaches to care planning
  B. Formats for nursing care plans
    1. Student care plans
    2. Computerized care plans
  C. Multidisciplinary (collaborative) care plans
  D. Guidelines for writing nursing care plans
III. The planning process
  A. Setting priorities
  B. Establishing client goals and desired outcomes
    1. The nursing outcomes classification
    2. Purpose of desired outcomes and goals
    3. Long- and short-term goals
    4. Relationship of desired outcomes and goals to nursing diagnoses
    5. Components of goal and desired outcome statements
    6. Guidelines for writing goals and desired outcomes
  C. Selecting nursing interventions and activities
    1. Types of nursing interventions
    2. Considering the consequences of each intervention
    3. Criteria for choosing nursing intervention
  D. Writing nursing orders
    1. Date
    2. Action verb
    3. Content area
    4. Time element
    5. Signature
    6. Relationship of nursing orders to problem status
  E. Delegating implementation
IV. The nursing interventions classification

FOCUSED STUDY TIPS

1. Define the following:
   critical pathways
   discharge planning
   initial planning
   nursing order
   protocols
   desired outcome
   formal care plan
   nursing intervention
   ongoing planning
2. List the characteristics found in the planning phase of the nursing care plan.
3. What is the purpose of standards of care, standardized care plans, protocols, and policies and procedures?
4. List the reasons for short-term goals.
5. List five factors that the nurse must consider when setting priorities for nursing care.
6. Provide two examples of independent nursing interventions.
7. Provide two examples of dependent nursing interventions.
8. Provide two examples of collaborative interventions.
9. Define a standing order.
10. List five nursing activities associated with planning of nursing care.
11. Identify which of the following goals or expected outcomes are well-stated by placing a check mark in front of them. Rewrite those that are incorrectly written.
    1. ____ Client will be able to successfully draw up and administer her own insulin by Thursday, 6/16.
    2. ____ Client will ambulate.

3. ____ By the end of the week, Mr. Teak will lose 20 pounds.
4. ____ The client will increase the amount of fluids ingested and participate in unit social activities.
5. ____ Fluid volume status will improve, as evidenced by a minimum of 1500cc intake every 24 hours beginning today, 1/18/02.

CASE STUDY

Ginger Harod is a 26-year-old woman with severe seasonal allergies. She is seen today in the outpatient clinic complaining of wheezing and shortness of breath. The nurse practitioner has outlined a rigorous treatment plan that includes an inhaled bronchodilator and an inhaled steroid. Ginger tells you, "I'm sick of being sick. I wheeze so much it affects everything about my life. I've got to get this under control, but I don't know anything about these medicines." As the nurse, you recognize that the client has a knowledge deficit about these new medications.

1. *Write an expected outcome/goal for this nursing diagnosis.*
2. *Write two nursing orders designed to accomplish this goal.*

NCLEX TEST QUESTIONS

1. The nurse admitted the client to the oncology unit. When does the nurse begin planning for client care?
   a. at the first contact
   b. after client has signed financial forms
   c. after the physician has established medical regime
   d. upon discharge
2. At the beginning of the day shift, the nurse established priorities for an adolescent client. Which type of planning is the nurse carrying out?
   a. initial planning
   b. ongoing planning
   c. discharge planning
   d. continuity of care planning
3. A client was admitted to the intensive care unit with a diagnosis of acute myocardial infarction. In planning for his care, which type of nursing care plan might the nurse use?
   a. informal nursing care plan
   b. formal nursing care plan
   c. standardized care plan
   d. individualized care plan
4. Which of the following becomes part of the client's permanent record?
   a. protocols
   b. policies
   c. procedures
   d. standing orders
5. In developing a plan of care for the client with left-sided cerebrovascular accident (CVA), the nurse outlined a plan that included both medical and other health care providers. This is an example of:
   a. student care plan.
   b. computerized care plan.
   c. collaborative care plan.
   d. standardized care plan.
6. When writing care plans, which of the following is the correct method?
   a. Turn and reposition the client every 2 hours.
   b. Clean the wound three times a day.
   c. Inspect the incision q8h.
   d. Clean the wound with hydrogen peroxide.
7. In caring for a client postoperatively, which of the following is considered a medium priority?
   a. loss of respiratory function
   b. loss of cardiac function
   c. decreased hygiene
   d. anxiety
8. The nurse developed a plan of care for a client with congestive heart failure. Which of the following is an appropriate goal statement?
   a. Client's ankle measures less than 10 inches in circumference.
   b. Restrict fluids to 1000 ml of fluid per day.
   c. Client identifies foods high in salt from a prepared list before time of discharge.
   d. Measure hourly urine.
9. In planning for care of a client with a seizure disorder, the nurse would order which of the following?
   a. 3/20/03 Administer Dilantin IM. J. Doe, R.N.
   b. 3/20/03 Pad side rails during periods of restlessness and confusion. M. Smith, R.N.

c. 3/20/03 Turn every 2 hours. J. Doe, R.N.
d. 3/20/03 Contact home health for evaluation. M. Smith, R.N.

10. In caring for a postpartal client, the nurse wrote on the care plan, "If fundus is boggy, massage until firm." This is an example of what type of nursing order?

a. observation order
b. prevention order
c. treatment order
d. health promotion order

CHAPTER 19

IMPLEMENTING AND EVALUATING

OVERVIEW

This chapter introduces the fourth and fifth steps of the nursing process: implementing and evaluating. The chapter stresses the interrelationship of all the steps in the nursing process to assist you in the practical application of the nursing process. You are introduced to several decision-making schemes for nursing care planning and for quality assurance (the ongoing evaluation of care).

LEARNING OUTCOMES

After completing this chapter, the student will be able to:

- Discuss the five activities of the implementing phase
- Explain how implementing relates to other phases of the nursing process
- Describe three categories of skills used to implement nursing interventions
- Identify guidelines for implementing nursing interventions
- Explain how evaluating relates to other phases of the nursing process
- Describe five components of the evaluation process
- Describe the steps involved in reexamining and modifying the client's care plan
- Name the two components of an evaluation statement
- Differentiate quality improvement from quality assurance
- Describe three components of quality evaluation: structure, process, and outcomes

www.prenhall.com/kozier

Additional resources for this chapter can be found on the Student CD-ROM accompanying this textbook, and on the Companion Website at www.prenhall.com/kozier. Click on Chapter 19 to select the activities for this chapter.

CD-ROM
- Audio Glossary
- NCLEX Review

Companion Website
- Additional NCLEX Review
- Case Study: Treating a Client for Pain
- MediaLink Application: Analyzing Effective Quality Assurance
- Links to Resources

KEY TOPICS

This study guide chapter reinforces the following terms/topics discussed in the textbook chapter:

- activities
- cognitive skills
- evaluating
- evaluation statement
- implementing
- interpersonal skills
- outcome
- evaluation
- evaluation process
- quality-assurance (QA) program
- quality improvement
- structure evaluation
- technical skills

LECTURE OUTLINE

I. Implementing
   A. Relationship of implementing to other nursing process phases
   B. Implementing skills
   C. Process of implementing
      1. Reassessing the client
      2. Determining the nurse's need for assistance
      3. Implementing nursing interventions
      4. Supervising delegated care
      5. Documenting nursing activities

II. Evaluating
   A. Relationship of evaluating to other nursing process phases
   B. Process of evaluating client responses
      1. Collecting data
      2. Judging achievement of desired outcomes
      3. Relating nursing actions to client goals and outcomes
      4. Drawing conclusions about problem status
      5. Continuing, modifying, and Terminating the nursing care plan
   C. Evaluating the quality of nursing care
      1. Quality assurance
      2. Quality improvement
      3. Nursing audit

FOCUSED STUDY TIPS

1. Define the following terms/phrases:
   cognitive skills
   evaluating
   implementing
   interpersonal skills
   nursing audit
   quality assurance
   quality improvement
   technical skills
2. What type of nursing skill is used to plan how to transport a ventilator-dependent client to another building for an MRI?
3. What is the role of the nurse when implementing nursing orders?
4. What is the key distinction between delegation and assignment?
5. What are the responsibilities of the nurse who delegates tasks to assistive personnel?
6. List characteristics for the evaluation phase of nursing care planning.
7. How do the assessment and evaluation phases of the nursing process differ?
8. If a nurse determines that the client's goals have not been met, what may he/she conclude?
9. What type of quality assurance program answers the question "What is the average time a client waits for lab results in the emergency department?"
10. What are the five components of the implementation phase of the nursing process?
11. What are the six components of the evaluation process?
12. List at least one question or area to evaluate in the first four phases of the nursing process.
    assessing
    diagnosing
    planning
    implementing
13. What are the three types of nursing audit?

CASE STUDY

The manager of a patient care area is planning a quality improvement initiative for the unit. The major care issues include documentation of narcotic medications given, documentation of patient care provided, and completion of prescribed dressings and treatments. Create a quality improvement study for these three patient care issues.

NCLEX TEST QUESTIONS

1. While caring for an unwed teenage mother, the nurse referred the client to a counseling center. What type of skill was the nurse using?
   a. cognitive
   b. intellectual
   c. interpersonal
   d. technical
2. For which of the following would the nurse need assistance?
   a. teaching the client how to give insulin injections
   b. using the one-person method of turning a client
   c. referring a client to home health
   d. setting up a new model of traction equipment
3. In caring for a client with a nursing diagnosis of "anxiety related to unfamiliar surroundings," the nurse decided to use an independent nursing action to help reduce anxiety. Which of the following is an independent nursing action?
   a. Administer Valium 10 mgm IM.
   b. Refer to social services.
   c. Perform back massage.
   d. Administer Lorezepam 5 mgm as needed.
4. The physician ordered 10 mg of morphine sulfate to be administered IM. The nurse assessed the client's respiratory rate to be 4 breaths/minute. What action should be done first?
   a. Give morphine sulfate as ordered.
   b. Withhold the morphine sulfate.
   c. Report respiratory rate to family members.
   d. Report respiratory rate to pharmacy.
5. During the evaluating phase of the nursing process, the nurse collects data for the purpose of:
   a. making diagnosis.
   b. developing a goal.
   c. implementing a nursing action.
   d. judging the effectiveness of the nursing care.
6. In caring for a client with congestive heart failure, which of the following outcomes is the most appropriate?
   a. Check the intake and output every shift.
   b. Urinary output will balance with fluid intake.
   c. Daily fluid intake will be minimal for 24 hours.
   d. Reduce pedal edema.
7. Which of the following subjective data need to be interpreted?
   a. restlessness of a client with pain
   b. degree of tissue turgor of a dehydrated client
   c. Client stating, "I am nauseated."
   d. relaxed facial muscles as indicators of pain relief
8. The physician ordered a client to drink 3,000 ml of fluids in a 24-hour period. The nurse charted the fluids taken in during the 7–3 shift to be 2,500 ml in the 24 hours. What conclusion can the nurse draw?
   a. Goal was met.
   b. Goal was partially met.
   c. Goal was not met.
   d. No goal established.
9. Which of the following is an example of an evaluation statement?
   a. Monitor respiratory status every 4 hours.
   b. Monitor level of consciousness.
   c. Administer prescribed expectorants.
   d. Goal met: Oral intake 300 ml more than output.
10. To continue professional accountability, the nurse questioned, "How many clients undergoing hip repairs develop pneumonia?" This is an example of:
    a. quality improvement.
    b. structure evaluation
    c. process evaluation
    d. outcome evaluation

CHAPTER 20

DOCUMENTING AND REPORTING

OVERVIEW

This chapter introduces the purpose and method of charting and communicating client information. Different types of charting, intraprofessional and interprofessional communication, and guidelines for charting are presented.

www.prenhall.com/kozier

Additional resources for this chapter can be found on the Student CD-ROM accompanying this textbook, and on the Companion Website at www.prenhall.com/kozier. Click on Chapter 20 to select the activities for this chapter.

CD-ROM
- Audio Glossary
- NCLEX Review

Companion Website
- Additional NCLEX Review
- Case Study: Client with Delirium Tremens
- MediaLink Application: Establishing a Document System
- Links to Resources

LEARNING OUTCOMES

After completing this chapter, the student will be able to:

- Discuss reasons for keeping client records
- Explain how various forms in the client record (e.g., flowsheets, progress notes, care plans, critical pathways, Kardexes, discharge/transfer forms) are used to document steps of the nursing process (assessment, diagnosis, planning, implementation, and evaluation)
- Compare and contrast different documentation methods: source-oriented and problem-oriented medical record, PIE, focus charting, charting by exception, computerized records, and the case management model
- Compare and contrast the documentation needed for clients in acute care, home health care, and long-term care settings
- Identify and discuss guidelines for effective recording that meets legal and ethical standards
- Identify abbreviations and symbols commonly used for charting
- List the measures used to maintain the confidentiality of client records
- Describe the nurse's role in reporting, conferring, and making referrals
- Identify essential guidelines for reporting client data

KEY TOPICS

This study guide chapter reinforces the following terms/topics discussed in the textbook chapter:

- change-of-shift report
- chart
- charting
- charting by exception (CBE)
- client record
- discussion
- documenting
- flow sheet
- focus charting
- Kardex
- narrative charting
- PIE
- problem-oriented medical record (POMR)
- problem-oriented record (POR)
- progress notes
- record
- recording
- report
- SOAP
- source-oriented record
- variance

LECTURE OUTLINE

I. Ethical and legal considerations
  A. Ensuring confidentiality of computer records
II. Purposes of client records
  A. Communication
  B. Planning client care
  C. Auditing health agencies
  D. Research
  E. Education
  F. Reimbursement
  G. Legal documentation
  H. Health care analysis
III. Documentation systems
  A. Source-oriented medical record
  B. Problem-oriented medical record
    1. Database
    2. Problem list
    3. Plan of care
    4. Progress notes
  C. PIE
  D. Focus charting
  E. Charting by exception
  F. Computerized documentation
  G. Case management
IV. Documenting nursing activities
  A. Admission nursing assessment
  B. Nursing care plans
  C. Kardexes
  D. Flow sheets
    1. Graphic record
    2. Fluid balance record
    3. Medication administration record
    4. Skin assessment record
  E. Progress notes
  F. Nursing discharge/referral summaries
V. Long-term care documentation
VI. Home care documentation
VII. General guidelines for recording
  A. Date and time
  B. Timing
  C. Legibility
  D. Permanence
  E. Accepted terminology
  F. Correct spelling
  G. Signature
  H. Accuracy
  I. Sequence
  J. Appropriateness
  K. Completeness
  L. Conciseness
  M. Legal prudence
VIII. Reporting
  A. Change-of-shift reports
  B. Telephone reports
  C. Telephone orders
  D. Care plan conference
  E. Nursing rounds

FOCUSED STUDY TIPS

1. Define the following:
   case management
   charting by exception
   computerized record
   CORE documentation

FACT system
focus charting
narrative charting
outcome documentation
PIE charting
problem-oriented medical record
SOAP format charting
source-oriented clinical record

2. List five suggestions for ensuring confidentiality of computerized client records.
3. What are the regulations influencing the kind and frequency of documentation required in long-term care facilities?
4. How has home care documentation been standardized?
5. List general guidelines for recording.
6. Discuss the key elements of a change-of-shift report.
7. What should the nurse know about taking telephone orders?

CASE STUDY

The hospital is changing the way patient care is documented from SOAP(IER) to computerized focus charting. List learning issues that the nursing staff might experience with the change in the documentation system.

Training is being conducted on the new computerized clinical documentation system. The nurses are experiencing confusion and want to continue documenting the "old" way. Identify ways to aid the nurses change their behavior toward the way patient care is documented.

Many of the nursing staff complain they don't know how to type, want to use the older "paper and pencil" approach, and want the hospital to pay transcriptionists to enter the data into the clients' medical records. What types of issues does this recommendation create? Would this be a viable approach to the documentation of client care?

NCLEX TEST QUESTIONS

1. When the nurse makes an entry on a client record, this is an example of:
   a. discussing.
   b. reporting.
   c. charting.
   d. dialoguing.
2. To ensure confidentiality of computer records, the nurse must:
   a. leave computer unattended.
   b. document sensitive material, such as AIDS.
   c. use someone else's password.
   d. shred all unneeded computer-generated worksheets.
3. Nurses use baseline and ongoing data to evaluate the effectiveness of the nursing care plan. The purpose of charting the plan of care in the client record is an example of:
   a. planning.
   b. quality assurance.
   c. research.
   d. reimbursement.
4. Which of the following documentation systems uses critical pathways, a multidisciplinary approach to planning and documenting client care?
   a. source-oriented record
   b. PIE charting
   c. case management
   d. charting by exception
5. The nurse was developing a Kardex for a client with pneumonia. Which of the following items are placed on the Kardex?
   a. number of family members
   b. flow sheet
   c. fluid balance record
   d. list of diagnostic procedures ordered
6. Which of the following documentations is on the discharge summary?
   a. activities of daily living
   b. behavioral modification assessments
   c. treatments that are to be continued
   d. safety measures needed

7. The enterostomal R.N. assessed and measured a client for a colostomy. In documenting the findings, the R.N. recorded on which part of the chart?
   a. nurses' note
   b. flow sheet
   c. progress note
   d. medication record
8. The local hospital uses standards of nursing care in developing nursing care plans. This is a form of:
   a. the SOAP format.
   b. the PIE documentation model.
   c. focus charting.
   d. charting by exception.
9. The client refused to accept medication. In documenting this information in the chart, the nurse would write which of the following:
   a. The client was uncooperative.
   b. The client refused medication.
   c. No problems in giving medication.
   d. Client refused medication because he is stubborn.
10. An example of reporting information about the client in home health is:
   a. change-of-shift report.
   b. taped recorded reports.
   c. care plan conferences.
   d. nursing rounds.

CHAPTER 21

CONCEPTS OF GROWTH AND DEVELOPMENT

OVERVIEW

This chapter presents the major concepts of growth and development and their application to nursing. You will read about the ideas and beliefs of the top theorists who have helped shape modern-day tenets of growth and development.

LEARNING OUTCOMES

After completing this chapter, the student will be able to:

- Describe essential facts related to growth and development
- Differentiate between the terms *growth* and *development*
- Describe the stages of growth and development according to various theorists
- List factors that influence growth and development
- Explain the principles of growth and development
- Identify developmental tasks associated with Havighurst's six age periods
- Describe characteristics and implications of Freud's five stages of development
- Identify Erikson's eight stages of development
- Compare Peck's and Gould's stages of adult development
- Explain Piaget's theory of cognitive development
- Compare Kohlberg's and Gilligan's theories of moral development
- Compare Fowler's and Westerhoff's stages of spiritual development

www.prenhall.com/kozier

Additional resources for this chapter can be found on the Student CD-ROM accompanying this textbook, and on the Companion Website at www.prenhall.com/kozier. Click on Chapter 21 to select the activities for this chapter.

CD-ROM
- Audio Glossary
- NCLEX Review

Companion Website
- Additional NCLEX Review
- Case Study: Treating a Six-Year Old Client
- Care Plan Activity: Child with Developmental Problems
- MediaLink Application: Discharging a Young Client
- Links to Resources

KEY TOPICS

This study guide chapter reinforces the following terms/topics discussed in the textbook chapter:

- accommodation
- adaptation
- adaptive mechanism
- assimilation
- cognitive development
- defense mechanism
- development
- developmental task
- ego
- fixation
- growth
- id
- libido
- moral
- moral behavior
- moral development
- morality
- personality
- superego
- unconscious mind

LECTURE OUTLINE

I. Factors influencing growth and development
II. Stages of growth and development
III. Growth and development Theories
   A. Developmental task theory (Havighurst)
   B. Psychosocial theories
      1. Freud
      2. Erikson
      3. Peck
      4. Gould
   C. Cognitive theory (Piaget)
   D. Moral theories
      1. Kohlberg
      2. Gilligan
   E. Spiritual theories
      1. Fowler
      2. Westerhoff
IV. Applying growth and development concepts to nursing practice
V. Focus on critical thinking

FOCUSED STUDY TIPS

1. What do the following terms mean?
   cephalocaudal
   developmental task
   growth
   development
   differentiated development
   personality
2. What are Freud's five stages of development?
3. Which theorist concentrated on the developmental tasks of old age?
4. What is the nurse's major role in relation to growth and development?
5. You are assigned to care for four clients on a pediatric unit. The ages of the clients are 6 months, 30 months, 5 years, and 12 years. Identify at least one key characteristic of each client and a related nursing implication.
6. Review the numerous growth and development theorists. Which theorist most accurately depicts your personal experience? Identify your current stage of growth and development in this theory.

CASE STUDY

The nurse is caring for a 35-year-old client who has recently experienced a miscarriage. If care is provided according to Peck's theory, what interventions would be the best for this client?

Throughout the course of care, the client tells the nurse that she doesn't ever want to have any more children. What would be the best response for the nurse to make to this client? Which theorist supports this response?

On the day of discharge, the client asks the nurse if the baby could be in heaven if the child wasn't actually "born." Identify approaches that would help this client with her spiritual needs.

NCLEX TEST QUESTIONS

1. While assessing a toddler, the nurse determined that the toddler was performing age-appropriate skills. The toddler was demonstrating:
   a. growth.
   b. development.
   c. cultural adherence.
   d. spirituality.
2. A young mother was attempting to toilet train her toddler. Based on your understanding of Freud's theory, what was the nurse's best response?
   a. "If the toddler does not become toilet trained now, he never will."
   b. "The toddler must be punished if he soils his diaper."
   c. "Make the toilet training a positive experience."
   d. "A negative experience of toilet training will affect his self-esteem."
3. A 50-year-old client decided to have her 76-year-old mother move in with her. Using your knowledge of Erickson's theory of development, in which stage is the client?
   a. middle adulthood
   b. young-old
   c. middle-old
   d. old-old
4. The nurse was helping a retired client find a hobby he would enjoy. What theorist best explains this type of adult development?
   a. Freud
   b. Piaget
   c. Erickson
   d. Peck
5. Which of the following is an example of Gould's Stage 4?
   a. an 18-year-old leaving for college
   b. a 25-year-old in the military service
   c. a 32-year-old graduate student
   d. a 68-year-old retired nurse
6. A 13-year-old was diagnosed with diabetes mellitus. Using Piaget's theory, the nurse would educate the client by:
   a. educating the parents on how to administer insulin.
   b. explaining the rationale and consequences of taking insulin.
   c. recognizing that the 13-year-old is not capable of administering insulin.
   d. recognizing that the 13-year-old is too anxious to administer insulin.
7. While assessing an adolescent's values about abortion, the adolescent stated, "Abortion is wrong." Based on your knowledge of moral theories, the adolescent was stating his:
   a. morals.
   b. morality.
   c. moral behavior.
   d. moral development.
8. In counseling battered women, the nurse would use which of the following moral theorists?
   a. Kohlberg
   b. Gilligan
   c. Freud
   d. Piaget
9. While doing a spiritual assessment on a client diagnosed with cancer, the nurse found that the client felt the need to have sacred articles placed around the hospital room. Which spiritual theorist best explains the client's behavior?
   a. Fowler
   b. Westerhoff
   c. Gilligan
   d. Kohlberg
10. A 5-year-old child was admitted for tonsillectomy. So that the child could express his fear about the pending surgery, the nurse gave the child a doll with removable body parts. Which theorist best explains the nurse's rationale for this intervention?
    a. Erickson
    b. Piaget
    c. Peck
    d. Westerhoff

CHAPTER 22

PROMOTING HEALTH FROM CONCEPTION THROUGH ADOLESCENCE

OVERVIEW

This chapter discusses growth and development from conception through adolescence. It emphasizes health assessment, promotion, and teaching throughout these age groups.

LEARNING OUTCOMES

After completing this chapter, the student will be able to:

- Identify tasks characteristic of different stages of development from infancy through adolescence
- Describe usual physical development from infancy through adolescence
- Trace psychosocial development according to Erikson from infancy through adolescence
- Explain cognitive development according to Piaget from infancy through adolescence
- Describe moral development according to Kohlberg from childhood through adolescence
- Describe spiritual development according to Fowler throughout childhood and adolescence
- Identify assessment activities and expected characteristics from birth through late childhood
- Identify essential activities of health promotion and protection to meet the needs of infants, toddlers, preschoolers, school-age children, and adolescents

MediaLink

www.prenhall.com/kozier

Additional resources for this chapter can be found on the Student CD-ROM accompanying this textbook, and on the Companion Website at www.prenhall.com/kozier. Click on Chapter 22 to select the activities for this chapter.

CD-ROM

- Audio Glossary
- NCLEX Review
- Animations
  - Oogenesis
  - Cell Division
  - Conception
  - Embryonic Heart Formation and Circulation
  - Formation of Placenta
  - Sperm Production

Companion Website

- Additional NCLEX Review
- Case Study: Motor and Social Development in Infancy
- Care Plan Activity: Teen with Lymphocytic Leukemia
- MediaLink Application: Safety Tips for Children
- Links to Resources

KEY TOPICS

This study guide chapter reinforces the following terms/topics discussed in the textbook chapter:

- adolescence
- adolescent growth spurt
- amblyopia
- Apgar scoring system
- apocrine glands
- Denver Developmental Screening Test (DDST)
- eccrine glands
- ectoderm
- ejaculation
- embryonic phase
- emmetropic
- endoderm
- entoderm
- failure to thrive
- fetal phase
- fontanelles
- hyperopic
- identification
- imagination
- introjection
- lanugo
- menarche
- mesoderm
- myopic
- normocephaly
- peer groups
- placenta
- primary sexual characteristics
- puberty
- regression
- repression
- sebaceous glands
- secondary sexual characteristics
- self-concept
- separation anxiety
- shaken baby syndrome (SBS)
- stereognosis
- strabismus
- sudden infant death syndrome (SIDS)
- sutures
- teratogen
- trimesters
- vernix caseosa

LECTURE OUTLINE

I. Conception and Prenatal development
  A. Health promotion
    1. Oxygen
    2. Nutrition and fluids
    3. Rest and activity
    4. Elimination
    5. Temperature maintenance
    6. Safety
II. Neonates and infants (Birth to 1 Year)
  A. Physical development
    1. Weight
    2. Length
    3. Hand and chest circumference
    4. Head molding
    5. Vision
    6. Hearing
    7. Smell and taste
    8. Touch
    9. Reflexes
    10. Motor development
  B. Psychosocial development
  C. Cognitive development
  D. Moral development
  E. Health problems
    1. Failure to thrive
    2. Infant colic
    3. Crying
    4. Child abuse
    5. Sudden Infant Death Syndrome
  F. Health assessment and promotion
    1. Apgar scoring
    2. Developmental screening tests
    3. Ongoing nursing assessments
III. Toddlers (1–3 years)
  A. Physical development
    1. Weight
    2. Height
    3. Head circumference
    4. Sensory abilities
    5. Motor abilities
  B. Psychosocial development
  C. Cognitive development
  D. Moral development
  E. Spiritual development
  F. Health problems
    1. Accidents
    2. Visual problems
    3. Dental caries

4. Respiratory tract and ear infections
G. Health assessment and promotion
IV. Preschoolers (4–5 years)
A. Physical development
1. Weight
2. Height
3. Vision
4. Hearing and taste
5. Motor abilities
B. Psychosocial development
C. Cognitive development
D. Moral development
E. Spiritual development
F. Health problems
G. Health assessment and promotion
V. School-age children (6–12 years)
A. Physical development
1. Weight
2. Height
3. Vision
4. Hearing and touch
5. Prepubertal changes
6. Motor abilities
B. Psychosocial development
C. Cognitive development
D. Moral development
E. Spiritual development
F. Health problems
G. Health assessment and promotion
VI. Adolescence (12–18 years)
A. Physical development
1. Physical growth
2. Glandular changes
3. Sexual characteristics
B. Psychosocial development
C. Cognitive development
D. Moral development
E. Spiritual development
F. Health problems
G. Health assessment and promotion

FOCUSED STUDY TIPS

1. Identify nursing activities to assess and promote health of the fetus.
2. Identify nursing activities to assess and promote health of infants.
3. How does health promotion for the preschooler differ from health promotion for the toddler?

CASE STUDY

During your pediatric rotation, you have the opportunity to work in a pediatric ambulatory care clinic. Children from birth through adolescence are treated in this clinic by a team of nurse practitioners, pediatricians, and registered nurses.

Your first client, Marianna Roberts, is a 14-year-old who is seeking gynecological care. During your interview, Marianna expresses much concern about her sexuality. How can you help Marianna deal with her concerns?

The next client is Martin Randall, a 3-week-old infant. Martin's mother is concerned that he may have colic. She reports that he cries periodically throughout the day but each evening he has crying periods of 2 hours.

How would you proceed?

At midday, 18-month-old Sherrie Bacon is scheduled to be seen. Sherrie's biological mother has recently died of breast cancer. She has just been adopted by a loving family. Her adoptive parents have scheduled Sherrie for a complete physical. The nurse practitioner has asked you to provide teaching on health promotion to the family.

What advice would you offer to the new parents?

In the afternoon, you work with two additional clients: 4-year-old Scott Parker and 9-year-old Sarah Burch. Scott's mother is concerned about school readiness. Scott will be 5 in September and is scheduled to begin kindergarten. His mother reports that he is extremely shy, that he has had difficulty with preschool due to his fear of leaving his mother, and that he does not play with other children. She is concerned about his ability to function in school.

Evaluate Scott's level of development.

In contrast, Sarah's parents tell you that their daughter is very gregarious and always playing with friends. They ask if their daughter is showing signs of adolescence.

What is your assessment?

CARE PLAN CRITICAL THINKING ACTIVITIES

Fill in the appropriate elements of the care plan for Marianna Roberts.
Assessment and Diagnosis
Planning and Implementation
Evaluation

NCLEX TEST QUESTIONS

1. An unwed teenager in her second trimester told the school nurse that she was experiencing a fluttering sensation in her abdomen. What is the nurse's best response?
   a. "You should not be feeling any movement yet."
   b. "Fetal movements usually begin about 5 months."
   c. "Are you dilated or having contractions?"
   d. "Are you sure it is not gas?"
2. Which of the following vitamins prevent neural tube defects in the fetus?
   a. vitamin A
   b. niacin
   c. folic acid
   d. vitamin D
3. Pregnant women should consume what kind of food to help reduce birth defects?
   a. leafy green vegetables
   b. protein
   c. bananas
   d. doughnuts
4. To reduce birth defects, the nurse instructs pregnant women to:
   a. soak for one hour in a hot tub.
   b. drink caffeine frequently.
   c. avoid hot whirlpool baths.
   d. have a routine chest X-ray.
5. A new father expressed concern about his infant's head. He said to the nurse, "Are you sure my son is normal? His head looks dented." The nurse's best response is:
   a. "Are you concerned about your son's appearance?"
   b. "His head seems to be larger than his body."
   c. "Most babies are not attractive right after the birth process."
   d. "Within a week, a newborn's head usually regains its symmetry."
6. The nurse assessed a newborn's Apgar score to be a 10. The nurse inferred that:
   a. the newborn was stillborn.
   b. the newborn was normal.
   c. the newborn was having difficulty breathing.
   d. 10 is not on the scale for the Apgar Scoring System.
7. A young mother phoned 911 and stated that she found her infant in bed not breathing. The most common cause of this is:
   a. failure to thrive.
   b. colic.
   c. meningitis.
   d. sudden infant death syndrome.
8. The most common health problem among school-age children is:
   a. colic.
   b. hearing impairment.
   c. obesity.
   d. smoking.
9. A preventive measure for preschoolers is:
   a. regular dental screenings and fluoride treatments.
   b. providing accurate information about sexual issues.
   c. using proper equipment when participating in sports.
   d. providing opportunities for a variety of organized group activities.
10. When conducting a developmental assessment on an adolescent, the nurse would ask which of the following types of questions?
    a. "Are you able to read, print, and manipulate numbers and letters easily?"
    b. "Do you enjoy riddles and read and understand comics?"
    c. "Do you have a concept of money?"
    d. "Are you planning to go to college?"

CHAPTER 23

PROMOTING HEALTH IN ADULTS AND OLDER ADULTS

OVERVIEW

This chapter discusses the expected changes that occur in adulthood. It emphasizes the diversity within this age group and distinguishes the needs of young, middle, and older adult clients. It identifies common health concerns and hazards affecting adults and presents nursing interventions for promoting health in this group.

LEARNING OUTCOMES

After completing this chapter, the student will be able to:

- Identify characteristic tasks of the different stages of development during young, middle, and older adulthood
- Describe the usual physical development occurring in young, middle, and older adulthood
- Compare psychosocial development according to Erikson during the various stages of adulthood
- Explain changes in cognitive development according to Piaget throughout adulthood
- Describe moral development according to Kohlberg throughout adulthood
- Describe spiritual development according to Fowler throughout adulthood
- Identify selected health problems associated with young, middle-aged, and older adults
- Identify developmental assessment guidelines for young, middle-aged, and older adults
- List examples of health promotion topics from young adulthood through older adulthood

www.prenhall.com/kozier

Additional resources for this chapter can be found on the Student CD-ROM accompanying this textbook, and on the Companion Website at www.prenhall.com/kozier. Click on Chapter 23 to select the activities for this chapter.

CD-ROM
- Audio Glossary
- NCLEX Review

Companion Website
- Additional NCLEX Review
- Case Study: Developmental Phases of Adulthood
- Care Plan Activity: Parenting Responsibilities
- MediaLink Application: Developing a Health Promotion Program
- Links to Resources

KEY TOPICS

This study guide chapter reinforces the following terms/topics discussed in the textbook chapter:

- activity theory
- cataracts
- climacteric
- continuity theory
- dementia
- disengagement theory
- dyspnea
- frail elderly
- generativity
- hypothermia
- kyphosis
- long-term theory
- maturity
- menopause
- osteoporosis
- Papanicolaou (Pap) test
- pathologic fractures
- perception
- presbycusis
- recent memory
- sensory memory
- short-term memory

LECTURE OUTLINE

I. Young adults (20–40 years)
   A. Physical development
   B. Psychosocial development
   C. Cognitive development
   D. Moral development
   E. Spiritual development
   F. Health problems
      1. Accidents
      2. Suicide
      3. Hypertension
      4. Substance abuse
      5. Sexually transmitted disease
      6. Violence
      7. Abuse of women
      8. Malignancies
   G. Health assessment and promotion
II. Middle-aged adults (40–65 years)
   A. Physical development
   B. Psychosocial development
   C. Cognitive development
   D. Moral development
   E. Spiritual development
   F. Health problems
      1. Accidents
      2. Cancer
      3. Cardiovascular disease
      4. Obesity
      5. Alcoholism
      6. Mental health alterations
   G. Health assessment and promotion
III. Older adults (over 65 years)
   A. Physical changes
      1. Integument
      2. Neuromusculoskeletal
      3. Sensory/perceptual
      4. Pulmonary
      5. Cardiovascular
      6. Gastrointestinal
      7. Urinary
      8. Genitals
   B. Psychosocial development
      1. Retirement
      2. Economic change
      3. Relocation
      4. Maintaining independence and self-esteem
      5. Facing death and grieving
   C. Cognitive development
   D. Moral development
   E. Spiritual development
   F. Health problems
      1. Accidents
      2. Chronic disabling illness
      3. Drug use and misuse
      4. Alcoholism
      5. Dementia
      6. Elder abuse
   G. Health assessment and promotion
IV. Considerations for adults of all ages
   A. Health promotion
   B. Culture
   C. Developmental nursing considerations

FOCUSED STUDY TIPS

1. Define the following:
   cataracts
   dementia
   dyspnea
   osteoporosis
   presbycusis
   climacteric
   disengagement theory
   kyphosis
   Pap test
2. What is a common health problem that is seen most often in the young adult?
3. List health promotion activities appropriate for the young adult.
4. Both men and women experience changes in hormonal production in the middle adult years. List some of these changes.
5. Older adults experience major psychosocial adjustments. Which adjustment is not commonly seen in this age group?
6. What is elder abuse? What is the role of the nurse in suspected elder abuse?
7. How do you define adulthood? What criteria do you use to determine this state?
8. Complete the table of normal sensory and perceptual changes associated with aging.

Sensory/Perceptual Function	Changes Associated with Aging
Vision	________________________________
Hearing	________________________________
Taste	________________________________
Smell	________________________________
Touch	________________________________

CASE STUDY

M. is an active 70-year-old woman. She has just retired from work as a real estate agent. She is considering working independently as a real estate agent so she can set her own schedule and will not be forced out of work. M. is being seen for an annual physical. She is examined by an FNP. M. tells the nurse that because she loved her job she is dis appointed she was forced to retire. She also tells the FNP, "I don't feel old. I'm active. I'm alert. I don't like being treated like a little old lady. What can I do to stay healthy and well as I age?"

1. *How should the nurse practitioner respond to M.?*
2. *Examine your own feelings about older adults. How do you feel about M. and other older persons? Do you enjoy caring for them or not?*
3. *Examine the resources in your community for elderly clients. Look at support services that help clients remain at home and at nursing home care, adult day care, and community groups. Evaluate the adequacy of these services.*

CARE PLAN CRITICAL THINKING ACTIVITIES

Fill in the appropriate elements of the Care Plan for M.:

Assessment and Diagnosis
Planning and Implementation
Evaluation

NCLEX TEST QUESTIONS

1. Which age group is more likely to return to the family home?
   a. young adults
   b. middle-aged adults
   c. older adults
   d. old-old adults
2. The leading cause of death for the young adult is:
   a. cancer.
   b. heart disease.
   c. AIDS.
   d. unintentional injuries.
3. According to Healthy People 2010, homicide is the leading cause of death in which of the following ethnic groups?
   a. Caucasian
   b. African-American
   c. Native American
   d. Asian-American
4. Which age group relies primarily on spiritual beliefs to help deal with illness, death, and tragedy?
   a. adolescent
   b. young adult
   c. middle-aged adult
   d. older adult
5. The most common cause of accidental death in the middle-aged adult is:
   a. drowning
   b. homicide
   c. suicide
   d. motor vehicle accidents
6. The fastest-growing group in the United States today is:
   a. newborns.
   b. adolescents.
   c. middle-aged adults.
   d. older adults.
7. By age 80, all elderly people have:
   a. respiratory problems.
   b. cataracts.
   c. presbycusis.
   d. coronary artery disease.
8. While volunteering at the local council-on-aging senior home, the nurse found the senior citizens playing card games and knitting quilts. What psychosocial aging theory best explains this behavior?
   a. growth and developmental theory
   b. disengagement theory
   c. activity theory
   d. continuity theory
9. An Alzheimer's client was living with her daughter at home. Which type of living choices provides the caregiver a respite from the daily care?
   a. nursing home
   b. assisted living
   c. adult day care
   d. adult group home
10. The most common cause of accidents in older people is:
    a. suicides.
    b. homicides.
    c. medications.
    d. falls.

CHAPTER 24

CARING, COMFORTING, AND COMMUNICATING

OVERVIEW

This chapter presents a concise discussion of the role of therapeutic relationships in the delivery of client care. It introduces techniques that facilitate communication and the helping relationship and alerts you to potential barriers to these goals. Through extensive examples, you examine the relationship of verbal and nonverbal communication and distinguish the skills necessary for interpersonal and group communication.

LEARNING OUTCOMES

After completing this chapter, the student will be able to:

- Discuss nursing theory related to caring
- Describe essential aspects of the comforting process
- Describe factors influencing the communication process
- Discuss nurse–patient communication as a dynamic process
- Describe four phases of the helping relationship
- Identify types of groups helpful in promoting health and comfort
- Identify features of effective groups

MediaLink

www.prenhall.com/kozier

Additional resources for this chapter can be found on the Student CD-ROM accompanying this textbook, and on the Companion Website at www.prenhall.com/kozier. Click on Chapter 24 to select the activities for this chapter.

CD-ROM
- Audio Glossary
- NCLEX Review

Companion Website
- Additional NCLEX Review
- Case Study: Providing Comfort
- Care Plan Activity: Treating an Immigrant Family
- MediaLink Application: Communication Resources
- Links to Resources

KEY TOPICS

This study guide chapter reinforces the following terms/topics discussed in the textbook chapter:

- attentive listening
- caring
- comfort
- comforting
- communication
- congruent communication
- decode
- empathy
- encoding
- feedback
- group
- group dynamics

- helping relationships
- nonverbal communication
- personal space
- process recording
- proxemics
- territoriality
- therapeutic communication
- verbal communication

LECTURE OUTLINE

I. Caring
II. Comforting
 A. The Comforting process
 B. Comfort
  1. Comfort needs
  2. Intensity (type) of comfort
 C. Comfort measures
III. Communicating
 A. The communication process
  1. Sender
  2. Message
  3. Receiver
  4. Response
 B. Modes of communication
  1. Verbal communication
   a. Pace and intonation
   b. Simplicity
   c. Clarity and brevity
   d. Timing and relevance
   e. Adaptability
   f. Credibility
   g. Humor
  2. Nonverbal communication
   a. Personal appearance
   b. Posture and gait
   c. Facial expression
   d. Gestures
 C. Factors influencing the communication process
  1. Development
  2. Gender
  3. Values and perceptions
  4. Personal space
  5. Territoriality
  6. Roles and relationships
  7. Environment
  8. Congruence
  9. Interpersonal attitudes
 D. Therapeutic communication
  1. Attentive listening
  2. Physical attending
 E. Barriers to communication
IV. The helping relationship
 A. Phases of the helping relationship
  1. Pre-interaction phase
  2. Introductory phase
  3. Working phase
   a. Exploring and understanding thoughts and feelings
   b. Facilitating taking action
  4. Termination phase
 B. Developing helping relationships
V. Group communication
 A. Group dynamics
 B. Types of health care groups
  1. Task groups
  2. Teaching groups
  3. Self-help groups
  4. Self-awareness/growth groups
  5. Therapy groups
  6. Work-related social support groups
VI. Communication and the nursing process

FOCUSED STUDY TIPS

1. Define the following phases of the helping relationship.
   introductory phase — termination phase
   preinteraction phase — working phase
2. What are the recommended distances for each of the personal spaces?
   intimate — public
   personal — social
3. Place an F in front of those factors that facilitate communication and a B in front of those factors that are barriers to communication.
   ____ showing a lack of interest
   ____ showing acceptance
   ____ demonstrating respect for the client
   ____ patting a client on the head and calling her "dear"
   ____ responding to a client's request by saying "What do you want?"
4. Define caring. Why is this concept so important for a nurse?

5. List the characteristics of a helping relationship.
6. What is nonverbal communication?
7. What is attentive listening?
8. List barriers to communication.
9. Identify at least five factors that may influence the nurse–client helping relationship.
10. J. B. is an 11-year-old boy admitted with asthma. His mother says that he is not consistent in taking his medications. You have planned an interview and teaching session with the child. Identify at least five actions you can take to facilitate a helping relationship.
11. Complete the communication process diagram. (Include the graphics.)
12. Give an example of a nursing activity that might be conducted in each of the four space distances.

Space Distance	Nursing Activity
Intimate	____________________
Personal	____________________
Social	____________________
Public	____________________

13. List the three main functions of a group.

CASE STUDY

J. L., a 24-year old college sophomore, was brought to the hospital emergency department complaining of severe abdominal pain. She was examined and scheduled for surgical excision this afternoon of an ectopic pregnancy (pregnancy out of the uterus, usually in the Fallopian tube). She has been brought to the surgical unit for preoperative care. She is teary-eyed and complaining of pain.

1. *In an effort to create a positive environment for the interview, what might the nurse want to do?*
2. *What will affect the interpersonal space between them?*
   During the interview, J. L. tells the nurse that she is very frightened. She has never had surgery, and she is concerned about her future ability to conceive. The nurse considers sharing her own personal experience with surgery.
3. *What is the primary consideration in using self-disclosure?*
   The nurse asks J. L. about her understanding of the planned surgery. She starts to sob and stops talking. The nurse recognizes the client's obvious emotional distress.
4. *What are at least three therapeutic responses that could be employed?*
   The client is very tearful. She is unable to make eye contact with the nurse. She says, "I can't believe this is happening."
5. *What should the nurse say?*

CARE PLAN CRITICAL THINKING ACTIVITIES

Fill in the appropriate elements of the care plan for J. L.:
Assessment and Diagnosis
Planning and Implementation
Evaluation

NCLEX TEST QUESTIONS

1. In the Native American cultures, the elders demonstrate caring by sharing the ancient stories of their people. Which theorist best explains this type of caring and communicating?
   a. Watson
   b. Leininger
   c. Miller
   d. Gadow and Noddings
2. A non–English-speaking Korean woman was scheduled for surgery. The nurse observed the client to be very agitated. The nurse contacted the client's daughter who could speak English and asked her to stay in the preoperative suite with her mother. What type of comfort was the nurse providing?
   a. physical
   b. psychospiritual
   c. social
   d. environmental
3. The nurse asked the client if she was in pain. The client answered, "No." However, the nurse observed the client making facial grimaces and holding her hand over her stomach. Which part of the communication process is important?
   a. sender
   b. receiver
   c. message
   d. feedback
4. The Asian client gestured "Come here" with her hand. The American nurse perceived this gesture to mean "Go away." This is a form of:
   a. verbal behavior.
   b. nonverbal behavior.
   c. inappropriate communication.
   d. culture-specific communication.
5. The nurse was administering an IM injection. The nurse was communicating what kind of personal space with the client?
   a. intimate
   b. personal
   c. social
   d. public
6. What is an example of congruent communication?
   a. The nurse did not make eye contact and said, "You will be fine."
   b. The nurse squinted her eyes and said, "This should not hurt."
   c. The nurse made direct eye contact with the client and said, "This colostomy looks good."
   d. While removing a dressing, the nurse physically moved away from the smell while saying, "Oh, this looks good."
7. The home health nurse developed a contract with the client. What phase of the helping relationship is being demonstrated?
   a. preinteraction phase
   b. introductory phase
   c. working phase
   d. termination phase
8. The nurse was preparing a diabetic education program. What type of health care group would the nurse be involved in?
   a. task
   b. teaching
   c. self-help
   d. self-awareness
9. A school-age client had bilateral hearing aids. He did not like to wear his hearing aids. An appropriate nursing diagnosis for this client is:
   a. powerlessness related to impaired verbal communication.
   b. low self-esteem related to impaired verbal communication.
   c. social Isolation related to impaired verbal communication.
   d. impaired social interaction related to impaired verbal communication.
10. The elderly client asked the nurse, "Should I move from my home to a nursing home?" The nurse stated, "If I were you, I would go to a nursing home where you will get your meals cooked for you." The nurse was demonstrating what kind of barrier to communication?
    a. stereotyping
    b. being defensive
    c. challenging
    d. giving common advice

CHAPTER 25

TEACHING

OVERVIEW

This chapter discusses the importance of teaching and learning in the delivery of health care, beginning with assessing learning needs. Practical tips are offered on how to facilitate learning and avoid barriers to the teaching/learning process.How to develop a teaching plan and evaluate the effectiveness of your teaching are also presented.

LEARNING OUTCOMES

After completing this chapter, the student will be able to:

- Discuss the importance of the teaching role of the nurse
- Describe the attributes of learning
- Compare and contrast andragogy, pedagogy, and geragogy
- Discuss the learning theory of Behaviorism, Cognitivism, and Humanism, and how nurses can use each of these theories
- Describe the three domains of learning
- Identify factors that affect learning
- Assess learning needs of learners and the learning environment
- Identify nursing diagnoses, outcomes, and interventions that reflect the learning needs of clients
- Describe the essential aspects of a teaching plan
- Discuss guidelines for effective teaching
- Discuss strategies to use when teaching clients of different cultures
- Identify methods to evaluate learning
- Demonstrate effective documentation of teaching–learning activities

www.prenhall.com/kozier

Additional resources for this chapter can be found on the Student CD-ROM accompanying this textbook, and on the Companion Website at www.prenhall.com/kozier. Click on Chapter 25 to select the activities for this chapter.

CD-ROM

- Audio Glossary
- NCLEX Review

Companion Website

- Additional NCLEX Review
- Case Study: Planning a Rural Health Education Program
- Care Plan Activity: Client Admitted to the Hospital for the First Time
- MediaLink Application: Overseeing a Health Fair
- Links to Resources

KEY TOPICS

This study guide chapter reinforces the following terms/topics discussed in the textbook chapter:

- adherence
- andragogy
- affective domain
- behaviorist theory
- cognitive domain
- cognitive theory
- compliance
- geragogy
- humanism
- imitation
- learning
- learning need
- modeling
- motivation
- pedagogy
- positive reinforcement
- psychomotor domain
- readiness

LECTURE OUTLINE

I. Teaching
   A. Teaching clients and their families
   B. Teaching in the community
   C. Teaching health personnel
II. Learning
   A. Learning theories
      1. Behaviorism
      2. Cognitivism
      3. Humanism
   B. Using learning theories
   C. Factors affecting learning
      1. Motivation
      2. Readiness
      3. Active involvement
      4. Relevance
      5. Feedback
      6. Nonjudgmental support
      7. Simple to complex
      8. Repetition
      9. Timing
      10. Environment
      11. Emotions
      12. Physiologic events
      13. Cultural aspects
      14. Psychomotor ability
III. Nurse as educator

FOCUSED STUDY TIPS

1. Define the following:
   androgogy
   learning
   affective
   learning objectives
2. Define the three domains of learning.
3. Evaluate whether the following teaching strategies are effective. Place an *E* in front of those items that are effective teaching techniques. Place an *I* in front of those items that are ineffective teaching strategies.
   ____ The student nurse decides that her client would benefit from information on weight loss.
   ____ The nurse introduces himself to the client and his family and gets to know them prior to beginnning cardiac rehabilitation teaching.
   ____ A minimum of 15 minutes is allotted at the end of the teaching session for questions on low-sodium foods.
   ____ A nurse who is teaching a sibling preparation class determines the age range of the participants and their experience with other children prior to beginning the class. She modifies the class each time she teaches it so she can be responsive to her audience.
4. The nurse is caring for a client with a wound that requires dressing changes. The client is scheduled for discharge from the hospital. The nurse plans a teaching session with the client. She will teach the client how, why, and when to change the dressing and what signs to report to the physician. What aspect of learning has the nurse omitted?
5. Your 6-year-old client was recently diagnosed with asthma. He tells you he wants to breathe better so he can play with his friends. He lives in a supportive family environment. His parents have requested a conference to discuss his medications, treatment plan, and coordination with the child's school. They state they are willing and able to provide any care to facilitate their son's treatment. Which element in the nursing history provides the greatest clues to the client's learning needs?

6. Your client has been newly diagnosed with hypertension. He speaks limited English, but a professional interpreter is available with advance notice. You attempt independently to communicate with him through nonverbal communication and the use of a teenage family member who is bilingual. What would be an appropriate nursing diagnosis for this client?
7. Determine which of the following learning objectives is written correctly. If it is incorrect, state why and correct it.
   By the end of the cardiac rehab teaching class, the client will understand the importance of taking his prescribed medications.
   The client will increase physical activity after the exercise training class.
   By the end of the week, the client will recognize which foods to avoid on a low-fat diet.
   Before discharge, the client will be able to demonstrate correct technique for measuring blood glucose using the Accu-check monitor.
8. When is the optimum time for a nurse to schedule a teaching session?
9. What can the nurse do to facilitate a learning environment?
10. What are the uses of computer-assisted instruction?
11. What should the nurse do when teaching a client of a different culture or ethnic background?
12. From your clinical agency, obtain a pamphlet or client handout on a health topic. What is the readability of the material? For which population is this material best suited?
13. You are planning a teaching session on safer sex with your client. What five characteristics should the information you present have?
14. Documentation of the teaching process is essential. What are the elements that must be documented?
15. Ms. S. will be caring for her elderly mother upon her mother's discharge from the hospital. Her mother has had a cerebrovascular accident (stroke). Physical therapy and occupational therapy will be provided in the home. Ms. S. will need to learn how to bathe her mother in bed. Devise a teaching plan for providing a bed bath. Include sample documentation of your teaching.

CASE STUDY

A. B. is a client newly diagnosed with diabetes. As part of her orientation to diabetes management, you will be teaching how to administer her own insulin.

1. *Identify at least five ways in which you can facilitate learning.*
2. *Identify three factors that could inhibit learning.*
3. *Readiness is essential for learning. Identify what you must assess to determine readiness to learn.*

CARE PLAN CRITICAL THINKING ACTIVITIES

Fill in the appropriate elements of the care plan for A. B.:
Assessment and Diagnosis
Planning and Implementation
Evaluation

NCLEX TEST QUESTIONS

1. A health promotion educational program was planned and implemented for school-age children. This is an example of what type of teaching?
   a. one-to-one teaching
   b. community health education
   c. instruction of professional colleague
   d. client education
2. Geragogy is:
   a. the art and science of teaching adults.
   b. the art and science of teaching children.
   c. the art and science of teaching elderly adults.
   d. learning.

3. In teaching a client how to care for a colostomy, the nurse would use which learning theory?
   a. behaviorist theory
   b. cognitive theory
   c. humanism theory
   d. feminism theory
4. In teaching adolescents about the consequences of untreated sexually transmitted diseases, what factor can facilitate client learning?
   a. motivation
   b. readiness
   c. active involvement
   d. allotted time
5. Which of the following is a barrier to learning?
   a. emotionally ready to learn
   b. adequate family support system
   c. low literacy skills
   d. English-speaking
6. The nurse developed which nursing diagnosis for a client undergoing cardiac rehab?
   a. deficient knowledge related to inexperience of newly ordered therapy
   b. risk for infection related to deficient knowledge
   c. health-seeking behavior related to desire to improve health behaviors
   d. ineffective coping related to deficient knowledge
7. Which of the following is a learning outcome for a teaching plan?
   a. Instruct the client about cardiac risk factors.
   b. The client will understand low-fat diet.
   c. The client will understand cardiac risk factors.
   d. Identify personal risk factors for heart disease.
8. A newly diabetic adolescent needs to learn how to administer insulin injections. What teaching strategy would be most effective?
   a. A videotape
   b. An orange to practice injections
   c. printed brochures
   d. role modeling
9. Which teaching strategy is effective for teaching clients with low literacy levels?
   a. lecture for 1 hour
   b. give handouts
   c. hands-on practice
   d. videos
10. In preparing a child for a tonsillectomy, the nurse used which teaching tool?
    a. video
    b. brochures
    c. coloring books
    d. role modeling

CHAPTER 26

DELEGATING, MANAGING, AND LEADING

OVERVIEW

This chapter focuses on leadership, management, change, and power. It explains the difference between leadership and management and exposes you to various styles of leadership. Creating change is the central theme of this chapter. While managers create a positive work environment using formal power, leaders may be vested with power or may be informal leaders from the group. Several change theories that leaders or managers may utilize are examined. This chapter also discusses the importance of power and political influence, as well as opportunities for political involvement.

www.prenhall.com/kozier

Additional resources for this chapter can be found on the Student CD-ROM accompanying this textbook, and on the Companion Website at www.prenhall.com/kozier. Click on Chapter 26 to select the activities for this chapter.

CD-ROM
- Audio Glossary
- NCLEX Review

Companion Website
- Additional NCLEX Review
- Case Study: Nurse as Manager and Delegator
- MediaLink Application: Go to Nursing World
- Links to Resources

LEARNING OUTCOMES

After completing this chapter, the student will be able to:

- Describe the characteristics of tasks appropriate to delegate to unlicensed and licensed assistive personnel
- List the five rights of delegation
- Compare and contrast leadership and management
- Differentiate formal from informal leaders
- Compare and contrast different leadership styles
- Identify characteristics of an effective leader
- Compare and contrast the levels of management
- Describe the four functions of management
- Discuss the roles and functions of nurse-managers
- Identify the skills and competencies needed by a nurse-manager
- Describe the role of the leader/manager in planning for and implementing change

KEY TOPICS

This study guide chapter reinforces the following terms/topics discussed in the textbook chapter:

- accountability
- authoritarian leader
- authority
- autocratic leader
- bureaucratic leader
- change agent
- charismatic leader
- coercive power
- consultative leader
- coordinating
- delegation
- democratic leader
- directing
- effectiveness
- efficiency
- expert power
- first-level manager
- formal leader
- influence
- informal leader
- laissez-faire leader
- leader
- leadership style
- legitimate power
- manager
- mentor
- middle-level manager
- networking
- nondirective leader
- nursing leadership
- organizing
- participative leader
- permissive leader
- planned change
- planning
- power
- preceptor
- productivity
- referent power
- responsibility
- reward power
- risk management
- shared governance
- shared leadership
- situational leader
- transactional leader
- transformational leadership
- unplanned change
- upper-level (top-level) manager
- vision

LECTURE OUTLINE

I. The nurse as delegator
II. The nurse as leader and manager
III. Leadership
    A. Leadership theory
        1. Classic leadership theories
        2. Contemporary leadership theories
    B. Effective leadership
IV. Management
    A. Levels of management
    B. Management functions
        1. Planning
        2. Organizing
        3. Directing
        4. Coordinating
    C. Principles of management
    D. Skills and competencies of nurse-managers
        1. Critical thinking
        2. Communicating
        3. Managing resources
        4. Enhancing employee performance
        5. Building and managing teams
V. Change
    A. Types of change
    B. Models of change

FOCUSED STUDY TIPS

1. Describe the differences between a manager and a leader.
2. Define the following:

   accountability — authority
   delegation — effectiveness
   efficiency — productivity

3. List the characteristics of an informal leader.
4. What activities does a charge nurse perform when making assignments for patient care?
5. What does a nurse liaison do?
6. What is resource management?
7. What does a change agent do?
8. List the different type of leadership styles. Which one(s) support the needs of patient care the most? What is your leadership style?

CASE STUDY

On Unit A, client care is currently provided by RNs, LVNs, and nurse's aides. Due to declining reimbursement from insurance companies, the manager has been directed to cut personnel costs. She is considering increased use of nurse's aides to deliver client care. Her proposal is to decrease RN positions by 10% and LVN positions by 25% and to increase nurse's aide use by 25%. The RNs and LVNs on the unit are extremely unhappy about the recent changes; however, the nurse's aides are happy with the changes and believe they are adequately prepared to take on more client care activities.

1. *As the manager of the unit, how would you handle this conflict?*
2. *Identify the motivating and restraining forces for RNs, LVNs, nurse's aides, and the manager.*
   A 56-year-old client is admitted to the hospital with multiple medical problems. The client is unable to care for herself, has financial issues, and is concerned about her young adult daughter. The nurse is concerned about the different needs this client has and wants to ensure each area is addressed.

CARE PLAN CRITICAL THINKING ACTIVITIES

Fill in the appropriate elements of the care plan for this client:
Assessment and Diagnosis
Planning and Implementation
Evaluation

NCLEX TEST QUESTIONS

1. The nurse manager of a patient care area discusses with a nurse her documentation of care for one particular patient. The manager claims the nurse did not utilize collaborative terminology when stating "The patient is compliant with the plan of care." How could this statement be worded to support the concept of collaboration?
   a. The patient doesn't want to follow the nursing orders.
   b. The patient complains about the plan of care.
   c. The patient is consistent with the plan of care.
   d. The patient is adhering to the plan of care.
2. A patient waiting in the emergency room demands to be seen by a doctor. Unable to have his wishes complied with, the patient then asks to see the "boss." Which role of the manager will be needed in this situation?
   a. figurehead
   b. liaison
   c. resource coordinator
   d. fearless leader
3. The nurses for a patient care area are known to have high on-the-job morale and seem very satisfied in their positions. Which type of

management style might their nurse manager be utilizing to create this positive work environment?
   a. autocratic
   b. laissez-faire
   c. democratic
   d. shared governance
4. When the nurse manager ensures that supplies are available, accounted for, and used with discretion, the nurse is acting in which of the following roles?
   a. controller
   b. resource coordinator
   c. organizer
   d. director
5. The nurse manager who makes all decisions for the group and believes that individuals are externally motivated and incapable of independent decision making is demonstrating which leadership theory?
   a. autocratic
   b. democratic
   c. laissez-faire
   d. bureaucratic
6. The nurse manager who allows much freedom within the group and exhibits no control over the group, with minimal leadership activity, is demonstrating which leadership theory?
   a. autocratic
   b. democratic
   c. laissez-faire
   d. bureaucratic
7. The manager who is responsible for managing the work of nonmangerial personnel and day-to-day activities of a specific work group or groups is considered a(n):
   a. first-level manager.
   b. middle-level manager.
   c. upper-level manager.
   d. organizational manager.
8. A nurse manaager who has power based on the fear of retribution or withholding of rewards is said to have which of the following powers?
   a. reward
   b. coercive
   c. legitimate
   d. referent
9. The type of change that is an intended, purposive attempt by an individual, group, organization, or larger social system to influence its own status quo or that of another organism or a situation is referred to as:
   a. natural change.
   b. situational change.
   c. overt change.
   d. planned change.
10. The transference of responsibility and authority for the performance of an activity to a competent individual is referred to as:
   a. change.
   b. directing.
   c. delegation.
   d. accountability.

CHAPTER 27

VITAL SIGNS

OVERVIEW

This chapter explores the importance of vital signs and the techniques for evaluating these cardinal signs. In this chapter, you examine the factors that affect all the vital signs and examine common errors in their measurement.

www.prenhall.com/kozier

Additional resources for this chapter can be found on the Student CD-ROM accompanying this textbook, and on the Companion Website at www.prenhall.com/kozier. Click on Chapter 27 to select the activities for this chapter.

CD-ROM
- Audio Glossary
- NCLEX Review

Companion Website
- Additional NCLEX Review
- Case Study: Assessing Vital Signs
- Care Plan Activity: Client with Pneumonia
- MediaLink Application: Joanna Briggs Institute
- Links to Resources

LEARNING OUTCOMES

After completing this chapter, the student will be able to:

- Describe factors that affect the vital signs and accurate measurement of them
- Identify the normal ranges for each vital sign
- Identify the variations in normal body temperature, pulse, respirations, and blood pressure that occur from infancy to old age
- Describe factors influencing the body's heat production and loss
- Compare oral, tympanic, rectal, and axillary methods of measuring body temperature
- Describe appropriate nursing care for alterations in body temperature
- Identify nine sites used to assess the pulse and state the reasons for their use
- List the characteristics that should be included when assessing pulses
- Explain how to measure the apical pulse and the apical-radial pulse
- Describe the mechanics of breathing and the mechanisms that control respirations
- Identify the components of a respiratory assessment
- Differentiate systolic and diastolic blood pressure
- Describe the five phases of Korotkoff's sounds
- Describe various methods and sites used to measure blood pressure
- Discuss measurement of blood oxygenation using pulse oximetry
- Identify when it is appropriate to delegate measurement of vital signs to unlicensed assistive personnel

KEY TOPICS

This study guide chapter reinforces the following terms/topics discussed in the textbook chapter:

- afebrile
- apical pulse
- apical–radial pulse
- apnea
- arrhythmia
- arterial blood pressure
- arteriosclerosis
- auscultatory gap
- basal metabolic rate (BMR)
- body temperature
- bradycardia
- bradypnea
- cardiac output
- cardinal signs
- chemical thermogenesis
- compliance
- conduction
- constant fever
- convection
- core temperature
- costal (thoracic) breathing
- diaphragmatic (abdominal) breathing
- diastolic pressure
- dysrhythmia
- elasticity of the arterial wall
- eupnea
- exhalation
- expiration
- external respiration
- febrile
- fever
- fever spike
- heat balance
- hematocrit
- hyperpyrexia
- hypertension
- hyperthermia
- hyperventilation
- hypotension
- hypothalamic integrator
- hypothermia
- hypoventilation
- inhalation
- insensible heat loss
- insensible water loss
- inspiration
- intermittent fever
- internal respiration
- Korotkoff's sounds
- meniscus
- orthostatic hypotension
- peripheral pulse
- point of maximal impulse (PMI)
- polypnea
- pulse
- pulse deficit
- pulse oximeter
- pulse pressure
- pulse rhythm
- pulse volume
- pyrexia
- radiation
- relapsing fever
- remittent fever
- respiration
- respiratory character
- respiratory quality
- respiratory rhythm
- stroke volume output
- surface temperature
- systolic pressure
- tachycardia
- tachypnea
- tidal volume
- vaporization
- ventilation
- viscous
- vital signs

LECTURE OUTLINE

I. Body temperature
   A. Regulation of body temperature
   B. Factors affecting body temperature
   C. Alterations in body temperature
      1. Pyrexia
      2. Hypothermia
   D. Assessing body temperature
      1. Types of thermometers
      2. Temperature scales

II. Pulse
   A. Factors affecting the pulse
   B. Pulse sites
   C. Assessing the pulse

III. Respirations
   A. Mechanics and regulation of breathing
   B. Assessing respirations
   C. Factors affecting respirations

IV. Blood pressure
   A. Determinants of blood pressure
      1. Pumping action of the heart
      2. Peripheral
      3. Vascular resistance
      4. Blood volume
      5. Blood viscosity
   B. Factors affecting blood pressure
   C. Hypertension
   D. Hypotension
   E. Assessing blood pressure
      1. Blood pressure sites
      2. Methods

V. Oxygen saturation
   A. Factors affecting oxygen saturation readings

FOCUSED STUDY TIPS

1. Define the following:
   basal metabolic rate
   core temperature
   external respiration
   pulse deficit
   pyrexia
   surface temperature
   ventilation
   cardiac output
   diastolic pressure
   internal respiration
   pulse pressure
   stroke volume
   systolic pressure
2. How is heat normally lost?
3. What does placing a febrile client in a cool bath accomplish in regard to body temperature? How is heat lost?
4. What is insensible heat loss? What is the role of insensible water loss?
5. What causes heat to be lost during everyday activities?
6. What can the nurse control in regard to a patient's body temperature?
7. Convert the temperature 38.5C to the Fahrenheit scale.
8. What type of temperature reading is the most accurate? Why?
9. What effects the pulse rate?
10. How long must the pulse be counted if the client has an irregular pulse?
11. What is included when respirations are assessed?
12. What is the way to estimate the correct size of blood pressure cuff for a client?
13. In which phase of Korotkoff's sounds is the systolic blood pressure measured?
14. Analyze the following vital signs: BP 80/50, P 112, RR 26, T 103.9F oral. What would be your assessment for this client?
15. Analyze the following vital signs: BP 130/78, P 84, RR 18, T 98.0F oral. What would be your assessment for this client?
16. Identify the five most important factors that affect heat production.
17. At 8:00 A.M. you note that your client's temperature is 35.0C. What questions should you consider to determine if this reading is accurate?
18. Identify the nine factors that significantly affect blood pressure.

CASE STUDY

Susan Santos, a 15-year-old high school student, reports to the urgent care clinic with complaints of fever, chills, and fatigue. Her vital signs upon admission are BP 120/70, P 116, RR 20, T (oral) 102.1F. She is examined by the nurse practitioner (NP). The NP orders blood and urine lab work.

1. *Evaluate Susan's vital signs.*
2. *During her stay at the urgent care clinic, how often should Susan's vital signs be assessed?*
3. *Identify at least three independent nursing interventions for Susan's fever.*
4. *Identify the data that should be evaluated when assessing Susan's pulse.*

A 37-year-old female is admitted to the hospital with a temperature of 103F. Blood cultures are drawn and the client receives one dose of an antipyretic.

CARE PLAN CRITICAL THINKING ACTIVITIES

Fill in the appropriate elements of the care plan for this client:
Assessment and Diagnosis
Planning and Implementation
Evaluation

NCLEX TEST QUESTIONS

1. The nurse who correctly takes a rectal temperature leaves the thermometer in place for:
   a. 1 minute.
   b. 3 minutes.
   c. 4 minutes.
   d. 5 minutes.
2. During a client assessment, the nurse notes the patient's respirations are 8 per minute. The nurse documents this as:
   a. eupnea.
   b. bradypnea.
   c. tachypnea.
   d. dyspnea.
3. The nurse assesses the apical pulse of an adult at the PMI, placing the stethoscope over the:
   a. midclavicular line at the fifth intercostal space.
   b. Erb's point area.
   c. midclavicular line at the fourth intercostal space.
   d. pulmonic region.
4. The diastolic reading of the blood pressure is recorded at which Korotkoff phase?
   a. II
   b. III
   c. IV
   d. V
5. The nurse implementing health teaching regarding pulse and blood pressure to a middle-aged male client recognizes the client requires further teaching when he states:
   a. "My heart rate will normally increase with activity."
   b. "Stress can increase my heart rate."
   c. "My heart rate will gradually increase as I get older."
   d. "Certain medications can affect my heart rate."
6. A postoperative patient tells the nurse she is so cold that she thinks she will never be warm again. While taking the patient's temperature, the nurse checks the patient's nail beds. The rationale for checking the patient's nail beds in relation to the patient's body temperature is:
   a. to ensure that neurological function is maintained.
   b. to check oxygenation of body tissues.
   c. to offer comfort by touching the patient's hands.
   d. to check for blood shunting to vital core organs.
7. A patient has an elevated temperature that is very high due to a systemic infection. The nurse caring for this patient knows that if the client begins to shiver, the body temperature will:
   a. lower.

b. remain the same.
c. raise.
d. drop below normal quickly.

8. When preparing to take a patient's temperature orally, the nurse should consider:
   a. orientation status, ability to follow directions, and age.
   b. body build and type.
   c. pulse rate and prognosis.
   d. accuracy ratings.
9. A nurse needs to take the body temperature of a neonate as part of the routine assessment done on all newborns. What route should the nurse use to assess the neonate?
   a. oral
   b. rectal
   c. axillary
   d. temperature blanket
10. What phase of the respiratory cycle happens when pressure inside the lungs is less than atmospheric pressure?
    a. inhalation
    b. exhalation
    c. ventilation
    d. diffusion
11. A nurse has taken a patient's temperature and notes it is elevated. She can anticipate that the respiratory rate of the patient will:
    a. not be altered.
    b. be irregular with a period of apnea.
    c. be below normal.
    d. elevate four breaths/minute for every 1F degree of elevation.
12. The nurse observes that the patient is having difficulty breathing while lying down. The nurse would label this condition as:
    a. dyspnea.
    b. orthopnea.
    c. hyperventilation.
    d. bradypnea.
13. A nurse is concerned because she cannot palpate a patient's pedal pulse although the color of the foot indicates profusion is occurring. To verify the pulse is present the nurse should:
    a. notify the physician.
    b. use a Doppler ultrasound stethoscope.
    c. do nothing.
    d. contact the nursing supervisor and provide her findings.
14. A nurse reviewing the nurse's notes for a patient for whom she will be caring noted that the pulse volume of the patient's right pedal pulse has been documented as 1+. This means that:
    a. the pedal pulse is absent.
    b. the pedal pulse is normal.
    c. the pedal pulse is strong and forceful.
    d. the pedal pulse is weak and easily obliterated.

CHAPTER 28

HEALTH ASSESSMENT

OVERVIEW

This chapter discusses health assessment through the use of physical examination techniques. The ample information in this chapter will help you begin learning how to become an excellent examiner.

LEARNING OUTCOMES

After completing this chapter, the student will be able to:

- Identify the purposes of the physical health examination
- Explain the four methods of examining
- Explain the significance of selected physical findings
- Identify expected outcomes of health assessment
- Identify the steps in selected examination procedures
- Describe suggested sequencing to conduct a physical health examination in an orderly fashion
- Discuss variations in examination techniques appropriate for clients of different ages

www.prenhall.com/kozier

Additional resources for this chapter can be found on the Student CD-ROM accompanying this textbook, and on the Companion Website at www.prenhall.com/kozier. Click on Chapter 28 to select the activities for this chapter.

CD-ROM
- Audio Glossary
- NCLEX Review

Animations:
- Otoscope Examination
- Middle Ear Dynamics
- Ear Abnormalities
- Mouth and Throat

Companion Website
- Additional NCLEX Review
- Case Study: Performing Physical Assessments
- MediaLink Application: Physical Exam
- Links to Resources

KEY TOPICS

This study guide chapter reinforces the following terms/topics discussed in the textbook chapter:

- adventitious breath sounds
- alopecia
- angle of Louis
- antihelix
- aphasia
- astigmatism
- auricle
- auscultation
- blanch test
- bruit
- caries
- cataract
- cerumen
- clubbing
- cochlea
- conduction hearing loss
- conjunctivitis
- crepitations
- cyanosis
- dacryocystitis
- diastole
- dullness
- duration
- edema
- erythema
- Eustachian tube
- exophthalmos
- external auditory meatus
- extinction
- fasciculation
- flatness
- gingivitis
- glaucoma
- glossitis
- goniometer
- helix
- hernia
- hordeolum (sty)
- hyperopia
- hyperresonance
- incus
- inspection
- intensity
- intention tremor
- jaundice
- lift
- lobule
- malleus
- manubrium
- mastoid
- miosis
- mixed hearing loss
- mydriasis
- myopia
- normocephalic
- one-point discrimination
- ossicles
- otoscope
- pallor
- palpation
- parotitis
- percussion
- perfusion
- periodontal disease
- pinna
- pitch
- plaque
- pleximeter
- plexor
- point of maximal impulse (PMI)
- precordium
- presbyopia
- proprioceptors
- pyorrhea
- quality
- reflex
- resonance
- resting tremor
- S_1
- S_2

- semicircular canals
- sensorineural hearing loss
- sordes
- stapes
- stereognosis
- sternum
- systole
- tartar
- thrill
- tragus
- tremor
- triangular fossa
- two-point discrimination
- tympanic membrane
- tympany
- vestibule
- visual acuity
- visual fields
- vitiligo

LECTURE OUTLINE

I. Physical health assessment
   A. Preparing the client
   B. Preparing the environment
   C. Positioning
   D. Draping
   E. Instrumentation
   F. Methods of examining
      1. Inspection
      2. Palpation
      3. Percussion
      4. Auscultation
II. General survey
   A. Appearance and mental status
   B. Vital signs
   C. Height and weight
III. The integument
IV. Skin
   A. Hair
   B. Nails
V. The Head
   A. The skull and face
   B. Lifespan considerations
   C. The Eyes and vision
   D. The Ears and hearing
   E. The Nose and sinuses
   F. The Mouth and oropharynx
VI. The neck
VII. The thorax and lungs
   A. Chest landmarks
   B. Chest shape and size
   C. Breath sounds
VIII. The cardiovascular and peripheral vascular systems
   A. Heart
   B. Central vessels
   C. The peripheral vascular system
IX. The breasts and axillae
X. The abdomen
XI. The musculoskeletal system
XII. The neurologic system
   A. Mental status
      1. Language
      2. Orientation
      3. Memory
      4. Attention span and calculation
   B. Level of consciousness
   C. Cranial nerves
   D. Reflexes
   E. Motor Function Sensory Function
XIII. The female genitals and inguinal area
XIV. The Male genitals and inguinal area
XV. The rectum and anus

FOCUSED STUDY TIPS

1. Define the following:
   bromhidrosis, cyanosis
   edema, erythema
   hyperhidrosis, jaundice
   melanin, pallor
   vitiligo
2. What is the purpose of a physical examination?
3. List characteristics of the physical examination.

4. What are the environmental issues that you should consider when preparing to physically examine a client?
5. What are the aspects of the general survey?
6. What does "normocephalic male with alopecia" mean?
7. Which structures can be visualized with an otoscope?
8. What type of hearing loss is the result of interrupted transmission of sound waves through the outer and middle ear structures?
9. Your client complains of irritation and pain in the roof of the mouth. You assemble the following equipment to examine the mouth: tongue blade, gauze square, and penlight. What else must you add to your equipment list to be complete?
10. You are auscultating the breath sounds of a client. You hear high-pitched harsh sounds. In a healthy client, what type of breath sound is this, and where is your stethoscope placed?
11. Which type of adventitious breath sound may be cleared by coughing?
12. List the correct order of examination techniques for the abdomen.
13. What does the examination of the neurologic system include?
14. In which position is the examination of the prostate usually conducted?
15. When describing a skin lesion, which points should you always include?
16. Describe the following five sounds elicited by percussion. Give an example of where these sounds may be heard.
    flatness dullness
    resonance hyperresonance
    tympany
17. What are two questions you should ask the client when assessing the musculoskeletal system?
18. Evaluate your own comfort with assessment of male and female genitalia. Can you successfully conduct a matter-of-fact examination?

CASE STUDY

As part of your clinical rotation, you have been assigned to an outpatient clinic. At the clinic, you are asked to conduct a head-to-toe physical assessment on several clients.

1. *The first client is an 82-year-old woman with severe rheumatoid arthritis. What considerations should you keep in mind while conducting this examination?*
2. *The second client is a 3-year-old boy with complaints of sore throat, earache, and fever. How should you alter the examination with this client?*

A 38-year-old male client comes into the clinic for a routine physical assessment. Upon this assessment, the nurse finds an alteration in skin status, facial muscle twitching, loss of hair, and abnormal vital signs.

CARE PLAN CRITICAL THINKING ACTIVITIES

Fill in the appropriate elements of the care plan for this client:
Assessment and Diagnosis
Planning and Implementation
Evaluation

NCLEX TEST QUESTIONS

1. The nurse is preparing to complete a health history on a patient who is being admitted to the hospital. As the nurse begins the interview, the client tells the nurse that she doesn't understand why all this information is necessary. The most appropriate approach is:
   a. to apologize to the patient and tell her that these questions are part of the assessment process.
   b. to stop the health history interview as the patient requested.
   c. to explain the purpose of the interview and confidentiality associated with it.
   d. to document that the patient is uncooperative and inform the doctor.

2. During the assessment process a nurse will encourage patients to discuss openly and without restraint their health problems and needs. An interviewing technique that conveys this message is:
   a. focusing.
   b. verbal observation.
   c. a direct question.
   d. an open-ended question.
3. When the nurse asks the patient why the patient is seeking health care the nurse is establishing the:
   a. patient's orientation.
   b. patient's cognitive development.
   c. patient's primary concern.
   d. social relationship.
4. A nurse is preparing to complete a physical exam on a patient's pelvis and vagina. The position the client is placed in for this exam is:
   a. Sim's.
   b. dorsal recumbent.
   c. knee–chest.
   d. lithotomy.
5. The nurse is assessing the patient's abdomen to detect areas of tenderness and/or muscle guarding. The correct technique to use is:
   a. light palpation.
   b. deep palpation.
   c. percussion.
   d. palpation above the pubic symphysis.
6. A client complains of painful cracks in the soles of his feet. Upon assessment, the nurse notes a linear crack that extends into the dermis. The nurse documents the finding as:
   a. a fissure.
   b. an erosion.
   c. an excoriation.
   d. an ulcer.
7. The nurse assessing a client's mouth and oropharynx notes inflammation of the oral mucosa. The nurse documents this finding as:
   a. gingivitis
   b. glossitis.
   c. stomatitis.
   d. parotitis.
8. A nurse performs a Buerger's test on a client with suspected peripheral vascular disease. The nurse assists the client to a supine position and asks the client to raise one leg about 1 foot above heart level and to move the foot up and down briskly for about 1 minute and then to sit up and dangle the leg. What action does the nurse then take?
   a. The nurse observes the time elapsed until return of original color and vein filling.
   b. The nurse asks the client to repeat the steps.
   c. The nurse observes skin temperature over lower extremities.
   d. The nurse observes capillary refill.
9. The nurse performing an abdominal assessment on an adult client notes the liver is palpable below the costal margin. The nurse recognizes this finding as:
   a. normal.
   b. indication of an enlarged liver.
   c. indication of incorrect assessment technique.
   d. indication of bladder distention.
10. The nurse is assessing a client who has lost the ability to express self by writing, making signs, or speaking. The nurse documents this finding as:
    a. sensory aphasia.
    b. auditory aphasia.
    c. expressive aphasia.
    d. visual aphasia.

CHAPTER 29

ASEPSIS

OVERVIEW

This chapter discusses your role in the control of infection. It highlights natural defenses that protect the body against infection and presents potential risk factors for development of infection. It emphasizes nursing interventions to protect clients and staff from transmission of microorganisms.

LEARNING OUTCOMES

After completing this chapter, the student will be able to:

- Explain the concepts of medical and surgical asepsis
- Identify risks for nosocomial infections
- Identify signs of localized and systemic infections
- Identify factors influencing a microorganism's capability to produce an infectious process
- Identify anatomic and physiologic barriers that defend the body against microorganisms
- Differentiate active and passive immunity
- Identify relevant nursing diagnoses and contributing factors for clients at risk for infection and those with infections
- Identify interventions to reduce risks for infections
- Identify measures that break each link in the chain of infection
- Compare and contrast category-specific, disease-specific, universal, body substance, standard, and transmission-based isolation precaution systems
- Describe the steps to take in the event of a bloodborne pathogen exposure
- Correctly implement aseptic practices, including hand washing, donning and removing a face mask, gowning, donning and removing disposable gloves, bagging articles, and managing equipment used for isolation clients

www.prenhall.com/kozier

Additional resources for this chapter can be found on the Student CD-ROM accompanying this textbook, and on the Companion Website at www.prenhall.com/kozier. Click on Chapter 29 to select the activities for this chapter.

CD-ROM
- Audio Glossary
- NCLEX Review

Companion Website
- Additional NCLEX Review
- Case Study: Client with Mycoplasma Pneumonia
- Care Plan Activity: Client on Radiation Therapy and Medication
- MediaLink Application: Go to "Infection Control Today"
- Links to Resources

KEY TOPICS

This study guide chapter reinforces the following terms/topics discussed in the textbook chapter:

- acquired immunity
- active immunity
- acute infection
- airborne precautions
- airborne transmission
- antibodies
- antigen
- antiseptics
- asepsis
- autoantigen
- bacteria
- bacteremia
- bacteriocins
- bloodborne pathogens
- body substance isolation (BSI)
- carrier
- cell-mediated defenses
- cellular immunity
- chemotaxis
- chronic infection
- cicatrix
- circulating immunity
- clean
- colonization
- communicable disease
- compromised host
- contact precautions
- cultures
- diapedesis
- dirty
- disease
- disinfectants
- droplet nuclei
- droplet precautions
- emigration
- endogenous
- exogenous
- exudate
- fibrinogen
- fibrous (scar) tissue
- fungi
- granulation tissue
- humoral immunity
- hyperemia
- iatrogenic infections
- immune defenses
- immunity
- immunoglobulins
- infection
- inflammation
- isolation
- leukocytes
- leukocytosis
- local infection
- macrophages
- margination
- medical asepsis
- nonspecific defenses
- nosocomial infections
- opportunistic pathogen
- parasites
- passive immunity
- pathogenicity
- phagocytes
- regeneration
- reservoir
- resident flora
- sepsis
- septicemia
- specific (immune) defenses
- sterile field
- sterile technique
- sterilization
- surgical asepsis
- systemic infection
- universal precautions (UP)
- vector-borne transmission
- vehicle-borne transmission
- virulence
- viruses

LECTURE OUTLINE

I. Types of microorganisms causing infections
II. Types of infections
III. Nosocomial infections
IV. Chain of infection
  A. Etiologic agent
  B. Reservoir
  C. Portal of exit from reservoir
  D. Method of transmission
  E. Portal of entry to the susceptible host
  F. Susceptible host
V. Body defenses against infection
  A. Nonspecific defenses
    1. Anatomic and physiologic barriers
    2. Inflammatory response
  B. Specific defenses
    1. Antibody-mediated defenses
    2. Cell-mediated defenses
VI. Factors increasing susceptibility to infection
  A. Supporting defenses of a susceptible host
  B. Cleaning, disinfecting, and sterilizing
    1. Cleaning
    2. Disinfecting
    3. Sterilizing
VII. Isolation precautions
  A. CDC (HICPAC) isolation precautions (1996: updated 1997)
    1. Standard precautions
    2. Transmission-based precautions
  B. Compromised clients
VIII. Isolation practices
  A. Personal protective equipment
    1. Gloves
    2. Gowns
    3. Face masks
    4. Eyewear
  B. Disposal of soiled equipment and supplies
  C. Transporting clients with infections
  D. Psychosocial needs of isolation clients
IX. Sterile technique
  A. Sterile field
  B. Sterile gloves
  C. Sterile gowns
X. Infection control for health care workers
XI. Role of the infection control nurse
XII. Evaluating
XIII. Chapter highlights
XIV. Review questions
XV. Readings and references
  A. Suggested readings
  B. Related research
  C. References
  D. Selected bibliography

FOCUSED STUDY TIPS

1. Define the following:
   asepsis
   communicable disease
   disease
   etiology
   infection
   normal flora
   opportunistic pathogen
   virulence
2. Describe the following types of immunity:
   active immunity
   antibody
   antigen
   cellular immunity
   humoral immunity
   immunity
   passive immunity
   primary immune response
   secondary immune response
3. Describe surgical asepsis.
4. List four microorganisms responsible for infections.
5. Your client has a small wound on his left hand. A culture of this wound is positive for skin flora and one pathogen. He has no fever. This wound could be described as?
6. Your client has a fever, localized pain, and purulent drainage from a wound. Your client is in which stage of the infectious process?
7. Your client has been exposed to chicken pox but does not display any signs or symptoms. Your client is in which stage of the infectious process?

8. Numerous factors have been identified that affect a person's resistance to infection. Which of these factors may be altered by the nurse?
9. Your client is a preschool teacher. She complains that since she started working with small children she has had numerous colds and infections. She reports that she showers twice daily and washes her hands frequently while at work. She eats a balanced diet, drinks plenty of water, and gets 7 to 8 hours of sleep per night. What other strategies might you recommend to your client to decrease her risk for infections?
10. How do antiseptics break the chain of infection?
11. How do disinfectants break the chain of infection?
12. List common sterilization methods.
13. You are caring for a toddler who is not toilet trained. The child is experiencing frequent episodes of vomiting and diarrhea. Identify the appropriate precautions you should utilize when changing the diaper of this child.
14. Define surgical asepsis.
15. Inflammation is a local and nonspecific defensive response to injury or infection. It destroys or dilutes the agent, prevents its spread, and promotes repair of damaged tissue. What are the five signs of inflammation?
16. Reggie is admitted to the hospital for initiation of treatment for pulmonary tuberculosis. What type of isolation precaution is appropriate for Reggie?
17. Marsha is admitted from the emergency department to the hospital with a closed head injury as a result of a motor vehicle accident. What type of isolation precaution is appropriate for Marsha?
18. Initiation of precautions to prevent the transmission of microorganisms is generally a nursing responsibility. You must assess the client to determine if any special precautions must be taken. What actions must you take in all client situations?
19. You are asked to speak to a neighborhood preschool about reducing the risk of infection among the students. The preschool staff will attend, as will the parents of the children. What instruction will you offer?
20. After administering an injection to an agitated client, you inadvertently stick yourself with the needle. What do you do?

CASE STUDY

You are a staff nurse on a busy medical-surgical unit at a community hospital. You realize that nosocomial infections are associated with increased risk for morbidity and mortality among clients, higher health care costs, and increased nursing time.

1. *How can you decrease the risk of nosocomial infections when providing routine care?*
2. *How would you modify your efforts if clients with known multidrug-resistant bacteria are on your unit?*

You are caring for a client with diarrhea who is incontinent of stool. This client also has a productive cough. Based on the client's history you suspect that he may have pneumonia. You enter the room to bathe the client and change the linen. The client is too weak to get out of bed and the linen is saturated with stool. What protective garb should you wear? What precautions should be taken with the dirty linen?

You receive an order to give Compazine to this client by intramuscular injection. What precautions must you take when disposing of the needle after giving the injection?

After a 7-day hospital stay, the client is discharged home. He is no longer incontinent of stool, but your suspicion of pneumonia has been confirmed. What process will you use to evaluate the client's ability to successfully manage his pneumonia at home?

CARE PLAN CRITICAL THINKING ACTIVITIES

Fill in the appropriate elements of the care plan for this client:
Assessment and Diagnosis
Planning and Implementation
Evaluation

NCLEX TEST QUESTIONS

1. An exposure to an organism that causes infection during hospitalization is called a:
   a. significant exposure.
   b. nosocomial infection.
   c. negligent occurrence.
   d. negligent exposure.
2. The single most important means of preventing the spread of infection is:
   a. wearing disposable gloves.
   b. handwashing.
   c. avoiding persons with known infections.
   d. wearing a face mask.
3. The nurse instructs the patient to use tissues when coughing or sneezing and to dispose of tissues properly after use. These instructions will prevent the spread of infection by:
   a. airborne route.
   b. droplet transmission.
   c. vehicle route.
   d. direct contact.
4. A nurse is planning preventive measures to reduce client susceptibility to infection. Which of the following is not a factor in supporting defenses of a susceptible host?
   a. hygiene
   b. nutrition
   c. gender
   d. rest and sleep
5. A nurse preparing to do a bladder catheterization prepares the patient for the procedure and sets up the sterile field. As the nurse begins to approach the patient to insert the catheter, the tip of the catheter touches the sterile drape. The nurse should:
   a. start the procedure from the beginning.
   b. wipe the tip of the catheter with sterile water and continue.
   c. continue with the procedure.
   d. change the sterile drape and continue with the procedure.
6. A patient has returned from surgery with a single lumen nasogastric tube in place for decompression. Physician orders are for low continuous suction. The nurse should:
   a. attach the tube to the connecting tubing, then to the suction source.
   b. check the tube for placement.
   c. assess the patient's bowel sounds.
   d. verify the physician orders.
7. A major focus of professional nurses is preventive care. In providing preventive care the nurse should focus on:
   a. developing nursing diagnoses.
   b. health education.
   c. research and development.
   d. scientific knowledge.
8. The priority nursing diagnosis for a client with impaired skin integrity is which of the following?
   a. risk for infection: inadequate primary defenses
   b. impaired physical mobility
   c. anxiety
   d. risk for infection: inadequate secondary defenses
9. A nurse is preparing a sterile field for a procedure. The nurse is adding sterile supplies to the sterile field. Which area around the edge of the field is considered contaminated?
   a. .5 inch
   b. 1 inch
   c. 1.5 inches
   d. 2 inches
10. When transporting a client with an infection from one department to another, which of the following would not be considered an appropriate action? The nurse:
    a. securely covers a draining wound.
    b. places a surgical mask on a client with an airborne infection.
    c. notifies personnel at the receiving area of any infection risk.
    d. requests delay in transporting client until infection is treated.

CHAPTER 30

SAFETY

OVERVIEW

This chapter provides working knowledge of common hazards and factors that affect client safety. It highlights your role as a nurse in assessing hazards and developing interventions to promote safety for your clients.

LEARNING OUTCOMES

After completing this chapter, the student will be able to:

- Discuss factors that affect people's abilities to protect themselves from injury
- Describe methods to assess clients at risk for injury
- Identify common potential hazards throughout the life span
- Give examples of nursing diagnoses, outcomes, and interventions for clients at risk for accidental injury
- Plan strategies to maintain safety in the health care setting, home, and community, including prevention strategies across the life span for thermal injury, falls, poisoning, suffocation or choking, electric hazards, firearms, and radiation
- Explain measures to prevent falls
- Discuss implementation of seizure precautions
- Discuss the use and legal implications of restraints
- Describe alternatives to restraints
- List desired outcomes to use in evaluating the selected strategies for injury prevention

www.prenhall.com/kozier

Additional resources for this chapter can be found on the Student CD-ROM accompanying this textbook, and on the Companion Website at www.prenhall.com/kozier. Click on Chapter 30 to select the activities for this chapter.

CD-ROM
- Audio Glossary
- NCLEX Review
- Animation: Lead Poisoning

Companion Website
- Additional NCLEX Review
- Case Study: Ensuring Client Safety
- Care Plan Activity: Safety at Home
- MediaLink Application: Safety in Nursing Issues
- Links to Resources

KEY TOPICS

This study guide chapter reinforces the following terms/topics discussed in the textbook chapter:

- asphyxiation
- burn
- carbon monoxide
- chemical restraints
- electric shock
- Heimlich maneuver
- physical restraints
- restraints
- safety monitoring device
- scald
- seizure
- seizure precautions
- status epilepticus

LECTURE OUTLINE

I. Factors affecting safety
  A. Age and development
  B. Lifestyle
  C. Mobility and health status
  D. Sensory-perceptual alterations
  E. Cognitive awareness
  F. Emotional state
  G. Ability to communicate
  H. Safety awareness
  I. Environmental factors
II. Assessing
  A. Nursing history and physical examination
    1. Risk assessment tools
    2. Home hazard appraisal
III. Diagnosing
IV. Planning
V. Implementing
  A. Promoting safety across the life span
    1. Newborns and infants
    2. Toddlers
    3. Preschoolers
    4. School-age children
    5. Adolescents
    6. Young adults
    7. Middle-aged adults
    8. Older adults
    9. Safety problems across the life span
  B. Preventing specific hazards
    1. Scalds and burns
    2. Fires
      a. Agency fires
      b. Home fires
    3. Falls
      a. Seizures
    4. Poisoning
    5. Carbon monoxide poisoning
    6. Suffocation or choking
    7. Excessive noise
    8. Electrical hazards
    9. Firearms
    10. Radiation
  C. Procedure and equipment-related accidents
  D. Restraining clients
    1. Legal implications of restraints
    2. Selecting a restraint
    3. Kinds of restraints
VI. Evaluating

FOCUSED STUDY TIPS

1. Define the following:
   Geri chair
   hand restraint
   jacket or vest restraint
   mummy restraint
   safety strap
2. Define environmental safety factors.
3. List interventions to improve infant safety.
4. You are a nurse working for a large school district. You have been asked to present a safety program to high school students. What important topics should be included in this talk?
5. You work in a community clinic that serves a large population of teenagers and young adults. Several clinic clients have committed suicide since you began working at this site. What is your role in suicide prevention?

6. A client reports to the urgent care clinic with a burn related to use of a hot pack on his lower back. He has no underlying health problems. He states that the hot pack was in proper working order and that he used the protective cover that came with the pack, that he followed the directions completely and propped the pack next to his back while lying on his side. What other questions must you ask to fully evaluate this burn?
7. Which two age groups are at greatest risk for falls?
8. List client teaching topics for poison prevention.
9. Carbon monoxide is a serious health hazard. Why is this chemical so potentially dangerous?
10. You are eating in the cafeteria when one of your classmates begins to choke. What action should you take?
11. Which factors must be evaluated when assessing a client's safety risk?
12. Conduct an assessment of your own safety awareness and practices. What are your strengths? Which areas need improvement?
13. Now that you have completed your own safety awareness assessment, consider how you might use this tool in the clinical setting. Identify at least three ways you could incorporate this assessment into your nursing care.
14. Name at least three environmental factors that may be modified to improve client safety.
15. In the event of a fire, what four priorities should guide the nurse's behavior?
16. Firearms in the home are a potential health hazard to all family members. Discuss with your family and classmates your experiences with firearms and your feelings about having them in the home.
17. Radiation injury can occur from overexposure to a radioactive source. What three factors determine the amount of radiation exposure?
18. What are the most significant threats to safety in your home environment?

CASE STUDY

Kylie Fallon is a 73-year-old widow who lives alone. She has been admitted to the hospital for surgical repair of a fractured ankle. As the nurse assigned to her care, you will need to modify her environment to protect her against hazards. List at least three nursing interventions that will help ensure Kylie's safety during her hospitalization.

Kylie has recovered well from her surgery but is experiencing pain and swelling on discharge. As the student nurse who has cared for her during her stay, you will continue to follow her after discharge. You have arranged to make a home visit the next day.

CARE PLAN CRITICAL THINKING ACTIVITIES

Fill in the appropriate elements of the care plan for this client:
Assessment and Diagnosis
Planning and Implementation
Evaluation

NCLEX TEST QUESTIONS

1. A major focus of professional nurses is preventive care. In providing preventive care the nurse should focus on:
   a. developing nursing diagnoses.
   b. health education.
   c. research and development.
   d. scientific knowledge.
2. When planning accident prevention for parents of newborns and infants, which of the following would not be a focus at this time?
   a. suffocation or choking
   b. falls
   c. poisoning
   d. tricycle safety
3. When evaluating a parent's understanding of safety measures for a toddler, which of the following statements indicates a need for further teaching?
   a. "I will teach my child to swim."
   b. "I will obtain a low bed when my child begins to climb."
   c. "I will teach my child to cross the street safely and obey traffic signals."
   d. "I will teach my child not to run or ride a tricycle into the street."

4. A nurse planning a safety instruction class for parents of preschoolers knows that the focus of the class should be on:
   a. teaching children to avoid hazards such as busy streets, swimming pools, and other potentially dangerous areas.
   b. teaching children not to play with fireworks, gunpowder, or firearms.
   c. teaching children the effects of drugs and alcohol on judgment and coordination.
   d. teaching children to use light or reflective clothing when walking or cycling at night.
5. The nurse planning to teach children safety measures regarding contact sports and activities in which children aim at a target knows this teaching should begin with which developmental level?
   a. toddlers
   b. preschoolers
   c. school-age children
   d. adolescents
6. Suicide is a leading cause of death among teenagers. When planning a workshop on adolescent suicide, the nurse knows that which of the following is not among the most common methods of adolescent suicide?
   a. firearms
   b. drugs
   c. automobile exhaust gases
   d. laceration of radial arteries with a sharp object
7. A nurse teaching a safety class for young adults identifies all of the following as main causes of death for young adults. Which of those identified is the *leading* cause of death?
   a. fires
   b. burns
   c. firearms
   d. motor vehicle accidents
8. When planning a safety inservice for a church group consisting of older adults, the nurse will include information on which of the following as the leading cause of accidents among older adults?
   a. falls
   b. fires
   c. motor vehicle accidents
   d. firearms
9. A nurse establishing a client's plan of care for the use of restraints should plan to include release of all restraints and range-of-motion exercises at least:
   a. every 30 minutes
   b. every 1 to 2 hours
   c. every 2 to 4 hours
   d. every 8 hours
10. A client presents to the emergency department complaining of headaches, dizziness, weakness, nausea, vomiting, and loss of muscle control. The nurse should immediately suspect:
    a. food poisoning.
    b. medication overdose.
    c. carbon monoxide poisoning.
    d. ingestion of toxic substance.

CHAPTER 31

HYGIENE

OVERVIEW

This chapter discusses the importance of hygiene in the maintenance of health. It provides information on common normal and abnormal findings while providing personal hygiene care. The chapter builds on assessment information presented in previous chapters. Client safety and the control of the transmission of microorganisms as you provide care are emphasized.

LEARNING OUTCOMES

After completing this chapter, the student will be able to:

- Describe hygienic care that nurses provide to clients
- Identify factors influencing personal hygiene
- Identify normal and abnormal assessment findings while providing hygiene care
- Apply the nursing process to common problems related to hygienic care of the skin, feet, nails, mouth, hair, eyes, ears, and nose
- Identify the purposes of bathing
- Describe various types of baths
- Explain specific ways in which nurses help hospitalized clients with hygiene
- Describe steps for identified hygienic care procedures
- Identify steps in removing contact lenses and for inserting and removing artificial eyes
- Describe steps for removing, cleaning, and inserting hearing aids
- Identify safety and comfort measures underlying bed-making procedures

www.prenhall.com/kozier

Additional resources for this chapter can be found on the Student CD-ROM accompanying this textbook, and on the Companion Website at www.prenhall.com/kozier. Click on Chapter 31 to select the activities for this chapter.

CD-ROM
- Audio Glossary
- NCLEX Review

Companion Website
- Additional NCLEX Review
- Case Study: Providing Basic Hygiene Care
- Care Plan Activity: Client on Radiation Therapy
- MediaLink Application: Caring for Dentures
- Links to Resources

KEY TOPICS

This study guide chapter reinforces the following terms/topics discussed in the textbook chapter:

- alopecia
- apocrine glands
- bactericidal
- callus
- cerumen
- cleaning bath
- corn
- dandruff
- dental caries
- eccrine glands
- fissures
- gingiva
- gingivitis
- hirsutism
- hygiene
- ingrown toenail
- lanugo
- pediculosis
- periodontal disease
- plantar warts
- plaque
- pyorrhea
- scabies
- sebum
- sudoriferous glands
- sweat glands
- tartar
- therapeutic baths
- ticks
- tinea pedis

LECTURE OUTLINE

I. Hygienic Care
II. Skin
  A. Assessing
    1. Nursing history
    2. Physical assessment
  B. Diagnosing
  C. Planning
    1. Planning for home care
  D. Implementing
    1. General guidelines for skin care
    2. Bathing
    3. Categories
    4. Long-term care setting
III. Feet
  A. Developmental variations
  B. Assessing
    1. Nursing history
    2. Physical assessment
    3. Identifying clients at risk
  C. Diagnosing
  D. Planning
  E. Implementing
IV. Nails
V. Mouth
  A. Developmental and biocultural variations
  B. Assessing
    1. Nursing history
    2. Physical assessment
    3. Identifying clients at risk
  C. Diagnosing
  D. Planning
  E. Implementing
    1. Promoting oral health through the life span
      a. Infants and toddlers
      b. Preschoolers and school-age children
      c. Adolescents and adults
      d. Brushing and flossing the teeth
      e. Caring for artificial dentures
      f. Assisting clients with oral care
      g. Clients with special oral hygiene needs
VI. Hair
  A. Developmental variations
  B. Assessing
  C. Nursing history
  D. Physical assessment
    1. Dandruff
    2. Hair loss
    3. Ticks
    4. Pediculosis (lice)
    5. Scabies
    6. Hirsutism
  E. Diagnosing
  F. Planning
  G. Implementing
    1. Brushing and combing hair
    2. Shampooing the hair
    3. Beard and mustache care
    4. Evaluating

VII. Eyes
  A. Assessing
  B. Nursing history
  C. Physical assessment
  D. Diagnosing
  E. Planning
  F. Implementing
    1. Eye care
    2. Eyeglass care
    3. Contact lens care
    4. Artificial eyes
    5. General eye care
  G. Evaluating
VIII. Ears
  A. Cleaning the ears
  B. Care of hearing aids
IX. Nose
  A. Supporting a hygienic environment
    1. Environment
      a. Room temperature
      b. Ventilation
      c. Noise
    2. Hospital beds
      a. Mattresses
      b. Side rails
      c. Footboards or footboot
      d. Bed cradles
      e. Intravenous rods
    3. Making beds
      a. Unoccupied beds

FOCUSED STUDY TIPS

1. Define the following:
   apocrine glands — eccrine glands
   fissures — gingivitis
   hirsutism — scabies
   sebum
2. Why is the skin considered the body's first line of defense?
3. A 27-year-old client who underwent an appendectomy for ruptured appendix last evening is sweating profusely. Her temperature is 103.5F. She is unable to perform personal hygiene care due to her acute illness. List the most appropriate nursing diagnoses for this client.
4. What is the most important factor that should be considered when planning to assist a client with personal hygiene?
5. You work in a small hospital in a rural area. It is not unusual for you to have clients of all ages on your unit. What important considerations must you keep in mind when bathing clients of all ages?
6. List reasons why oral hygiene is important in the provision of client care.
7. What can be done to improve hair care for clients who are debilitated and bedridden?
8. What is an appropriate technique for eye care?
9. Name the purpose of the following equipment:
   bed cradle — footboard
   IV pole
10. What is the correct way to make an occupied bed?
11. List what you must do before bathing a client.
12. When should gloves be worn when providing care to a client?
13. Identify three ways you assess your client's skin and hygiene practices.
14. Josie Keefer is a 97-year-old woman who has just been admitted to your unit at the skilled nursing facility. She has lived independently until a recent fall that resulted in a severe head laceration. During your intake interview, Josie complains of dry and itchy skin. What nursing actions would you take to correct this problem?
15. Anna Treffel is incontinent of urine and stool. What nursing actions would you take to protect her skin?
16. Identify at least three health concerns that may affect a client's ability to provide foot care independently.

CASE STUDY

You are assigned to provide care to Bryan White, a 16-year-old boy who recently suffered a C-5 fracture as a result of a diving accident. As a result of this accident, Bryan is a quadriplegic. He is awake, alert, and oriented. Bryan is hospitalized on a neurological unit at a major medical center.

1. *What can you do to you provide the most comfortable environment for Bryan?*
2. *Due to his injury, Bryan is dependent on nursing staff for hygienic care. How can you make this a comfortable experience for him?*

CARE PLAN CRITICAL THINKING ACTIVITIES

Fill in the appropriate elements of the care plan for this client:
Assessment and Diagnosis
Planning and Implementation
Evaluation

NCLEX TEST QUESTIONS

1. An 18-month-old infant is noted to have profuse diaper dermatitis. What is the appropriate nursing diagnosis for this infant?
   a. risk for impaired skin integrity related to wearing diapers
   b. risk for impaired tissue integrity related to wearing diapers
   c. impaired skin integrity related to wearing diapers as evidenced by diaper dermatitis
   d. impaired tissue integrity related to knowledge deficit as evidenced by the presence of diaper dermatitis
2. During discharge planning, the nurse is teaching a patient how to prevent pruritis. Which of the following statements is true?
   a. Using alkaline soaps is one way to prevent pruritis.
   b. The patient should take a Sitz bath at least once a day.
   c. The patient should be sure to change his laundry detergent when he gets home.
   d. The patient should decrease the frequency of bathing or should avoid all soap except on the face, axilla, and perineal area.
3. A nurse is shaving a male patient with a razor. Which of the following actions is incorrect?
   a. The nurse applies a moist, warm washcloth to the face and neck for several minutes before shaving.
   b. The nurse dons gloves prior to shaving the patient.
   c. The nurse shaves against the direction of hair growth.
   d. The nurse holds the razor at a 45-degree angle.
4. The nurse is evaluating the outcomes of the nursing diagnosis of altered oral mucous membranes related to dehydration. Which of the following outcome criteria would indicate that the goal was met?
   a. tongue and oral mucosa pink and moist
   b. adequate skin turgor
   c. moist and pink conjunctiva
   d. adequate saliva formation
5. A patient reports to a home care nurse that her wound is healing. Which of the following are indications that a wound is not healing?
   a. The wound tissue color has changed from yellow to red.
   b. The depth of the wound has decreased from 2cm to 1cm.
   c. The wound tissue color has changed from yellow to black.
   d. The wound tissue color has changed from black to yellow.
6. When providing a bed bath for a client, the nurse correctly adjusts the temperature of the water to which of the following?
   a. 100°F to 105°F
   b. 105°F to 110°F
   c. 110°F to 115°F
   d. 115°F to 120°F
7. When performing oral care for an unconscious client, which of the following would be inappropriate? The nurse:
   a. provides oral care every 2 to 4 hours.
   b. uses a gauze square wrapped around a tongue blade and dipped into lemon juice and oil to cleanse the mouth.
   c. uses hydrogen peroxide to remove dried, crusty particles from mouth.
   d. uses normal saline solution to clean the mucous membranes.
8. A nurse is evaluating a nursing student's eye care for a comatose client. Which of the following

actions demonstrates a need for further teaching? The student:

a. cleanses the eyes with saline solution and cotton balls.
b. uses a new cotton ball for each wipe.
c. instills artificial tears into the lower lids.
d. wipes from the outer canthus to the inner canthus.

9. The spouse of a client is cleaning the client's dentures. Which of the following indicates a need for further teaching? The spouse:

a. places a washcloth in the bowl of the sink while cleaning the dentures.
b. uses hot water to clean the dentures.
c. uses a toothbrush to scrub the dentures.
d. soaks the dentures in vinegar and warm water.

10. A nurse is evaluating a client's understanding of foot care. Which of the following statements indicates a need for further teaching?

a. "I wash my feet every day and dry them well, especially between the toes."
b. "I file my toenails instead of cutting them."
c. "I wear clean socks every day."
d. "I avoid creams or lotions since I have calluses."

CHAPTER 32

DIAGNOSTIC TESTING

OVERVIEW

This chapter reviews the role of diagnostic testing when planning care of clients in acute, long-term, and home care environments. It highlights the different types of diagnostic tests, preparation for testing, and any applicable post-testing care.

LEARNING OUTCOMES

After completing this chapter, the student will be able to:

- Describe the nurse's role for each of the phases involved in diagnostic testing
- List common blood tests
- Discuss the nursing responsibilities for specimen collection
- Explain the rationale for the collection of each type of specimen
- Accurately measure blood glucose from a capillary blood specimen using a blood glucose meter
- Compare and contrast the different types of urine specimens
- Collect sputum and throat specimens
- Describe visualization procedures that may be used for the client with gastrointestinal, urinary, and cardiopulmonary alterations
- Compare and contrast CT, MRI, and nuclear imaging studies
- Describe the nurse's role in caring for clients undergoing aspiration/biopsy procedures

www.prenhall.com/kozier

Additional resources for this chapter can be found on the Student CD-ROM accompanying this textbook, and on the Companion Website at www.prenhall.com/kozier. Click on Chapter 32 to select the activities for this chapter.

CD-ROM

- Audio Glossary
- NCLEX Review
- Animation: PET and SPECT Scans

Companion Website

- Additional NCLEX Review
- Case Study: Checking Lab Results
- Care Plan Activity: Client Waiting for Diagnosis
- MediaLink Application: Diagnostic Tests
- Links to Resources

KEY TOPICS

This study guide chapter reinforces the following terms/topics discussed in the textbook chapter:

- abdominal paracentesis
- angiography
- anoscopy
- arterial blood gases
- ascites
- aspiration
- biopsy
- blood chemistry
- blood urea nitrogen (BUN)
- cannula
- clean catch
- clean voided
- colonoscopy
- complete blood count (CBC)
- computed tomography (CT)
- creatinine
- cystoscope
- cystoscopy
- echocardiogram
- electrocardiogram (ECG)
- electrocardiography
- expectorate
- guaiac test
- hematocrit
- hemoglobin
- hemoglobin A1C
- hemoptysis
- intravenous pyelography (IVP)
- kidney/ureter/bladder (KUB)
- leukocyte
- lumbar puncture
- lung scan
- magnetic resonance imaging (MRI)
- manometer
- midstream urine specimen
- occult blood
- peak level
- phlebotomist
- polycythemia
- positron emission tomography (PET)
- proctoscopy
- proctosigmoidoscopy
- radiopharmaceutical
- reagent
- red blood cell (RBC) indices
- retrograde pyelography
- saliva
- serum osmolality
- specific gravity
- sputum
- steatorrhea
- stress electrocardiography
- thoracentesis
- trocar
- trough level
- ultrasonography
- urine osmolality
- venipuncture
- white blood cell (WBC)

LECTURE OUTLINE

I. Diagnostic testing phases
    A. Pretest
    B. Intratest
    C. Post-test
    D. Nursing diagnosis
II. Blood tests
    A. Complete blood count
    B. Serum electrolytes
    C. Serum osmolality
    D. Drug monitoring
    E. Arterial blood gases
    F. Blood chemistry
    G. Capillary blood glucose
    H. Stool specimens
        1. Collecting stool specimens
        2. Testing feces for occult blood
    I. Urine specimens
        1. Clean voided urine specimen
        2. Clean-catch or midstream urine specimen
        3. Timed urine specimen
        4. Indwelling catheter specimen
        5. Urine testing
            a. Specific gravity
            b. Urinary pH

c. Glucose
d. Ketones
e. Protein
f. Occult blood
g. Osmolality
J. Sputum specimens
K. Throat culture
III. Visualization procedures
A. Clients with gastrointestinal alterations
B. Clients with urinary alterations
C. Clients with cardiopulmonary alterations
D. Computed tomography
E. Magnetic resonance imaging
F. Nuclear imaging studies
IV. Aspiration/biopsy
A. Lumbar puncture
B. Abdominal paracentesis
C. Thoracentesis
D. Bone marrow biopsy
E. Liver biopsy
V. Chapter highlights
VI. Review questions
VII. Readings and references
A. Suggested readings
B. Related research
C. References
D. Selected bibliography

FOCUSED STUDY TIPS

1. Define the following:
aspiration
biopsy
computed tomography (CT)
creatinine
cystoscope
cystoscopy
hemoptysis
intravenous pyelography (IVP)
paracentesis
polycythemia
positron emission tomography (PET)
reagent
retrograde pyelography
trocar
trough level
ultrasonography
2. List the phases of diagnostic testing.
3. What is typically done during the intraphase of diagnostic testing?
4. What is the most commonly used diagnostic test?
5. List the parts of the complete blood count.
6. Which diagnostic tests are commonly prescribed to help assess a client's acid-base balance?
7. A client is prescribed Dilantin 300 mg PO TID. Which type of diagnostic test could be prescribed to assess the therapeutic level of this medication?
8. Which diagnostic test measures an average of the amount of glucose in a client's blood?
9. What are the purposes for obtaining a capillary blood sample from a client?
10. List responsibilities of the nurse with specimen collection.
11. A stool specimen for ova and parasites is ordered for a client with a possible parasite infection. What instructions would you provide to the client prior to collecting the stool specimen?
12. List foods that could provide a falsely positive result on a stool specimen test for occult blood.
13. While obtaining a clean catch urine specimen, the client contaminates the outside of the container. What should you do with the specimen?
14. What are the purposes of timed urine specimens?
15. What steps should you follow when collecting a timed urine specimen?
16. What is the difference between obtaining a urine specimen from an indwelling catheter and from an external catheter?
17. What type of apparatus is used to obtain a sputum specimen through suctioning?
18. List diagnostic tests that require an informed consent from the client prior to conducting.
19. Which diagnostic test uses a magnet?
20. How are cerebrospinal fluid pressure measurements taken during a lumbar puncture?
21. Which positions are used when a client needs a thoracentesis?
22. List actions you should take to provide care to a client who has just had a liver biopsy.

CASE STUDY

Marvin Williams, a 55-year-old male, is admitted to the hospital with weight loss, night sweats, and hemoptysis.

1. *Upon admission, the physician orders the client to have three sputum samples for AFB. What does this mean?*
2. *How should you collect these specimens?*
3. *A few hours later, the results of Mr. Williams' complete blood count are phoned. He has a significant elevation in white blood cells. What does this mean?*
4. *What is the relationship between the sputum AFB sample and the elevated white blood cell count?*
5. *Mr. Williams' urine is extremely cloudy. Upon closer examination, you see flecks of white matter floating near the surface. What should you do about the findings with Mr. Williams' urine specimen?*
6. *After several days, Mr. Williams is no longer experiencing night sweats. However, he is having difficulty moving his bowels. What should you do to help this client?*
7. *With the next bowel movement, Mr. Williams puts on his call-light to let you know that "Something is wrong." Upon analysis of his bowel movement, you see streaks of blood and mucous. What should you do?*

CARE PLAN CRITICAL THINKING ACTIVITIES

Fill in the appropriate elements of the care plan for Mr. Williams:
Assessment and Diagnosis
Planning and Implementation
Evaluation

NCLEX TEST QUESTIONS

1. The nurse is assessing a newly admitted male client's serum laboratory values. Which of the following values is abnormal and should be reported immediately?
   a. platelet count 20,000 $\times$ 10^3/mL^3
   b. white blood cell count 7 $\times$ 10^3/mL^3
   c. red blood cell count 5 $\times$ 10^6/mL^3
   d. hematocrit 44%
2. The nurse assessing a client's serum laboratory values recognizes that the normal hemoglobin (Hgb) level for an adult male is:
   a. 14–18 g/dL.
   b. 12–16 g/dL.
   c. 42–52%.
   d. 37–47%.
3. When evaluating the serum laboratory values of a client, which of the following is abnormal and requires the nurse to report it immediately?
   a. potassium 2.8 mEq/L
   b. sodium 140 mEq/L
   c. chloride 98 mEq/L
   d. magnesium 2.0 mEq/L
4. When monitoring serum levels of drugs, the nurse recognizes that the highest concentration of the drug in the blood serum is the:
   a. trough level.
   b. peak level.
   c. therapeutic level.
   d. subtherapeutic level.
5. Which of the following is incorrect technique for the collection of a 24-hour urine collection?
   a. The nurse obtains a specimen container with preservative and labels with client's name.
   b. The nurse provides a clean receptacle for the client to collect urine.
   c. The nurse has the client void at the start of the collection period and includes the urine in the specimen.
   d. The nurse instructs the client to completely empty the bladder at the end of the collection period and saves this voiding as part of the specimen.
6. The nurse is preparing a client for a thoracentesis. The correct position for this client is:
   a. supine in bed.
   b. in the sitting position.
   c. in the prone position.
   d. in the semi-Fowler's position.

7. The nurse is preparing a client for a bone marrow biopsy. Which is the preferred site for this procedure?
   a. posterior superior iliac crest
   b. sternum
   c. anterior iliac spine
   d. posterior iliac spine
8. Which of the following actions taken by the nurse preparing a client for an abdominal paracentesis is inappropriate?
   a. The nurse informs the client of the importance of remaining still during the procedure.
   b. The nurse assists the client to assume a sitting position on the bed or in a chair.
   c. The nurse instructs the client to drink plenty of liquids in order to achieve a full bladder.
   d. The nurse has the client void just prior to the procedure.
9. A client who recently underwent a liver biopsy begins complaining of severe abdominal pain. The nurse's most appropriate action is to:
   a. administer the client's PRN pain medication.
   b. inform the physician.
   c. encourage the client to reposition in bed.
   d. encourage relaxation techniques.
10. The nurse assisting a physician with an abdominal paracentesis knows that normally the maximum amount of fluid drained out at one time to avoid hypovolemic shock is:
    a. 500 mL.
    b. 1,000 mL.
    c. 1,500 mL.
    d. 2,000 mL.

CHAPTER 33

MEDICATIONS

OVERVIEW

This chapter introduces you to the safe administration of medications. You will learn the variety of routes for drug administration, as well as the skills required to administer drugs through these routes. Client safety and bloodborne pathogen precautions are emphasized.

www.prenhall.com/kozier

Additional resources for this chapter can be found on the Student CD-ROM accompanying this textbook, and on the Companion Website at www.prenhall.com/kozier. Click on Chapter 33 to select the activities for this chapter.

CD-ROM

- Audio Glossary
- NCLEX Review
- Injections Animation
  Agonist/Antagonist Mechanism of Action
- Videos
  Metered Dose Inhaler (MDI)
  Small Volume Nebulizer Treatment (SVN)

Companion Website

- Additional NCLEX Review
- Case Study: Preparing Medications
- Care Plan Activity: Client on Insulin
- MediaLink Application: Calculating Dosage
- Links to Resources

LEARNING OUTCOMES

After completing this chapter, the student will be able to:

- Define selected terms related to the administration of medications
- Describe legal aspects of administering medications
- Identify physiologic factors and individual variables affecting medication action
- Describe various routes of medication administration
- Identify essential parts of a medication order
- Give examples of various types of medication orders
- Recognize abbreviations commonly used in medication orders
- List six essential steps to follow when administering medication
- State the six "rights" to accurate medication administration
- Describe physiologic changes in older adults that alter medication administration and effectiveness
- Outline steps required to administer oral medications safely
- Outline steps required for nasogastric and gastrostomy tube medication administration
- Identify equipment required for parenteral medications
- Describe how to mix selected drugs from vials and ampules
- Recognize systems of measurement that are used in the administration of medications
- Identify sites used for subcutaneous, intramuscular, and intradermal injections

- Describe essential steps for safely administering parenteral medications by intradermal, subcutaneous, intramuscular, and intravenous routes
- Describe essential steps in safely administering the following topical medications: dermatologic, ophthalmic, otic, nasal, vaginal, respiratory inhalation, and rectal preparations

KEY TOPICS

This study guide chapter reinforces the following terms/topics discussed in the textbook chapter:

- absorption
- adverse effects
- agonist
- ampule
- anaphylactic reaction
- bevel
- biotransformation
- brand name
- buccal
- cannula
- chemical name
- cumulative effect
- desired effect
- detoxification
- distribution
- drug
- drug abuse
- drug allergy
- drug dependence
- drug habituation
- drug half-life
- drug interaction
- drug polymorphism
- drug tolerance
- drug toxicity
- elimination half-life
- epidural
- excretion
- gastrostomy tube
- gauge
- generic name
- hub
- hypodermic
- hypodermic syringe
- iatrogenic disease
- idiosyncratic effect
- illicit drugs
- inhibiting effect
- insulin syringe
- intradermal
- intradermal (ID) injection
- intramuscular
- intramuscular (IM) injection
- intraspinal
- intrathecal
- intravenous
- irrigation
- lavage
- medication
- meniscus
- metabolism
- metabolites
- metered-dose inhaler (MDI)
- minim
- nasogastric tube
- NPO
- official name
- onset of action
- ophthalmic
- oral
- otic
- parenteral
- peak plasma level
- percutaneous
- pharmacist
- pharmacodynamics
- pharmacokinetics
- pharmacology
- pharmacopoeia
- pharmacy
- physiologic dependence
- piggyback
- plateau
- potentiating effect
- prefilled unit-dose system
- prescription
- PRN order
- psychologic dependence

- reconstitution
- shaft
- side effect
- single order
- specific antagonists
- standing order
- stat order
- subcutaneous
- sublingual
- synergistic effect
- tandem
- therapeutic effect
- topical
- trademark
- transdermal patch
- tuberculin syringe
- vial
- volume control infusion set

LECTURE OUTLINE

I. Drug standards
II. Legal aspects of drug administration
III. Effects of drugs
IV. Drug misuse
V. Actions of drugs on the body
  A. Pharmacodynamics
  B. Pharmacokinetics
    1. Absorption
    2. Distribution
    3. Biotransformation
    4. Excretion
VI. Factors affecting medication action
  A. Developmental factors
  B. Gender
  C. Cultural, ethnic, and genetic factors
  D. Diet
  E. Environment
  F. Psychologic factors
  G. Illness and disease
  H. Time of administration
VII. Routes of administration
  A. Oral
  B. Sublingual
  C. Buccal
  D. Parenteral
  E. Topical
VIII. Medication orders
  A. Types of medication orders
  B. Essential parts of a drug order
  C. Communicating a medication order
IX. Systems of measurement
  A. Metric system
  B. Apothecaries' system
  C. Household system
  D. Converting units of weight and measure
    1. Converting weights within the metric system
    2. Converting weights and measures between systems
    3. Converting units of volume
    4. Converting units of weights
  E. Calculating dosages
    1. Dosages for children
    2. Body surface area
X. Administering medications safely
  A. Medication-dispensing systems
  B. Process of administering medications
  C. Developmental considerations
    1. Infants and children
    2. Older adults
XI. Oral medication
XII. Nasogastric and gastrostomy medications
XIII. Parenteral medications
  A. Equipment
    1. Syringes
    2. Needles
    3. Preventing needle-stick injuries
  B. Preparing injectable medications
  C. Ampules and vials
  D. Mixing medications in one syringe
  E. Intradermal injections
  F. Subcutaneous injections
  G. Intramuscular injections
    1. Ventrogluteal site
    2. Vastus lateralis site
    3. Dorsogluteal site
    4. Deltoid site
    5. Rectus femoris site
    6. Injection technique
  H. Intravenous medications
    1. Large volume infusions
    2. Intermittent intravenous infusions
    3. Volume-control infusions
    4. Intravenous push (IVP)
    5. Intermittent infusion devices
  I. Topical medications
    1. Skin applications
    2. Ophthalmic medications

FOCUSED STUDY TIPS

1. Define the following:
   absorption
   anaphylactic reaction
   brand name
   drug interaction
   drug toxicity
   half-life
   metabolites
   side effect
   agonist
   biotransformation
   drug allergy
   drug tolerance
   excretion
   idiosyncratic effect
   peak plasma level
   therapeutic effect
2. A nurse is caring for a 61-year-old client. The client returned from surgery 6 hours earlier after undergoing a bowel resection and removal of a tumor. The physician has ordered morphine 100 mg q1h IV. The nurse recognizes that this order is potentially lethal as written. If the nurse administers this medication as prescribed, who would be responsible for the error? Why?
3. What is important to know about controlled substances?
4. Your client drinks 12 beers per day. His wife is concerned about his daily beer intake and fears he is becoming an alcoholic. She suggests that he stop drinking. After 24 hours without a beer, he says he is "craving" a beer. He elaborately describes the way an imagined glass of beer looks and tastes. To get his mind off beer, he takes a long walk. What do his cravings demonstrate? Why?
5. Which route of medication administration is the most common, least expensive, and most convenient?
6. You have received an order to administer a drug via the sublingual route. What is the correct way to give this medication?
7. The physician orders Cefotetan 1 gm q12h IV. What type of order is this?
8. The physician orders Valium 2 mg IV stat. When should this medication be given? Why?
9. Your client is a young male, 69 inches tall and weighing 70 kg. You will be administering a subcutaneous injection. What type of needle would be appropriate for his body size?
10. Your client has insulin-dependent diabetes. He states that he uses a #28-gauge needle and only uses his abdomen for insulin administration. He shows you how he pinches a skinfold in his abdomen and administers the injection at a 45-degree angle. What health teaching does this client need relative to insulin administration?
11. You are preparing to give your client an intramuscular injection and have selected the right dorsogluteal site. As you turn the client over to expose the site, you note that multiple injections have been given previously at this site and that a portion of the area is erythematous. What should you do?
12. You will be administering an immunization via intramuscular route to a 5-month-old infant. Where should this injection be given?
13. You are administering an immunization via intramuscular route to a 35-year-old adult. Where should this injection be given?
14. Percodan, a controlled substance, is ordered for your client. Where will you find this medication?
15. When should medications be given via the intravenous route?
16. For which medication routes should sterile technique be used?
17. Identify the factors that influence medication action.
18. Identify the seven essential aspects of a drug order.

19. Complete the following equivalency problems.

    3 g = ____________ mg
    198 lbs = ____________ kg
    500 mcg = ____________ mg
    1.5 L = ____________ mL
    gr X = ____________ mg
20. The physician has ordered tetracycline 500 mg po q6h times 10 days. You have tetracycline 250 mg tablets on hand. How many would you give?
21. Demerol 35 mg IM stat is ordered. You have on hand prefilled syringes that contain 50 mg of Demerol in 1 mL. What would you administer?
22. List at least three nursing actions to avoid puncture injuries.

CASE STUDY

You will be administering digoxin 0.5 mg po to Rose Banda, an awake and alert client.

1. *To safely administer the medication you must follow the five rights. The five rights are:*
2. *Describe your process for administering the medication.*
3. *Rose is complaining of severe nausea. The physician has ordered Compazine 10 mg IM q4h PRN. In the ward stock drawer is an ampule marked "Compazine 5 mg/mL, 2 mL vial." Calculate the volume of medication you will administer.*
4. *How will you draw up the medication from the ampule?*
5. *What are the potential sites for administration?*
6. *After her nausea subsides, Rose is examined by the nurse practitioner. Additional medications are ordered as follows:*
   Pilocarpine 1% i gtt OS q6h
   D5/.9NS @ 150 cc/hr
   Strict NPO
   Describe how you will instill the pilocarpine as ordered.
7. *After the IV infusion has been established, how can additional medications be given through the IV route?*

CARE PLAN CRITICAL THINKING ACTIVITIES

Fill in the appropriate elements of the care plan for this client:
Assessment and Diagnosis
Planning and Implementation
Evaluation

NCLEX TEST QUESTIONS

1. The nurse preparing to administer an intramuscular injection using the Z-track technique knows that the correct angle to use when administering intramuscular medications is:
   a. 30 degrees.
   b. 45 degrees.
   c. 60 degrees.
   d. 90 degrees.
2. The nurse understands that drugs may produce a response by stimulating enzyme activity or hormone production. This is called
   a. synergistic effect.
   b. agonist effect.
   c. distribution.
   d. biotransformation.
3. A client experiences respiratory depression after two days of morphine sulfate administration for

pain manangement. The nurse recognizes that the client has experienced:

a. a side effect of the drug.
b. drug toxicity.
c. a drug allergy.
d. an anaphylactic reaction.

4. A nurse planning a seminar on drug misuse plans to explain the differences between drug dependence and drug habituation. A person's reliance on or need to take a drug or substance identifies:
   a. drug abuse.
   b. drug dependence.
   c. drug habituation.
   d. drug interaction.
5. A nurse assessing a client after the administration of penicillin notes shortness of breath, acute hypotension, and tachycardia. The nurse plans immediate interventions for:
   a. drug toxicity.
   b. drug allergy.
   c. anaphylactic reaction.
   d. drug tolerance.
6. A nurse planning an orientation inservice for new nurses to a geriatric unit will discuss factors affecting medication action in the older adult. Which of the following is not a factor affecting medication action in the older adult?
   a. decreased gastric acid production and blood flow
   b. decreased adipose tissue
   c. decreased total body fluid proportionate to the body mass
   d. decreased number of protein-binding sites and changes in the blood-brain barrier
7. A client in the emergency department is to receive ¼ gr of morphine sulfate. The nurse administering the medication knows that ¼ gr is equivalent to:
   a. .25 mg.
   b. 10 mg.
   c. 15 mg.
   d. 25 mg.
8. The nurse practitioner in the clinic has written an order for an ophthalmic solution to be administered 1 gtt OU bid. The nurse instructs the client to do which of the following?
   a. Instill one drop in each eye twice a day.
   b. Instill one drop in the left eye twice a day.
   c. Instill one drop in the right eye twice a day.
   d. Instill one drop in each eye once a day.
9. Which of the following actions taken by a client self-administering eye medications indicates to the nurse a need for further teaching?
   a. The client instills the medication into the conjunctival sac.
   b. The client squeezes eyes closed after instilling the medication.
   c. The client presses on the nasolacrimal duct for at least 30 seconds.
   d. The client gently wipes the eyelids from the inner to the outer canthus to collect excess medication.
10. Which of the following actions is inappropriate for the nurse administering a rectal suppository to an adult?
   a. The nurse positions the client in the left lateral position, with the upper leg flexed.
   b. The nurse lubricates the smooth rounded end of the suppository.
   c. The nurse lubricates the gloved index finger.
   d. The nurse inserts the suppository 5 cm (2 inches).

CHAPTER 34

SKIN INTEGRITY AND WOUND CARE

OVERVIEW

This chapter presents your role in caring for clients with wounds and pressure ulcers. It presents assessment guidelines and interventions to promote skin integrity, prevent and treat pressure ulcers, and support wound healing. You are introduced to a variety of wound care procedures as well as dressing and bandage equipment and techniques.

LEARNING OUTCOMES

After completing this chapter, the student will be able to:

- Describe factors affecting skin integrity
- Identify clients at risk for pressure ulcer formation
- Describe the four stages of pressure ulcer development
- Differentiate primary and secondary wound healing
- Describe the three phases of wound healing
- Identify three major types of wound exudate
- Identify the main complications of and factors that affect wound healing
- Identify assessment data pertinent to skin integrity, pressure sites, and wounds
- Identify nursing diagnoses associated with impaired skin integrity
- Identify essential aspects of planning care to maintain skin integrity and promote wound healing
- Discuss measures to prevent pressure ulcer formation
- Describe nursing strategies to treat pressure ulcers, promote wound healing, and prevent complications of wound healing
- Identify purposes of commonly used wound dressing materials and binders
- Identify physiologic responses to heat and cold, and purposes of heat and cold
- Describe methods of applying dry and moist heat and cold
- Identify essential steps of obtaining wound specimens, applying dressings, and irrigating a wound

www.prenhall.com/kozier

Additional resources for this chapter can be found on the Student CD-ROM accompanying this textbook, and on the Companion Website at www.prenhall.com/kozier. Click on Chapter 34 to select the activities for this chapter.

CD-ROM
- Audio Glossary
- NCLEX Review
- Animations:
  - Pressure Ulcer
  - Feature Integument
  - Layers of the Skin
  - Integumentary Repair

Companion Website
- Additional NCLEX Review
- Case Study: Client with Chronic Illnesses
- Care Plan Activity: Client with Pressure Ulcer
- MediaLink Application: Enterostomal Therapist
- Links to Resources

KEY TOPICS

This study guide chapter reinforces the following terms/topics discussed in the textbook chapter:

- aerobic
- anaerobic
- approximated
- bandage
- binder
- collagen
- compress
- debridement
- decubitus ulcer
- dehiscence
- eschar
- evisceration
- excoriation
- exudate
- fibrin
- friction
- granulation tissue
- hematoma
- hemorrhage
- hemorrhagic exudate
- hemostasis
- immobility
- irrigation (lavage)
- ischemia
- keloid
- lavage
- maceration
- packing
- phagocytosis
- pressure
- pressure ulcer
- primary intention healing
- purulent exudate
- pus
- pyogenic bacteria
- reactive hyperemia
- regeneration
- sanguineous exudate
- secondary intention healing
- serous exudate
- shearing force
- sitz bath
- suppuration
- vasoconstriction
- vasodilation

LECTURE OUTLINE

I. Skin integrity
II. Types of wounds
III. Pressure ulcers
    A. Etiology of pressure ulcers
    B. Risk factors
        1. Immobility
        2. Inadequate nutrition
        3. Fecal and urinary incontinence
        4. Decreased mental status
        5. Diminished sensation
        6. Excessive body heat
        7. Advanced age
        8. Chronic medical conditions
        9. Other factors
    C. Stages of pressure ulcer formation
IV. Wound healing
    A. Types of wound healing
    B. Phases of wound healing
        1. Inflammatory phase
        2. Proliferative phase
        3. Maturation phase
    C. Kinds of wound drainage
    D. Complications of wound healing
        1. Hemorrhage
        2. Infection
        3. Dehiscence with possible evisceration
    E. Factors affecting wound healing
        1. Developmental considerations
        2. Nutrition
        3. Lifestyle
        4. Medications
        5. Assessing
    F. Assessment of skin integrity
        1. Nursing history and physical assessment
        2. Risk assessment tools
    G. Assessment of wounds
        1. Untreated wounds
        2. Treated wounds
        3. Pressure ulcers
        4. Laboratory data

V. Diagnosing
VI. Planning
   A. Planning for home care
   B. Implementing
   C. Supporting wound healing
      1. Nutrition and fluids
      2. Preventing infection
      3. Positioning
   D. Preventing pressure ulcers
      1. Providing nutrition
      2. Maintaining skin hygiene
      3. Avoiding skin trauma
      4. Providing supportive devices
   E. Treating pressure ulcers
   F. The RYB color code
   G. Dressing wounds
      1. Types of dressing
      2. Securing dressings
   H. Cleaning wounds
   I. Wound irrigation and packing
   J. Heat and cold applications
      1. Local effects of heat
      2. Local effects of cold
      3. Systemic effects of heat and cold
      4. Thermal tolerance
      5. Adaptation of thermal receptors
      6. Rebound phenomenon
   K. Applying heat and cold
      1. Hot water bag
      2. Aquathermia pad
      3. Hot and cold packs
      4. Electric pads
      5. Ice bag, ice glove, ice collar
      6. Compresses
      7. Soak
      8. Sitz bath
      9. Cooling sponge bath
   L. Supporting and immobilizing wounds
      1. Bandages
      2. Basic turns for roller bandages
      3. Binders
   M. Evaluating
VII. Chapter highlights
VIII. Review questions
IX. Readings and references
   A. Suggested readings
   B. Related research
   C. References
   D. Selected bibliography

FOCUSED STUDY TIPS

1. Define the following:
   debridement
   dehiscence
   evisceration
   exudate
   hemostasis
   ischemia
   keloid
   maceration
   phagocytosis
   pressure ulcer
   reactive hyperemia
   shearing force
2. Your client is a 6-year-old boy who sustained a fracture of the right humerus when he fell off his bike. The skin of the upper arm is erythematous and tender to the touch. The bone is not protruding through the skin. How would you classify this wound?
3. Your client had abdominal surgery for incision and drainage of an abscess. The wound margins have not been approximated. The wound is being irrigated and packed every 4 to 6 hours. The client is receiving IV antibiotics. The surgeon believes that this wound can be surgically closed within 2 weeks. How will this wound heal?
4. When you remove the old dressing on a surgical wound, you note a large pool of pus on the dressing and in the central portion of the wound. What phrase would best describe this exudate?
5. What is the major advantage of a wet-to-damp dressing over a wet-to-dry dressing?
6. When should heat and cold be used in wound care?
7. Earl Mason has a pressure ulcer on his coccyx that must be irrigated and packed. When you remove the old dressing, you note that there is a long sinus tract extending down the left thigh. Muscle tissue is visible and a yellow exudate is present in the wound. This is evidence of which pressure ulcer stage?
8. On your morning rounds, you note that one of your clients has a reddened area on her right hip. When you apply pressure to the erythematous region, it does not blanch. This is evidence of which pressure ulcer stage?
9. Your client is terminally ill and is being cared for at home by his family. His family is overwhelmed by the amount of care he currently requires. On his admission to the hospice unit, you perform a complete assessment. You note reddened and abraded areas on both heels. This is evidence of which pressure ulcer stage?

10. Your client is febrile and uncomfortable. You are considering giving her a tepid sponge bath. What technique would be appropriate for this bath?
11. What are the risk factors for pressure ulcer formation?
12. Report has just finished for the evening shift on a medical-surgical unit. One of your clients returned from the operating room during the change of shift. You find the client sleepy but arousable. The dressing is saturated with bloody drainage. When you remove the dressing, you see a constant flow of bright red blood from the suture line. What should you do?
13. Aaron Souza is 4 days postoperative from a colon resection. You are assisting him to get out of bed when he starts coughing. He grimaces in pain and states, "Oh, that hurt. I swear it felt like my insides popped." You assist Aaron back to bed and place him in a semi-Fowler's position. The wound dressing appears disheveled. When you remove the dressing to examine the wound, you find a loop of bowel protruding through the suture line. What should you do?
14. Grant Martin reports to the emergency department with a laceration to his left hand. While pruning roses, he accidentally cut his hand. How would you assess this wound?
15. Robert Wayne successfully underwent knee surgery 24 hours ago. When you examine the wound, you find dried blood on the old dressing. The wound edges are approximated, but the margins are slightly red and inflamed. There is no odor. Robert complains of moderate pain which he describes as "burning" in nature. He reports that the pain medication provides significant relief. What is your assessment?
16. Identify at least five purposes of a wound dressing.
17. What safeguards should be taken when irrigating a wound?

CASE STUDY

Martin Rogers is a 19-year-old college freshman who sustained a C-5 spinal cord injury as a result of a diving accident 1 week ago today. Martin has no movement or sensation below his shoulders. Martin's vital signs are BP 100/48, P 124, RR 24, and T 39.0C. A chest X-ray reveals bibasilar pneumonia. Martin is receiving IV fluids at 100 cc/hr. You have observed that he is despondent about his recent injury. He was placed on a diet as tolerated 3 days ago, but he has refused food. He is only taking sips of liquid by mouth. He has not had a bowel movement since his hospitalization. A Foley catheter is to straight drainage.

1. *Identify Martin's risk factors for development of a pressure ulcer.*
2. *Martin continues to refuse to eat. By the twelfth day of hospitalization, Martin weighs 10 pounds less than his preinjury weight. As you turn Martin, you note that he has developed a pressure ulcer. Which aspects of your findings should be recorded in the chart?*
3. *You determine that Martin's existing pressure sore is at Stage II. What type of dressing might be appropriate for this pressure ulcer?*

CARE PLAN CRITICAL THINKING ACTIVITIES

Fill in the appropriate elements of the care plan for this client:
Assessment and Diagnosis
Planning and Implementation
Evaluation

NCLEX TEST QUESTIONS

1. While assessing a 29-year-old Caucasian patient, the nurse notices an area of skin that has normal coloring but is surrounded by patchy areas without pigmentation. What conclusion can the nurse make from this assessment finding?
   a. The patient has a suntan.
   b. The patient has vitiligo.
   c. The patient is an albino.
   d. The patient has erythema.
2. A nurse is assessing a pressure ulcer and notes that the wound is superficial and involving the epidermis only. The nurse later reports to the physician that the patient has a stage 2 pressure ulcer. Which of the following statements is true?

a. The nurse correctly assessed the pressure ulcer as stage 2.
b. The nurse was incorrect in her assessment and should have noted that the pressure ulcer is at stage 3.
c. The nurse was incorrect in her assessment and should have noted that the pressure ulcer is at stage 4.
d. The nurse's scope of practice does not allow for staging of pressure ulcers and the nurse should have called the physician for this assessment.

3. The nurse is assessing a wound and notes that the exudate is serosanguineous. What would you expect the exudate to look like?
a. The exudate is thick with dead bacteria and leukocytes with a yellow or green color.
b. The exudate is clear and thin.
c. The exudate is bright red and bloody.
d. The exudate is red to pink and watery.

4. During discharge planning, the nurse is teaching a patient how to prevent pruritis. Which of the following statements is true?
a. Using alkaline soaps is one way to prevent pruritis.
b. The patient should take a sitz bath at least once a day.
c. The patient should be sure to change his laundry detergent when he gets home.
d. The patient should decrease the frequency of bathing, or avoid all soap except on the face, axilla, and perineal area.

5. The nurse is preparing to apply a wet-to-dry dressing to a stage 3 wound on a patient's coccyx. Which of the following actions is incorrect?
a. The nurse verifies the medical order and reviews the nursing and medical progress notes prior to changing the dressing.
b. The nurse places the patient in a supine position to prepare for wound care.
c. When the nurse gathers supplies, she/he includes clean gloves and sterile gloves to prepare for the procedure.
d. The nurse should cleanse the wound with a solution ordered by the physician.

6. The nurse performs postsurgical wound care on a patient who has had an incision and drainage of an abscess. The nurse recognizes this type of wound as a:
a. clean wound.
b. clean-contaminated wound.
c. contaminated wound.
d. infected wound.

7. The nurse is performing a skin assessment of a newly admitted nursing home patient. The nurse notes a shallow, reddened, craterlike opening over the coccyx and documents this as a:
a. stage 1 ulcer.
b. stage 2 ulcer.
c. clean wound.
d. contaminated wound.

8. The nurse performs a wet-to-dry treatment to a hip ulcer on a nursing home patient. The nurse notes muscle tissue, which is exposed. This type of wound is documented as a:
a. stage 3 ulcer.
b. stage 4 ulcer.
c. clean wound.
d. contaminated wound.

9. While changing a dressing on a patient's surgical incision, the nurse notes reddish-pink drainage coming from the incision. The nurse recognizes this as:
a. serous drainage.
b. serosanguineous drainage.
c. purulent drainage.
d. purosanguineous drainage.

10. During a discharge teaching session on postsurgical wound care, the nurse stresses the need to report the following signs of infection:
a. itching and tingling around the surgical incision
b. presence of serous drainage
c. pain and swelling at surgical site
d. sloughing off of scab formation

11. The nurse caring for a client with an open wound recognizes that the process whereby a wound is left open to heal is called healing by:
a. primary intention.
b. secondary intention.
c. tertiary intention.
d. open reduction.

12. During a postsurgical dressing change, the nurse notes that the wound edges have pulled apart, exposing the underlying tissue. This separation of a wound is called:
a. superficial separation.

b. hemorrhage.
c. dehiscence.
d. evisceration.

13. In planning wound care interventions for a stage 2 skin ulcer, the most effective treatment would be:
    a. gauze packing dressings
    b. a dry sterile dressing
    c. hydrocolloid-type dressings
    d. a wet-to-dry dressing

CHAPTER 35

PERIOPERATIVE NURSING

OVERVIEW

This chapter examines the perioperative experience from the belief that surgery is a unique human experience that creates stress. It emphasizes your role in preparing the client for surgery and preventing postoperative complications.

LEARNING OUTCOMES

After completing this chapter, the student will be able to:

- Describe the phases of the perioperative period
- Discuss various types of surgery according to degree of urgency, degree of risk, and purpose
- Identify essential aspects of preoperative assessment
- Give examples of pertinent nursing diagnoses for surgical clients
- Identify nursing responsibilities in planning perioperative nursing care
- Describe essential preoperative teaching, including pain control, moving, leg exercises, and coughing and deep-breathing exercises
- Describe essential aspects of preparing a client for surgery, including skin preparation
- Compare various types of anesthesia
- Identify essential nursing assessments and interventions during the immediate postanesthetic phase
- Demonstrate ongoing nursing assessments and interventions for the postoperative client
- Identify potential postoperative complications, and describe nursing interventions to prevent them
- Identify essential aspects of managing gastrointestinal suction
- Describe appropriate wound care for a postoperative client
- Evaluate the effectiveness of perioperative nursing interventions

www.prenhall.com/kozier

Additional resources for this chapter can be found on the Student CD-ROM accompanying this textbook, and on the Companion Website at www.prenhall.com/kozier. Click on Chapter 35 to select the activities for this chapter.

CD-ROM
- Audio Glossary
- NCLEX Review

Companion Website
- Additional NCLEX Review
- Case Study: Clients Having Surgical Procedures
- Care Plan Activity: Coronary Artery Bypass Procedure
- MediaLink Application: Developing Operative Care Policies
- Links to Resources

KEY TOPICS

This study guide chapter reinforces the following terms/topics discussed in the textbook chapter:

- ambulatory surgery center (ASC)
- atelectasis
- Bier block
- circulating nurses
- closed wound drainage system
- conscious sedation
- elective surgery
- emboli
- emergency surgery
- epidural anesthesia
- general anesthesia
- intraoperative phase
- intravenous block
- local anesthesia
- major surgery
- minor surgery
- nerve block
- Penrose drain
- peridural anesthesia
- perioperative period
- postoperative phase
- preoperative phase
- regional anesthesia
- scrub nurse
- spinal anesthesia
- subarachnoid block (SAB)
- surface anesthesia
- suture
- thrombophlebitis
- thrombus
- tissue perfusion
- topical anesthesia

LECTURE OUTLINE

I. Types of surgery
  A. Purpose
  B. Degree of urgency
  C. Degree of risk
    1. Age
    2. General health
    3. Medications
    4. Mental status
II. Preoperative phase
  A. Preoperative consent
  B. Assessing
    1. Nursing history
    2. Physical assessment
    3. Screening tests
  C. Diagnosing
  D. Planning
    1. Planning for home care
  E. Implementing
    1. Preoperative teaching
  F. Physical preparation
    1. Nutrition and fluids
    2. Elimination
    3. Hygiene
    4. Medications
    5. Rest and sleep
    6. Valuables
    7. Prostheses
    8. Special orders
    9. Skin preparation
    10. Vital signs
    11. Antiemboli stockings
    12. Sequential compression devices
  G. Evaluating
III. Intraoperative phase
  A. Types of anesthesia
  B. Assessing
  C. Diagnosing
  D. Planning
  E. Implementing
    1. Surgical skin preparation
    2. Positioning
  F. Documentation
IV. Postoperative phase
  A. Immediate post-anesthetic phase
  B. Preparing for ongoing care of the postoperative client
  C. Assessing
  D. Diagnosing
  E. Planning
    1. Planning for home care
  F. Implementing
    1. Pain management

2. Positioning
3. Deep-breathing and coughing exercises
4. Leg exercises
5. Moving and ambulation
6. Hydration
7. Diet
8. Urinary elimination
9. Suction

G. Wound care
1. Surgical dressings
2. Wound drains and suction
3. Sutures

H. Home care teaching
1. Maintaining comfort
2. Promoting healing
3. Restoring wellness
4. Community agencies and other sources of help
5. Referrals

I. Evaluating

V. Chapter highlights

VI. Review questions

VII. Readings and references
A. Suggested readings
B. Related research
C. References
D. Selected bibliography

FOCUSED STUDY TIPS

1. Define the following:
   conscious sedation
   epidural anesthesia
   general anesthesia
   local anesthesia
   patient-controlled analgesia
   regional anesthesia
   spinal anesthesia
2. Your client is scheduled for same-day surgery. You have assessed her preoperative status, knowledge of the planned surgery, previous experience with surgery and anesthesia, and emotional/psychological concerns. What other aspects must be assessed for this client?
3. What is the purpose of the preoperative assessment?
4. There is always risk involved with any surgical procedure. List the types of clients who have a high surgical risk.
5. What should preoperative teaching for a hospitalized client include?
6. Surgical clients are usually instructed to fast for 6 to 8 hours before surgery. What is the purpose of fasting?
7. Who should obtaining legal, informed consent to perform a surgical procedure?
8. What are the purposes of leg exercises and sequential compression devices?
9. Surgical nurses may function in either the scrub or circulating position. What is a key distinction between these roles?
10. The client is scheduled for cardiac surgery. In which position will the client most likely be placed for surgery?
11. Which is the immediate postoperative position of choice for a client who has had spinal anesthesia?
12. Why should splinting be done while coughing?
13. Until when does a postoperative client usually remain in the PAR?
14. Which assessments should you perform when receiving a postoperative client from the recovery room?
15. Your postoperative client returns from surgery with a nasogastric tube. What is your role in managing the client who requires gastric suctioning?
16. What are your responsibilities when caring for a client with a closed wound drainage system?

CASE STUDY

David Lipscomb is a 51-year-old client admitted to Mercy Medical Center for abdominal surgery on an inpatient basis. What preparation for surgery is required?

During your assessment David states, "No one ever explained this surgery to me. The doctor told me I needed this surgery, but I don't understand why. I'm really not sure about all this." A signed consent form is on the chart and the operating room transporter has just arrived to transport the client. How would you handle this situation?

As you prepare David for surgery, you note that his chest and abdomen are very hairy. He will undoubtedly need hair removal prior to surgery. What should you do?

David undergoes resection of a loop of bowel and returns to the unit later that evening. An NG tube is in place for 48 hours and then removed. On the third postoperative day, he asks you when he will be able to eat and drink again. What is your best response?

CARE PLAN CRITICAL THINKING ACTIVITIES

Fill in the appropriate elements of the care plan for this client:
Assessment and Diagnosis
Planning and Implementation
Evaluation

NCLEX TEST QUESTIONS

1. The nurse assessing a patient admitted to the hospital for gall bladder surgery would assess the patient's primary concern by:
   a. reviewing the patient's diagnostic test to determine the seriousness of the gall bladder problems.
   b. completing the nursing physical assessment.
   c. taking a nutritional history and assessing the effect diet has on the patient.
   d. asking the patient, "What about your problem bothers you the most?"
2. The plan of care for a patient admitted to the hospital for heart surgery has identified the nursing diagnosis as "Powerlessness R/T illness-related regimen AEB patient statement, 'I hate not being able to do things for myself.'" A nursing intervention related to this diagnosis may be to:
   a. assess the patient's personal strengths and set realistic goals for change.
   b. discuss the patient's favorite topics during treatments.
   c. provide information regarding techniques to control pain.
   d. help the patient identify factors of care under his or her control.
3. When caring for a patient in the immediate postoperative period, the priority intervention for the nurse is which of the following?
   a. pain management
   b. maintenance of patent airway
   c. wound care
   d. assessment of neurological status
4. During a discharge teaching session on postsurgical wound care, the nurse stresses the need to report the following signs of infection:
   a. itching and tingling around the surgical incision
   b. presence of serous drainage
   c. pain and swelling at surgical site
   d. sloughing off of scab formation
5. During a postsurgical dressing change, the nurse notes that the wound edges have pulled apart, exposing the underlying tissue. What is this separation of a wound called?
   a. superficial separation
   b. hemorrhage
   c. dehiscence
   d. evisceration
6. A client undergoing a procedure asks the nurse to clarify what "conscious sedation" is. Which of the following is the most appropriate response by the nurse?
   a. "It is an injection of an anesthetic agent into the epidural space."
   b. "It is minimal depression of the level of consciousness in which you will retain the ability to consciously maintain a patent airway."
   c. "It is the temporary interruption of the transmission of nerve impulses to and from a specific area or region of the body."
   d. "It is the loss of all sensation and consciousness."
7. A client is 4 hours postoperative abdominal surgery. Over the past 2 hours, he has exhibited

an increase in pulse, a decrease in urine output, and a decrease in blood pressure. The nurse suspects the client is experiencing which postoperative complication?
   a. pulmonary embolism
   b. atelectasis
   c. hypovolemic shock
   d. hypovolemia

8. A postoperative client complains of sudden chest pain and shortness of breath. Upon assessment, cyanosis, hypotension, and tachycardia are noted. The nurse's immediate intervention is to implement measures related to which of the following?
   a. pneumonia
   b. pulmonary embolism
   c. atelectasis
   d. hypovolemic shock

9. While irrigating a gastrointestinal tube on a postoperative client, the nurse encounters difficulty withdrawing the solution injected. Which of the following is not an appropriate action for the nurse to take?
   a. The nurse injects 60 mL of air and aspirates again.
   b. The nurse repositions the nasogastric tube.
   c. The nurse gently attempts to withdraw the solution.
   d. The nurse notifies the physician after repeated attempts to aspirate the solution are unsuccessful.

10. The nurse is assessing a client's spouse demonstrating surgical wound care. Which of the following indicates a need for further teaching?
   a. The spouse uses a clean sterile cotton ball for each stroke of cleansing.
   b. The spouse cleanses around the drain site by swabbing in half or full circles from around the drain site outward.
   c. The spouse maintains forcep tips higher than the handles at all times.
   d. The spouse places the bulk of the dressing over the drain area and below the drain.

CHAPTER 36

SENSORY PERCEPTION

OVERVIEW

This chapter discusses the importance of sensory and perceptual function in the maintenance of health. The chapter emphasizes the detection of sensory alterations and your role in caring for clients experiencing alterations in sensory reception or perception.

LEARNING OUTCOMES

After completing this chapter, the student will be able to:

- Discuss anatomic and physiologic components of the sensory-perception process
- Describe factors influencing sensory function
- Discuss factors that place a client at risk for sensory disturbances
- Describe essential components in assessing a client's sensory-perception function
- Identify clinical signs and symptoms of sensory overload and deprivation
- Develop nursing diagnoses and outcome criteria for clients with impaired sensory function
- Discuss nursing interventions to promote and maintain sensory function
- Identify strategies to promote and maintain orientation to person, place, time, and situation for the confused client
- Identify community resources for clients with chronic sensory disturbances

www.prenhall.com/kozier

Additional resources for this chapter can be found on the Student CD-ROM accompanying this textbook, and on the Companion Website at www.prenhall.com/kozier. Click on Chapter 36 to select the activities for this chapter.

CD-ROM
- Audio Glossary
- NCLEX Review
- Animations:
  - Brain and Brainstem 3D
  - Visceral Effectors A & P Review
  - Components of a Reflex Arc
  - Meninges of the Brain A & P Review
  - Head and Trunk 3D
  - The Ear 3D
  - The Ear A & P Review
  - The Eye 3 D
  - The Eye A & P Review
  - Lower Limb 3D
  - Upper Limb 3D

Companion Website
- Additional NCLEX Review
- Case Study: Clients with Altered Sensory Perception
- Care Plan Activity: The Confused and Agitated Client
- MediaLink Application: Client with Second-Degree Burns
- Links to Resources

KEY TOPICS

This study guide chapter reinforces the following terms/topics discussed in the textbook chapter:

- auditory
- awareness
- cultural care deprivation
- cultural deprivation
- CultureCare
- gustatory
- kinesthetic
- olfactory
- sensoristasis
- sensory deficit
- sensory deprivation
- sensory overload
- sensory perception
- sensory reception
- stereognosis
- tactile
- visceral
- visual

LECTURE OUTLINE

I. Components of the sensory experience
  A. Arousal mechanism
II. Sensory alterations
  A. Sensory deprivation
  B. Sensory overload
  C. Sensory deficits
III. Factors affecting sensory function
  A. Developmental stage
  B. Culture
  C. Stress
  D. Medications and illness
  E. Lifestyle and personality
IV. Assessing
  A. Nursing history
  B. Mental status
  C. Physical examination
  D. Clients at risk for sensory deprivation or overload
  E. Client environment
  F. Social support network
V. Diagnosing
  A. Disturbed sensory perception as the diagnostic label
  B. Sensory-perception problem as the etiology
VI. Planning
  A. Planning independent of setting
  B. Planning for home care
VII. Implementing
  A. Promoting healthy sensory function
  B. Adjusting environmental stimuli
    1. Preventing sensory overload
    2. Preventing sensory deprivation
VIII. Managing acute sensory deficits
  A. Sensory aids
  B. Promoting the use of other senses
  C. Communicating effectively
  D. Ensuring client safety
    1. Impaired vision
    2. Impaired hearing
    3. Impaired olfactory sense
    4. Impaired tactile sense
  E. The confused client
  F. The unconscious client
IX. Evaluating
X. Chapter highlights
XI. Review questions
XII. Readings and references
  A. Suggested readings
  B. Related research
  C. References
  D. Selected bibliography

FOCUSED STUDY TIPS

1. Define the following:
   awareness
   kinesthetic
   sensoristasis
   sensory overload
   visceral
   cognition
   reticular activating system
   sensory deprivation
   stereognosis

2. Your client has experienced a cerebrovascular accident, or stroke, which has resulted in severe damage to the visual center in the brain. As a consequence, her sensory process is altered. Which aspect of the sensory process has been altered?
3. Numerous factors affect the quality and quantity of sensory stimulation and function. List factors that play an important role in sensory stimulation.
4. Which stimuli in the health care environment may produce sensory deprivation?
5. You are communicating with an elderly client who has a hearing impairment. You are in a quiet room and directly facing the client. What else can you do to improve communication?
6. You have admitted a client who is blind to your unit. What is the most appropriate nursing action for this client?
7. A client with peripheral neuropathy secondary to diabetes is being prepared for discharge. The client has an ulceration on his foot, which must be soaked in warm water three times per day. Due to the neuropathy, the client cannot sense the temperature of the water with his extremities. What instructions should be given to this client?
8. Your client is sleepy but arouses to touch and the call of his name. Describe his state of awareness.
9. When conducting a nursing history, what sensory perceptual aspects should be evaluated?
10. Identify the types of clients who are most likely to experience social isolation.
11. Identify at least one health promotion activity in each area to prevent sensory deficits.

    hearing
    taste
    vision

CASE STUDY

Marla Nicholson is an 87-year-old widow with severe osteoporosis. Her numerous compression fractures and recent fractured hip limit her activities. Marla rarely ventures out of the house. Her children and grandchildren live over 1,000 miles away. Marla's daughter is concerned about her mother. On a recent visit she contacts you, the nurse at the community geriatric program. She requests that her mother be evaluated for participation in an adult day health care program. As part of your evaluation, you arrange to meet Marla at her home.

1. *Identify three areas that you would evaluate during your visit to Marla.*
2. *Marla is interested in being part of the adult day health care program. She realizes that she will be able to meet other seniors and engage in social activities while still living in her home. She eagerly agrees to participate. Approximately 1 month after joining the program, Marla falls and refractures her hip. She is hospitalized at the community hospital affiliated with the adult day health care program. You visit Marla 2 days after surgery. She appears tense, restless, and disoriented. What do you suspect is wrong with Marla? What interventions would you suggest?*
3. *After a 10-day hospital stay, Marla is discharged to a skilled nursing facility (SNF). Marla is reluctant to enter the SNF, but the orthopedic surgeon insists that she stay in the SNF while receiving daily physical therapy. Two weeks after her admission to the SNF, you arrange a visit to evaluate when she will be able to return to the adult day health care program. Marla yawns frequently and appears tired. She seems apathetic and depressed. What do you suspect is wrong with her? What interventions would you suggest?*

CARE PLAN CRITICAL THINKING ACTIVITIES

Fill in the appropriate elements of the care plan for this client:
Assessment and Diagnosis
Planning and Implementation
Evaluation

NCLEX TEST QUESTIONS

1. A young child is at the clinic to receive an immunization. When the nurse enters the room, the child becomes fearful and agitated. The parent asks the nurse how to respond appropriately to this behavior. Which of the following explanations is correct?
   a. The child has developed a bad habit and should be gently punished for his or her behavior. Restraining for the immunization procedure may be necessary.
   b. The nurse explains to the parent that this behavior is normal and is most likely due to the child having been conditioned to associate nurses and physicians with pain from previous immunization visits. The child will eventually outgrow his fears and punishment is not justifiable.
   c. The child has been sensitized to the health-care setting and is responding to fear from the impending immunization. This behavior is normal and should not be punished.
   d. The child's behavior is not acceptable and the nurse should discuss with the parent and the physician a plan to premedicate the child for anxiety prior to every clinic visit.
2. An elder male reports to the nurse that "I finally got myself a pair of glasses. After nearly 78 years of perfect vision, I can no longer read without difficulty." What is the appropriate term for this man's condition?
   a. Myopia
   b. Diplopia
   c. Glaucoma
   d. Presbyopia
3. A patient is complaining of partial hearing loss. The nurse inspects the ears and notes that both ears are impacted with cerumen. What type of hearing loss does this patient most likely have?
   a. conductive hearing loss
   b. sensorineural hearing loss
   c. mixed hearing loss
   d. pathological hearing loss
4. The nurse performs a neurosensory assessment of a patient and finds the patient to be unresponsive to voice, but responsive to noxious stimuli as demonstrated by soft moaning. The nurse documents the patient's level of consciousness as:
   a. coma
   b. semicoma
   c. somnolent
   d. disoriented
5. While assesing a client, the nurse notes decreased attention span, impaired memory, and the client is experiencing hallucinations. The nurse recognizes that these signs may be indicative of which of the following?
   a. sensory deprivation
   b. sensory overload
   c. sensory deficits
   d. sensory awareness
6. The nurse providing care to a newly admitted client who is also blind recognizes the client is at increased risk for injury related to which of the following?
   a. blind individuals are at higher risk for injuries in their homes and other places
   b. blind individuals are at higher risk for injuries in unfamiliar settings
   c. blind individuals are at higher risk for injuries in general
   d. blind individuals are at higher risk for injuries because they are unable to adapt to new environments
7. A client being instructed on managing an impaired olfactory sense requires further teaching when which of the following statements is made?
   a. "I will keep my gas stove and heater in good working order."
   b. "I will inspect my food for color, texture, and expiration dates."
   c. "I can use ammonia to clean my bathroom since I can't smell it anymore."
   d. "I will check all my dairy products for expiration dates."
8. When planning interventions during hospitalization for clients with visual impairments, which of the following plans would be inappropriate?
   a. orienting the client to the arrangement of room furnishings
   b. maintaining clear pathways
   c. organizing self-care articles within the client's reach and orienting the client to their location
   d. assisting the client with ambulation by standing to the client's side about 1 foot behind them and allowing the client to grasp your arm

9. When planning interventions to prevent sensory overload, which of the following would not be included in the client's plan of care?
   a. minimize unnecessary light, noise, and distraction
   b. provide a private room
   c. maintain clean dressing on wound
   d. encourage family member to visit frequently to reduce client's anxiety

10. The nurse evaluating measures to communicate with a client who has a hearing deficit recognizes that which of the following is inappropriate?
   a. upon entering the client's room, the nurse moves to a position where she can be seen
   b. the nurse addresses the client directly
   c. the nurse speaks clearly and accurately
   d. the nurse talks in a louder than normal voice

CHAPTER 37

SELF-CONCEPT

OVERVIEW

This chapter presents your role in maintaining and enhancing the client's perception of self. It emphasizes assessment of clients with altered self-concept and interventions to facilitate positive self-esteem.

www.prenhall.com/kozier

Additional resources for this chapter can be found on the Student CD-ROM accompanying this textbook, and on the Companion Website at www.prenhall.com/kozier. Click on Chapter 37 to select the activities for this chapter.

CD-ROM
- Audio Glossary
- NCLEX Review

Companion Website
- Additional NCLEX Review
- Case Study: Refusal to Accept a Medical Diagnosis
- Care Plan Activity: Client Who Lost His Job
- MediaLink Application: A Change in Attitude
- Links to Resources

LEARNING OUTCOMES

After completing this chapter, the student will be able to:

- Identify four personal and social dimensions of self-concept
- Give Erikson's explanation of the effects of psychosocial tasks on self-concept and self-esteem
- Describe the four components of self-concept
- Identify common stressors affecting self-concept and coping strategies
- Describe the essential aspects of assessing role relationships
- Identify nursing diagnoses related to altered self-concept
- Describe nursing interventions designed to achieve identified outcomes for clients with altered self-concept
- Describe ways to enhance client self-esteem

KEY TOPICS

This study guide chapter reinforces the following terms/topics discussed in the textbook chapter:

- body image
- core self-concept
- global self
- global self-esteem
- ideal self
- role
- role ambiguity
- role conflict
- role development
- role mastery

- role performance
- role strain
- self-concept
- self-esteem
- specific self-esteem

LECTURE OUTLINE

I. Self-concept
II. Formation of self-concept
III. Components of self-concept
  A. Personal identity
  B. Body image
  C. Role performance
  D. Self-esteem
IV. Factors that affect self-concept
  A. Development
  B. Family and culture
  C. Stressors
  D. Resources
  E. History of success and failure
  F. Illness
V. Assessing
  A. Personal identity
  B. Body image
  C. Role performance
  D. Self-esteem
VI. Planning
VII. Implementing
  A. Identifying areas of strength
  B. Enhancing self-esteem
VIII. Evaluating
IX. Chapter highlights
X. Review questions
XI. Readings and references
  A. Suggested readings
  B. Related research
  C. References
  D. Selected bibliography

FOCUSED STUDY TIPS

1. Define the following:
   body image / global self
   personal identity / role
   self-concept / self-esteem
2. When asked about how she sees herself, your client states that she has been told by others that she is bright, articulate, and attractive. She is unable to voice a personal opinion about herself. What does this say about your client?
3. Your client has a large discrepancy between his ideal self and perceived self. His ideal self is unrealistic. What can you conclude?
4. What is the importance of role?
5. Which four criteria do people use to form their concept of self?
6. What is the purpose of self-esteem?
7. Which behaviors may indicate low self-esteem?
8. You are assessing your client's self-concept. You have identified the client's age, developmental level, health history, and family and cultural values. What other aspects must be evaluated?
9. What is the nurse's role in dealing with self-concept and self-esteem?
10. Evaluate your own self-concept. Are you me-centered or other-centered?
11. Using the Framework for Identifying Personality Strengths, as presented in the textbook, identify your own personality strengths.
12. Phillipa Jonas is a 7-year-old child with myopia and astigmatism. Corrective glasses have been prescribed, but Phillipa does not wear them in school because many of the other children make fun of her. Phillipa's mother believes her daughter has low self-esteem and cannot tolerate the other children's taunting. As the nurse, what advice would you give the mother?

CASE STUDY

You are working in a long-term care facility. The majority of residents are elderly. You note that the facility is very institutional: the walls are bare, the rooms and floor are beige, and the hallways are dark.

1. *What changes would you make in the setting to enhance the self-esteem of the residents?*
2. *What suggestions would you make to encourage professional self-concept among the staff?*
3. *What suggestions would you make to enhance client self-esteem?*

CARE PLAN CRITICAL THINKING ACTIVITIES

Fill in the appropriate elements of the care plan for this client:
Assessment and Diagnosis
Planning and Implementation
Evaluation

NCLEX TEST QUESTIONS

1. A client tells the nurse that he doesn't think he is a good person. The nurse would conclude that:
   a. he has low self-esteem.
   b. he has a problem with gender identification.
   c. he has a bad personality.
   d. this is an abnormal role performance.
2. Characteristics of clients with low self-esteem are:
   a. they accept themselves despite failures.
   b. they are not critical of others.
   c. they accept their gender role.
   d. they minimize their positive attributes.
3. Clients' perceptions of the health care environment are important to their understanding of their health care needs. What factors influence clients' perceptions?
   a. role identification and personality of health care workers
   b. gender identification and sexual development
   c. cognitive ability and psychosocial development
   d. self-concept, learning, and sensory functions
4. A nurse is caring for a client who seems to be focusing on the fact that his telephone is not in working order, instead of on his health condition. The nurse knows that:
   a. he is denying he is ill.
   b. he has an unmet need.
   c. his health is not important to him.
   d. he is unhappy with the care he is receiving.
5. Coping is the manner in which individuals attempt to manage stress. Many nursing procedures are implemented to assist a client in coping with stressors. The rationale behind these interventions is:
   a. that explaining procedures assures clients their health care problems will be resolved.
   b. to control client behavior.
   c. to control client response.
   d. to decrease the physiological response to stress.
6. What behaviors of a client will help the nurse identify ineffective coping?
   a. elevated blood pressure
   b. irritability
   c. diminished attention span
   d. upset stomach
7. The nurse who interacts with a patient who avoids eye contact and verbalizes distrust of the nurse's positive encouragement realizes that the patient has:
   a. a high sense of self-worth.
   b. low self-esteem.
   c. unmet physiological needs.
   d. mental incapacitation.
8. According to Erickson's stages of psychosocial development, the early adulthood stage is:
   a. Intimacy vs. Isolation
   b. Generativity vs. Stagnation

c. Industry vs. Inferiority
d. Identity vs. Identity Confusion

9. When people feel or are made to feel inadequate or unsuited to a role, they are experiencing which of the following?
   a. role development
   b. role ambiguity
   c. role strain
   d. role conflicts

10. Which of the following is considered to be a stressor affecting self-esteem?
   a. repeated failures
   b. hospitalization
   c. loss of body parts
   d. sexuality concerns

CHAPTER 38

SEXUALITY

OVERVIEW

This chapter examines your nursing role in caring for clients with sexual health needs. The focus is on the identification of sexual health issues and health promotion in order to maintain or restore sexual health.

LEARNING OUTCOMES

After completing this chapter, the student will be able to:

- Define sexual health
- Describe the components of psychologic sexual health
- Describe sexual development and concerns across the life span
- Identify factors influencing sexuality
- Identify common illnesses affecting sexuality
- Discuss essential aspects of sexual stimulation, intercourse, and the sexual response cycle
- Describe physiologic changes in males and females during the sexual response cycle
- Identify the forms of male and female sexual dysfunction
- Gain the ability to conduct a sexual history
- Recognize health-promotion teaching related to reproductive structures
- Identify nursing diagnoses and interventions for the client experiencing sexuality problems

www.prenhall.com/kozier

Additional resources for this chapter can be found on the Student CD-ROM accompanying this textbook, and on the Companion Website at www.prenhall.com/kozier. Click on Chapter 38 to select the activities for this chapter.

CD-ROM
- Audio Glossary
- NCLEX Review
- Animations:
  - Female Pelvis 3D
  - Male Pelvis 3D
  - Spermatogenesis
  - Oogenesis and Spermatogenesis Compared
  - Oogenesis and Spermatogenesis A & P Review
  - Oogenesis and Spermatogenesis Terms and Definitions
  - Female Reproductive System A & P Review
  - Female Reproductive System Terms & Definitions
  - Male Reproductive System A & P Review
  - Male Reproductive System Terms & Definitions
  - Ovulation A & P Review

Companion Website
- Additional NCLEX Review
- Case Study: Client in an Automobile Accident
- Care Plan Activity: Client with a Mastectomy
- MediaLink Application:
  - Society for Human Sexuality
- Links to Resources

KEY TOPICS

This study guide chapter reinforces the following terms/topics discussed in the textbook chapter:

- desire phase
- dysmenorrhea
- erectile dysfunction
- excitement/plateau phase
- gender
- gender identity
- hypoactive sexual desire disorder
- impotence
- menopause
- menstruation
- orgasmic disorder
- orgasmic phase
- rapid ejaculation
- resolution phase
- retarded ejaculation
- sex
- sexual arousal disorder
- sexual health
- sexuality
- sexual orientation
- sexual pain disorders
- sexual self-concept

LECTURE OUTLINE

I. Sexual health
  A. Components of sexual health
II. Development of sexuality
  A. Birth to 12 years
  B. Adolescence
  C. Young and middle adulthood
  D. Older adulthood
III. Factors influencing sexuality
  A. Culture
  B. Religious values
  C. Personal ethics
  D. Health status
    1. Heart disease
    2. Prostate cancer
    3. Hysterectomy
    4. Diabetes mellitus
    5. Spinal cord injury
    6. Surgical procedures
    7. Joint disease
    8. Chronic pain
    9. Sexually transmitted disease (STD)
    10. Mental disorders
  E. Medications
IV. Sexual response and love play
  A. Sexual response cycle
  B. Love play
V. Altered sexual function
  A. Male dysfunction
  B. Female dysfunction
  C. Effects of medications on sexual function
VI. Assessing
  A. Nursing history
  B. Physical examination
  C. Identifying clients at risk
VII. Diagnosing
VIII. Planning
IX. Implementing
  A. Providing sexual health teaching
    1. Sex education
      a. Teaching self-examination
    2. Responsible sexual behavior
      a. STD prevention
      b. Prevention of unwanted pregnancies
  B. Counseling for altered sexual function
    1. Permission giving
    2. Limited information
    3. Specific suggestions
    4. Intensive therapy
X. Dealing with inappropriate sexual behavior
XI. Evaluating
XII. Chapter highlights
XIII. Review questions
XIV. Readings and references
  A. Suggested readings
  B. Related research
  C. References
  D. Selected bibliography

FOCUSED STUDY TIPS

1. Define the following:

biologic sex	chemical barriers
coitus interruptus	fertility awareness
gender identity	gender role behavior
hormonal contraceptives	mechanical barriers
sexual identity	sexuality
surgical contraceptive methods	

2. Psychological sexual health consists of several critical elements. What are they?
3. You have been asked to discuss sexual development of children with a parent–teacher group. What will you include about sexual development?
4. Sexual issues are of major importance to adolescents. You are designing a teaching project for a group of high school students. What topics will you include?
5. What are some myths about sexuality in older adults?
6. List factors that influence a person's sexuality.
7. Sexually transmitted diseases (STDs) may affect sexuality and comfort. What are some common thoughts about STDs?
8. List the four phases of the sexual response cycle.
9. What are some common thoughts about sexual dysfunction?
10. Identify the five nursing skills required to help clients in the area of sexuality.
11. Nurses must help to identify clients at risk for altered sexual patterns. Once the problem has been identified and diagnosed, what are the overall goals?
12. The PLISSIT model of intervention is often used to help clients with sexual problems. Identify the four progressive levels of this model. Also, give an example of each type of intervention.

CASE STUDY

Michael Leonard is a 26-year-old man admitted to the hospital after being struck by a truck while riding his bicycle. Michael is being evaluated for a neurological deficit. He has impaired motor and sensory function below the level of the umbilicus. While you are caring for Michael, he makes sexual advances toward you.

1. *How would you handle this situation?*
2. *Why might this behavior be occurring?*

CARE PLAN CRITICAL THINKING ACTIVITIES

Fill in the appropriate elements of the care plan for this client:
Assessment and Diagnosis
Planning and Implementation
Evaluation

NCLEX TEST QUESTIONS

1. Behavior related to the development of sexuality in a toddler would include:
   a. integration of biologic sex, gender roles, and sexual expression.
   b. strong socialization regarding gender roles, with gender role identity becoming stronger.
   c. recognition of the differences between males and females.
   d. sexual experimentation with a partner.
2. The female patient recovering from a hysterectomy has the nursing diagnosis of sexual dysfunction related to altered reproductive system structure and function due to

hysterectomy. The nurse can facilitate healthy self-expression by:

a. providing factual information about sexual functioning after the hysterectomy.
b. respecting the patient's request not to discuss her changes in function.
c. discussing all the details of the hysterectomy with the patient.
d. referring the patient to a fertility specialist.

3. The nurse planning a sexual health workshop recognizes that the belief or awareness that individuals have of being male or female is called:
   a. sexual identity.
   b. biologic sex.
   c. gender identity.
   d. sexual orientation.
4. The nurse evaluating a sexual health class recognizes that further teaching is necessary when which of the following statements is made by a participant?
   a. "Alcohol is a relaxant and may affect the ability to have sex."
   b. "Conceiving is not related to experiencing orgasm."
   c. "There is no evidence that sexual activity weakens a person."
   d. "I should avoid intercourse during my period."
5. A male client routinely lies in bed uncovered and unclothed. The female nurse caring for the client best handles this inappropriate sexual behavior by:
   a. refusing to enter the client's room.
   b. reporting the client's behavior to the nursing supervisor.
   c. informing the client that the staff expects him to keep himself covered when they are in the room.
   d. ignoring the client's behavior.
6. The nurse evaluating a male client's understanding of instructions for testicular self-examination recognizes that further teaching is required when the client states:
   a. "I will perform the testicular self-examination before I take my bath."
   b. "I will perform the testicular self-examination every month."
   c. "I will notify my primary health care provider if I detect any abnormalities."
   d. "I will use a mirror to inspect my testicles for swelling or enlargement."
7. A female client presents to the clinic with complaints of intense vaginal itching and thick, white, cheesy discharge. Upon examination, the vulva is noted to be red and excoriated. The nurse recognizes that the client has clinical signs of which sexually transmitted disease?
   a. gonorrhea
   b. syphilis
   c. trichomoniasis
   d. candidiasis
8. A female client confides in the nurse practitioner that she is experiencing pain during intercourse. After a thorough assessment, the nurse practitioner recommends the use of a lubricant before intercourse. The nurse recognizes that the client described which of the following female dysfunctions?
   a. orgasmic dysfunction
   b. vaginismus
   c. dyspareunia
   d. vulvodynia
9. A male client is experiencing erectile dysfunction. In planning to assist the client to recognize the factors identified that may affect erection, which of the following is a physiologic factor?
   a. fatigue, anger, or stress
   b. boredom associated with partner
   c. prolonged use of alcohol
   d. doubts about ability to perform
10. A couple in a parenting class states that when their 4-year-old child asked where babies come from, they told the child that babies are brought by the "stork." The nurse recognizes that the couple requires further information based on the fact that at age 4:
    a. the child is too young to be asking questions about where babies come from.
    b. the child's questions about "where babies come from" should be answered honestly and simply.
    c. the child is not old enough to understand answers regarding the birth cycle.
    d. the child should be given a book on the birth cycle.

CHAPTER 39

SPIRITUALITY

OVERVIEW

This chapter distinguishes between spirituality and religion. You are introduced to the beliefs of selected religions. The chapter emphasizes your role in assessing, diagnosing, and intervening for clients with spiritual distress.

LEARNING OUTCOMES

After completing this chapter, the student will be able to:

- Define the concepts of spirituality and religion as they relate to nursing and health care
- Identify characteristics of spiritual well being
- Identify factors associated with spiritual distress and manifestations of it
- Describe the spiritual development of the individual across the life span
- Describe the influence of spiritual and religious beliefs about diet, dress, prayer and meditation, and birth and death on health care
- Assess the spiritual needs of clients, and plan nursing care to assist clients with spiritual needs
- Describe nursing interventions to support clients' spiritual beliefs and religious practices
- Identify desired outcomes for evaluating the client's spiritual well-being

www.prenhall.com/kozier

Additional resources for this chapter can be found on the Student CD-ROM accompanying this textbook, and on the Companion Website at www.prenhall.com/kozier. Click on Chapter 39 to select the activities for this chapter.

CD-ROM

- Audio Glossary
- NCLEX Review

Companion Website

- Additional NCLEX Review
- Case Study: Supporting a Client's Religions Practice
- Care Plan Activity: Treating a Client Who Is Paralyzed
- MediaLink Application: Atheism as a Client's Religious Preference
- Links to Resources

KEY TOPICS

This study guide chapter reinforces the following terms/topics discussed in the textbook chapter:

- agnostic
- atheist
- faith
- forgiveness
- holy day
- hope
- kosher
- meditation

- monotheism
- polytheism
- prayer
- presencing
- religion
- spiritual distress
- spiritual health
- spiritual well-being
- spirituality
- transcendence

LECTURE OUTLINE

I. Spirituality described
  A. Spiritual needs
  B. Spiritual well-being
  C. Spiritual distress
II. Related concepts
  A. Religion
  B. Faith
  C. Hope
  D. Transcendence
  E. Forgiveness
III. Spiritual development
IV. Spiritual practices affecting nursing care
  A. Holy days
  B. Sacred writings
  C. Sacred symbols
  D. Prayer and meditation
  E. Beliefs affecting diet and nutrition
  F. Beliefs related to healing
  G. Beliefs related to dress
  H. Beliefs related to birth
  I. Beliefs related to death
V. Spiritual health and the nursing process
VI. Assessing
  A. Nursing history
  B. Clinical assessment
VII. Diagnosing
  A. Spiritual problems as the diagnostic label
  B. Spiritual distress as the etiology
VIII. Planning
IX. Implementing
  A. Providing "presence"
  B. Supporting religious practices
  C. Assisting clients with prayer
  D. Referring clients for spiritual counseling
X. Evaluating
XI. Chapter highlights
XII. Review questions
XIII. Readings and references
  A. Suggested readings
  B. Related research
  C. References
  D. Selected bibliography

FOCUSED STUDY TIPS

1. Define the following:
   agnostic
   atheist
   faith
   hope
   meditation
   religion
   spiritual distress
   spirituality
2. What is the basis of religion?
3. All religions share some common spiritual needs, yet spirituality and religion are distinct entities. What aspects of spirituality extend beyond the common needs of religion?
4. What role does spiritual beliefs and practices play?
5. How does the nurse meet the spiritual needs of clients?
6. Identify ways that you can assess a client's spiritual health and beliefs.
7. Jennifer Parcel has just been told she has breast cancer. She is quite distraught. She asks you, "How long until I die?" Identify approaches you could take to alleviate Jennifer's spiritual distress.

CASE STUDY

Joseph Stallings is 35 years old and has AIDS. His condition is rapidly deteriorating. Joseph has been living at home with his partner during his illness. He now expresses fear and anger about his condition and states that he does not believe he will live much longer.

1. *As a nurse working for a home health agency, describe your process for assessing Joseph's spiritual health and practices.*
2. *Joseph asks you to pray with him. How would you handle this situation if you are uncomfortable with the request?*

CARE PLAN CRITICAL THINKING ACTIVITIES

Fill in the appropriate elements of the care plan for this client:
Assessment and Diagnosis
Planning and Implementation
Evaluation

NCLEX TEST QUESTIONS

1. The parish priest of a patient comes to see the patient in the hospital and uses holy water to bless the patient. The nurse recognizes this activity as being:
   a. societal expectation.
   b. culture shock.
   c. territoriality.
   d. religious practice.
2. When preparing a patient for surgery, the nurse asks the patient to remove a religious medal from around her neck. The patient becomes very upset and refuses to have the surgery. What could this nurse do?
   a. Offer to pin the religious medal to the patient's gown.
   b. Call the operating room.
   c. Call the doctor.
   d. Tape the medal to the patient's chest.
3. An elderly patient of the Jewish faith died at 4:00 in the morning. Which of the following actions must the nurse take to ensure this patient's spirituality?
   a. Complete all necessary care to prepare for burial within 24 hours.
   b. Position the body to face Mecca.
   c. Wear gloves when preparing the body.
   d. Prepare for the sacrament of holy unction.
4. While providing care to a patient, the patient stops the nurse from performing a certain procedure because it goes against her beliefs. Which of the following could help this nurse?
   a. Ask the patient to explain the beliefs.
   b. Do the procedure anyway.
   c. Call the physician.
   d. Talk the patient into the procedure.
5. Nurses caring for clients experiencing blood loss should recognize that members of which particular religion may refuse blood transfusions?
   a. Christian Scientist
   b. Jehovah's Witness
   c. Mormon
   d. Episcopalian
6. The nurse who is planning dietary interventions for the Orthodox Jew client knows that:
   a. pork and shellfish may not be eaten.
   b. no caffeinated or alcoholic beverages are allowed.
   c. the client may choose not to eat meat on Fridays.
   d. during the month of Ramadan, the client may eat no food and will avoid beverages during daylight hours.
7. The belief that food must be kosher (prepared according to religious law) is held by many people of:
   a. Catholic faith.
   b. Jewish faith.
   c. Baptist faith.
   d. Jehovah's Witness faith.
8. When a Native American is found sprinkling cornmeal around a patient's bed, the nurse:
   a. recognizes this as a health hazard and cleans up the cornmeal.
   b. explains that this is of no value to the client.
   c. understands this to be an important, sacred ceremony.
   d. calls security to have the offender removed from the hospital.
9. Nurses provide care to others during times of spiritual distress by conveying:
   a. respect and trust.
   b. a willingness to listen.

c. love and belonging.
d. self-disclosure and acceptance.

10. A terminally ill client chooses to participate in prayer with family and friends. The nurse's major responsibility during this situation is to:
    a. ensure a quiet environment and privacy.
    b. ensure the client does not become emotional.
    c. ensure the family and friends understand the client's prognosis.
    d. ensure the nursing care is complete before allowing the prayer.

CHAPTER 40

STRESS AND COPING

OVERVIEW

This chapter introduces you to multiple views on stress and its various manifestations. It emphasizes your role in minimizing client stress and presents numerous tips on how to control your professional stress.

LEARNING OUTCOMES

After completing this chapter, the student will be able to:

- Differentiate the concepts of stress as a stimulus, as a response, and as a transaction
- Describe the three stages of Selye's general adaptation syndrome
- Identify physiologic, psychologic, and cognitive indicators of stress
- Differentiate the four levels of anxiety
- Identify behaviors related to specific ego defense mechanisms
- Discuss types of coping and coping strategies
- Identify essential aspects of assessing a client's stress and coping patterns
- Identify nursing diagnoses related to stress
- Describe interventions to help clients minimize and manage stress

www.prenhall.com/kozier

Additional resources for this chapter can be found on the Student CD-ROM accompanying this textbook, and on the Companion Website at www.prenhall.com/kozier. Click on Chapter 40 to select the activities for this chapter.

CD-ROM
- Audio Glossary
- NCLEX Review

Companion Website
- Additional NCLEX Review
- Case Study: Becoming Parents
- Care Plan Activity: Client Going Through a Divorce
- MediaLink Application: Resources for Helping a Client to Manage Stress
- Links to Resources

KEY TOPICS

This study guide chapter reinforces the following terms/topics discussed in the textbook chapter:

- alarm reaction
- anger
- anxiety
- burnout
- caregiver burden
- coping
- coping mechanism
- coping strategy
- countershock phase
- crisis counseling
- crisis intervention
- depression

- ego defense mechanisms
- fear
- general adaptation syndrome (GAS)
- local adaptation syndrome (LAS)
- shock phase
- stage of exhaustion
- stage of resistance
- stimulus-based stress model
- stress
- stressor
- transactional stress theory

LECTURE OUTLINE

I. Concept of stress
  A. Sources of stress
  B. Effects of stress
II. Models of stress
  A. Stimulus-based models
  B. Response-based models
    1. Alarm reaction
    2. Stage of resistance
    3. Stage of exhaustion
  C. Transaction-based models
III. Indicators of stress
  A. Physiologic indicators
  B. Psychologic indicators
    1. Anxiety
    2. Fear
    3. Anger
    4. Depression
    5. Unconscious ego defense mechanisms
  C. Cognitive indicators
IV. Coping
V. Assessing
VI. Diagnosing
VII. Planning
  A. Planning for home care
VIII. Implementing
  A. Encouraging health-promotion strategies
    1. Exercise
    2. Nutrition
    3. Rest and sleep
    4. Time management
  B. Minimizing anxiety
  C. Mediating anger
  D. Using relaxation techniques
  E. Crisis intervention
  F. Stress management for nurses
IX. Evaluating
X. Chapter highlights
XI. Review questions
XII. Readings and references
  A. Suggested readings
  B. Related research
  C. References
  D. Selected bibliography

FOCUSED STUDY TIPS

1. Define the following:
   alarm reaction
   coping mechanism
   stage of exhaustion
   stage of resistance
   transactional stress theory
2. Tomorrow is your first clinical day as a nursing student. How might this event relate to stress?
3. Describe the mannerisms of a person with a high level of stress.
4. List body responses to stressors.
5. Describe anxiety.
6. Your client is experiencing depression related to recent loss of a loved one. If this depression continues unabated for a full year, how must you proceed?
7. Which stage of anxiety actually enhances perception and abilities?
8. What are two examples of short-term coping strategies?
9. In the space below, draw and label a scale illustrating the four levels of anxiety. Record your current level of anxiety.

10. Identify at least five ways in which you can successfully manage your stress.
11. Reflect on your most recent experience with stress. What were your verbal and motor manifestations of stress?
12. Jeff Drew is a 20-year-old client with insulin-dependent diabetes. During his first month at college, Jeff has trouble controlling his blood sugar. He attributes this difficulty to a hectic college schedule, erratic eating, and a dislike for dormitory food. By the second month, he requires hospitalization for control of his diabetes. What factors must be considered when evaluating Jeff's level of stress?

CASE STUDY

José Rojas is a 41-year-old mechanic who sustained a partial amputation of his left index finger while operating a machine at work. He is admitted to your unit after surgical repair of the injury. José is quite concerned about future use of his hand. He also voices concern about the cost of the hospitalization and the length of time he must be off of work.

1. *How can you help to minimize his anxiety?*
2. *What are the goals of nursing care for José?*
3. *On the third day of hospitalization, José becomes very angry and threatens to leave the hospital against medical advice (signing out AMA). How would you respond to José?*

CARE PLAN CRITICAL THINKING ACTIVITIES

Fill in the appropriate elements of the care plan for this client:
Assessment and Diagnosis
Planning and Implementation
Evaluation

NCLEX TEST QUESTIONS

1. During the assessment of an elderly patient, the nurse learns the patient is very unhappy with her new health insurance plan. She can't go to the same doctor when she wants to, and she doesn't like the long drive to the new doctor's office. The nurse identifies this patient's behavior as being:
   a. resistant to change.
   b. resistant to stability.
   c. seeking change.
   d. unstable.
2. The nurse, completing a patient interview, learns the patient identifies herself as being a wife, mother, sister, and aunt. Into which of the following systems is this patient categorizing herself?
   a. global
   b. societal
   c. community
   d. family
3. A patient is brought into the emergency department with profound bronchoconstriction and a slow heart rate. The nurse recognizes these symptoms as being:
   a. sympathetic effects on the kidneys.
   b. parasympathetic effects on glandular secretions.
   c. sympathetic effects on skeletal muscles and basal metabolism.
   d. parasympathetic effects on breathing and circulation.
4. The nurse, assessing a 40-year-old male patient, notes an increase in the patient's blood pressure after talking about his employment. The change in the blood pressure is identified as a(n):
   a. stressor.
   b. stress.
   c. response.
   d. adaptation.
5. A married couple is sitting in the physician's waiting room discussing the wife's stressful reaction to information she heard on the news. The husband can't understand why the information has caused her to become so upset. The nurse, observing this interaction, realizes the husband's response to the news is an example of:
   a. the alarm stage.
   b. the resistance stage.

   c. the exhaustion stage.
   d. cognitive appraisal.

6. A patient comes into the emergency department with shortness of breath, sweating, dizziness, and trembling. After a thorough examination, the physician determines the patient is having a reaction to stress. Which level of stress is this patient exhibiting?
   a. panic
   b. severe anxiety
   c. moderate anxiety
   d. mild anxiety
7. The nurse learns that a young female patient is a widow. After the death of her husband, the patient improved her eating habits, started to exercise, and looks upon life as an adventure to be lived. The nurse identifies these characteristics as being:
   a. maturational response to stress.
   b. situational response to stress.
   c. hardiness.
   d. defense mechanisms.
8. A medical-surgical patient care area nurse has become progressively quiet and disinterested in activities beyond providing basic patient care. At one point in time, this nurse was positive and motivated. Now, it appears this nurse just wants to get the job done and go home. What might this nurse be experiencing?
   a. stress
   b. moderate anxiety
   c. burnout
   d. panic attack
9. A patient, learning that the results of a breast biopsy show she does not have breast cancer, expresses relief. While talking with the nurse, the patient states this experience was a "wake-up call," and now she has a chance to change her negative health behaviors. This patient is viewing the health crisis as being:
   a. a coping mechanism.
   b. a stressor.
   c. a stress management technique.
   d. an opportunity for growth.
10. The nurse assisting a client experiencing acute stress would not anticipate which of the following assessment findings?
   a. increased heart rate
   b. increased diaphoresis
   c. decreased respirations
   d. decreased urinary output

CHAPTER 41

LOSS, GRIEVING, AND DEATH

OVERVIEW

This chapter discusses the processes of loss and grief. It presents coping with death, the ultimate loss, as an example of handling loss. The chapter emphasizes your role in assisting clients with successful transition through the grieving process. To facilitate personal growth, you are encouraged to evaluate your own beliefs about death and grief.

www.prenhall.com/kozier

Additional resources for this chapter can be found on the Student CD-ROM accompanying this textbook, and on the Companion Website at www.prenhall.com/kozier. Click on Chapter 41 to select the activities for this chapter.

CD-ROM
- Audio Glossary
- NCLEX Review

Companion Website
- Additional NCLEX Review
- Case Study: Helping a Family Accept a Terminal Illness
- Care Plan Activity: Client Who Suffered an Arm Amputation
- MediaLink Application: Resource for Client Dealing with a Pet Loss
- Links to Resources

LEARNING OUTCOMES

After completing this chapter, the student will be able to:

- Describe types and sources of losses
- Discuss selected frameworks for identifying stages of grieving
- Identify clinical symptoms of grief
- Discuss factors affecting a grief response
- Identify measures that facilitate the grieving process
- List clinical signs of impending and actual death
- Describe essential aspects of the Patient Self-Determination Act
- Identify the nurse's legal responsibilities regarding client death and issues such as advance health care directives, autopsy, certification of death, do-not-resuscitate orders, euthanasia, inquest, and organ donation
- Describe helping clients die with dignity
- Describe nursing measures for care of the body after death
- Describe the role of the nurse in working with families or caregivers of dying clients

KEY TOPICS

This study guide chapter reinforces the following terms/topics discussed in the textbook chapter:

- actual loss
- advance health care directive
- algor mortis
- anticipatory loss
- anticipatory grief
- autopsy
- bereavement
- cerebral death
- closed awareness
- coroner
- do-not-resuscitate (DNR) order
- dysfunctional grief
- end-of-life care
- euthanasia
- grief
- health care proxy
- heart-lung death
- higher brain death
- hospice
- living will
- livor mortis
- loss
- medical examiner
- mortician
- mourning
- mutual pretense
- open awareness
- palliative care
- perceived loss
- postmortem examination
- rigor mortis
- shroud
- undertaker

LECTURE OUTLINE

I. Loss and Grief
   A. Types and sources of loss
      1. Aspect of self
      2. External objects
      3. Familiar environment
      4. Loved ones
   B. Grief, bereavement, and mourning
      1. Types of grief responses
   C. Stages of grieving
      1. Manifestations of grief
   D. Factors influencing the loss and grief responses
      1. Age
         a. Childhood
         b. Early and middle adulthood
         c. Late adulthood
      2. Significance of the loss
         a. Culture
         b. Spiritual beliefs
         c. Gender
         d. Socioeconomic status
         e. Support systems
         f. Cause of loss or death
II. Assessing
III. Diagnosing
IV. Planning
   A. Planning for home care
V. Implementing
   A. Facilitating grief work
   B. Providing emotional support
VI. Evaluating
VII. Dying and death
   A. Responses to dying and death
   B. Definitions and signs of death
   C. Legalities related to death
      1. Advance health care directives
      2. Autopsy
      3. Certification of death
      4. Do-Not-Resuscitate orders
      5. Euthanasia
      6. Inquest
      7. Organ donation
   D. Death-related religious and cultural practices
VIII. Assessing
IX. Planning
   A. Planning for home care
X. Implementing
   A. Helping clients die with dignity
   B. Hospice and palliative care
   C. Meeting physiologic needs of the dying client
   D. Providing spiritual support
   E. Supporting the family
   F. Postmortem care

FOCUSED STUDY TIPS

1. Define the following:
   bereavement
   grief
   loss
   mourning
2. Which type of loss may be viewed as a developmental crisis and can be anticipated to some extent?
3. What is dysfunctional grief? Describe characteristics of the disorder.
4. Your client has recently been notified that he has metastatic colon cancer. The physician believes that he has less than 12 months to live. When you enter the room, he is cheerful and smiling. He tells you that he has decided that the physician must have gotten someone else's test results. He says, "I'm healthy and happy. He made a mistake. I'm not going to worry about things." According to Kübler-Ross, what stage of grieving is the client experiencing?
5. What is the most effective way to help the client presented in question 4?
6. On the oncology unit, you provide care for many middle-age adults with life-threatening illnesses. What are the characteristics of this specific age group?
7. A client in the intensive care unit has been unresponsive to verbal or tactile stimuli for over 3 weeks; has shallow, spontaneous respirations; and relies on a pacemaker to sustain an adequate blood pressure. How would you describe this client?
8. What is "closed awareness of death"?
9. Palliative care has been ordered for your client. What does this mean?
10. Your client is a devout Christian. As his condition deteriorates, his family requests that you immediately contact the hospital chaplain for spiritual support. You, however, are an atheist. How should you respond?
11. The physician has written a do-not-resuscitate order for a client. In the event that this client experiences a cardiopulmonary arrest, what should you do?
12. Your client was pronounced dead 5 minutes ago. The client's family is in transit to the hospital. Your goal is to prepare the body before the family arrives in 1 hour. What are you going to do?
13. What are the factors that determine how an individual deals with a loss?
14. What are the major goals of dying clients?
15. Shelli Jenkins is terminally ill with breast cancer. You are coordinating Shelli's care. Identify at least five appropriate nursing actions.
16. Have you ever experienced the death or loss of a significant other? If so, identify the relationship of this person to you and the effect this loss had on you.
17. React to the following statement: "Death is always a negative experience, and health professionals should strive to forestall death at all costs."
18. You are caring for an 11-year-old boy with leukemia. While you are giving him his morning medications he asks you, "What happens when you die?" How would you respond to him?
19. Your terminally ill client asks you what happens after death. How would you respond?

CASE STUDY

Anna Bradley is a healthy 71-year-old woman. Anna race-walks 5 miles three times per week, does not smoke, consumes limited alcohol, and consistently eats a low-fat, low-salt, high-fiber diet. She keeps active in the community by volunteering as a teacher's aide at the elementary school. Anna is known in the neighborhood as a model of healthy aging. Anna's husband recently died suddenly due to a lethal cardiac dysrhythmia (altered cardiac rhythm). He had no history of cardiac disease and was pronounced "in excellent health" at a recent physical examination.

Anna is devastated. She tells you she no longer has "the strength to go on." She can't imagine living without her spouse of 50 years.

1. *How would you respond to Anna's statements?*

CARE PLAN CRITICAL THINKING ACTIVITIES

Fill in the appropriate elements of the care plan for Anna:
Assessment and Diagnosis
Planning and Implementation
Evaluation

NCLEX TEST QUESTIONS

1. A veteran nurse was in an automobile accident after leaving work. This accident has caused a severe back injury that will affect her ability to return to work for some time. The nurse is at risk for developing:
   a. altered body image.
   b. altered sexuality.
   c. altered role performance.
   d. altered decision-making.
2. A young widow comes into the clinic with complaints of chest pain. This woman is wearing the leather jacket and sunglasses of her late spouse. The nurse recognizes this behavior as being which stage of the grieving process?
   a. shock and disbelief
   b. yearning and protest
   c. anguish, disorganization, and identification
   d. reorganization
3. A female patient has just been told she has cervical cancer. Which of the following approaches could the nurse use to help this patient?
   a. Leave the patient alone.
   b. Tell her to accept it.
   c. Encourage her to move on.
   d. Offer to contact a family member for her.
4. A female client comes into the clinic a few months after the death of her husband. During the interview, the nurse learns the patient has also just lost her job and is now facing multiple financial issues. Which of the following nursing diagnoses would address this patient's situation?
   a. alteration in body changes
   b. anxiety
   c. unresolved grief
   d. anticipatory grieving
5. During a clinic visit, the nurse learns a patient has just lost his job. Which of the following approaches would be appropriate for this patient?
   a. Encourage the verbalization of inadequate feelings.
   b. Promote self-esteem–building activities.
   c. Promote realistic adaptation.
   d. Encourage family intervention to strengthen support base.
6. The coping, planning, and psychosocial reorganization that occur when a person discovers he or she is about to lose a loved one is referred to as:
   a. anticipatory loss.
   b. perceived loss.
   c. actual loss.
   d. bereavement.
7. The nurse can facilitate healthy self-expression in a young woman whose husband has just been killed in an accident by:
   a. referring the woman to a social support group.
   b. encouraging the woman to take up a new hobby.
   c. discussing the need to maintain healthy social relationships with other men.
   d. providing information about raising children alone.
8. The nurse assessing a dying client's and family's state of awareness determines that the client and family know about the impending death and feel

comfortable discussing it, even though it is difficult. This type of awareness is identified as:

a. closed awareness.
b. mutual pretense.
c. open awareness.
d. conscious awareness.

9. A nurse providing family counseling to the 6-year-old and 7-year-old children of a terminally ill client recognizes that children in this age group:

a. do not understand the concept of death.
b. understand that death is final.
c. understand that death is the inevitable end of life.
d. believe that death is reversible, a temporary departure, or sleep.

10. A 32-year-old male has experienced a traumatic amputation of the left leg. The client refuses to believe that his leg was amputated and states that he will be walking out of the hospital. The nurse recognizes that the client is exhibiting which of Kübler-Ross's stages of grieving?

a. denial
b. anger
c. bargaining
d. depression

CHAPTER 42

ACTIVITY AND EXERCISE

OVERVIEW

This chapter emphasizes safety and health promotion in moving, transferring, and exercising clients. It emphasizes good body mechanics to prevent injury and to ensure efficiency of effort. It also highlights the essential skills of range-of-motion exercises, ambulation, and transfer.

www.prenhall.com/kozier

Additional resources for this chapter can be found on the Student CD-ROM accompanying this textbook, and on the Companion Website at www.prenhall.com/kozier. Click on Chapter 42 to select the activities for this chapter.

CD-ROM
- Audio Glossary
- NCLEX Review
- Animations
  - 3D Anatomical Joint and Muscle
  - Anatomical Movements
  - A & P Review

Companion Website
- Additional NCLEX Review
- Case Study: Treating a Client with Mobility Problems
- Care Plan Activity: Activity and Exercise
- MediaLink Application: Promoting Exercise for Seniors
- Links to Resources

LEARNING OUTCOMES

After completing this chapter, the student will be able to:

- Describe the four basic elements of normal movement
- Differentiate isotonic, isometric, isokinetic, aerobic, and anaerobic exercise
- Compare the effects of exercise and immobility on body systems
- Identify factors influencing a person's body alignment and activity
- Assess activity–exercise pattern, alignment, mobility capabilities and limitations, activity tolerance, and potential problems related to immobility
- Develop nursing diagnoses, outcomes, and interventions related to activity, exercise, and mobility problems
- Use proper body mechanics when positioning, moving, lifting, and ambulating clients

KEY TOPICS

This study guide chapter reinforces the following terms/topics discussed in the textbook chapter:

- active ROM exercises
- activity-exercise pattern
- activity tolerance
- aerobic exercise
- ambulation
- anaerobic exercise

- anabolism
- ankylosed
- anorexia
- atrophy
- basal metabolic rate
- base of support
- bed rest
- calculi
- catabolism
- center of gravity
- contracture
- crepitation
- embolus
- exercise
- dorsal position
- dorsal recumbent position
- flaccid
- Fowler's position
- gait
- high Fowler's position
- hypertrophy
- isokinetic (resistive) exercise
- isometric (static or sitting) exercise
- isotonic (dynamic) exercise
- lateral position
- line of gravity
- logrolling
- lordosis
- low Fowler's position
- metabolism
- mobility
- orthopneic position
- osteoporosis
- pace
- passive ROM exercises
- physical activity
- prone position
- range of motion (ROM)
- semi-Fowler's position
- SIMS position
- spastic
- supine position
- thrombophlebitis
- thrombus
- tripod (triangle) position
- urinary incontinence
- urinary reflux
- urinary retention
- urinary stasis
- Valsalva maneuver
- vital capacity

LECTURE OUTLINE

I. Normal movement
   A. Alignment and posture
   B. Joint mobility
   C. Balance
   D. Coordinated movement
II. Exercise
   A. Types of exercise
   B. Benefits of exercise
      1. Musculoskeletal system
      2. Cardiovascular system
      3. Respiratory system
      4. Gastrointestinal system
      5. Metabolic system
      6. Urinary system
      7. Psychoneurologic system
   C. Factors affecting body alignment and activity
      1. Growth and development
      2. Physical health
      3. Mental health
      4. Nutrition
      5. Personal values and attitudes
      6. External factors
      7. Prescribed limitations
   D. Effects of immobility
      1. Musculoskeletal system
      2. Cardiovascular system
      3. Respiratory system
      4. Metabolic system
      5. Urinary system
      6. Gastrointestinal system
      7. Integumentary system
      8. Psychoneurologic system
III. Assessing
   A. Nursing history
   B. Physical examination
      1. Body alignment
      2. Gait
      3. Appearance and movement of joints
      4. Capabilities and limitations for movement
      5. Muscle mass and strength

6. Activity tolerance
7. Problems related to immobility

IV. Diagnosing
V. Planning
A. Planning for home care
VI. Implementing
A. Using body mechanics
1. Lifting
2. Pulling and pushing
B. Pivoting
C. Preventing back injury
D. Positioning clients
1. Fowler's position
2. Orthopneic position
3. Dorsal recumbent position
4. Prone position
5. Lateral position
6. Sims' position
E. Moving and turning clients in bed
F. Assessment
G. Planning
1. Delegation
2. Equipment
H. Implementation
1. Preparation
2. Performance
VII. Implementation
A. Preparation
B. Performance
VIII. Implementation
A. Preparation
B. Performance
IX. Implementation
A. Preparation
B. Performance
X. Evaluation
XI. Transferring clients
XII. Assessment
XIII. Planning
A. Delegation
B. Equipment
XIV. Implementation
A. Preparation
B. Performance
XV. Assessment
XVI. Planning
A. Delegation
B. Equipment
XVII. Implementation
A. Preparation
B. Performance
XVIII. Evaluation
XIX. Using a hydraulic lift
XX. Providing ROM exercises
XXI. Ambulating clients
A. Preambulatory exercises
B. Assisting clients to ambulate
XXII. Assessment
XXIII. Planning
A. Delegation
B. Equipment
XXIV. Implementation
A. Preparation
B. Performance
XXV. Evaluation
XXVI. Using mechanical aids for walking
A. Canes
B. Walkers
C. Crutches
XXVII. Evaluating
XXVIII. Chapter highlights
XXIX. Review questions
XXX. Readings and references
A. Suggested readings
B. Related research
C. References
D. Selected bibliography

FOCUSED STUDY TIPS

1. Define the following:
   abduction
   adduction
   circumduction
   eversion
   inversion
   pronation
   supination
2. Body movement requires coordinated muscle activity and neurologic integration. Which four elements are required for body movement?
3. Your client is involved in an exercise program. She states that she regularly walks around the track at the local high school. The speed of her walk allows her to speak to her exercise partner in short answers. What type of exercise is she engaged in?
4. What is the major reason for using proper body mechanics?
5. What elements are involved in body mechanics?

6. Which factor do you not evaluate when you conduct an assessment of a client's activity and exercise patterns?
7. How should you lift to avoid injury while lifting?
8. Your client is positioned on his side with both his legs flexed in front of him. The upper leg is more acutely flexed than the lower. The lower arm is behind the client, and the upper arm is flexed at the shoulder and elbow. What position is your client in?
9. What are active range-of-motion exercises?
10. Describe an appropriately sized axillary crutch.
11. Your client has been on prolonged bed rest and is very fatigued. What can you do to help manage his fatigue?
12. What factors are involved in coordination of body movement?
13. You must turn a 315-pound client who is unable to assist with movement. Describe the principles you will follow in order to prevent injury to yourself or the client.
14. What are the key factors that affect body alignment and mobility?
15. What are the major components that must be addressed when designing a physical activity plan?

CASE STUDY

Mr. Miller is a 45-year-old male recovering from spinal fusion surgery. Immediately after surgery, he started complaining of severe lower spine pain.

1. *Which position might be more comfortable for this client?*
2. *The physician orders this client to be out of bed and ambulating at least 3 times each day. He will need an assistive device since he has residual left lower-extremity weakness. Which types of devices might be appropriate for him?*
3. *The nurse needs to help Mr. Miller move from a lying to a sitting position. What should the nurse do to avoid a personal spine injury?*

CARE PLAN CRITICAL THINKING ACTIVITIES

Fill in the appropriate elements of the care plan for Mr. Miller:
Assessment and Diagnosis
Planning and Implementation
Evaluation

NCLEX TEST QUESTIONS

1. While assessing a patient, the nurse asks the patient to turn the palm of the hand forward or upward. What is the appropriate term for this type of movement?
   a. supination
   b. pronation
   c. inversion
   d. eversion
2. A patient inquires whether lifting free weights is an appropriate form of exercise. The nurse assures the patient that isotonic exercises promote strength by:
   a. movement through a joint's full range of motion while maintaining consistent muscle tension.
   b. ensuring that the tension within the muscle remains constant as its length changes to move the weight.
   c. ensuring near-maximal contraction against a fixed object.
   d. developing increasing flexibility of the muscles and joints.
3. An elder female is discouraged that she is "not as strong as I used to be." The nurse is teaching the female about her strength. Which of the following statements made by the nurse is inaccurate?
   a. "You should become active in non-strength-related activities such as sewing and knitting."
   b. "A loss of strength is normal as we age due to a decrease in the size of the muscle fibers."

c. "A loss of strength is possibly due to normal hormonal changes due to the aging process."

d. "A loss of strength is possibly due to metabolic changes as a result of getting old."

4. Several bed-rest-related phenomena interfere with perfusion. The nurse is teaching a family to avoid such complications when caring for their elderly mother at home. Which of the following statements made by a family member indicates the need for more teaching?

a. "Avoiding the valsalva maneuver is an important intervention."

b. "We should be sure to limit fluids to decrease the risk of deep vein thrombosis."

c. "We should be sure to go from lying to standing slowly to avoid orthostatic hypotension."

d. "We should be sure to change our mother's position in bed at least every hour to avoid pressure ulcers."

5. The nurse is assessing a patient's home for barriers to mobility. Which of the following should not be a concern for this nurse during her assessment?

a. The nurse should assess any stairs in or out of the home for general condition and safety.

b. The nurse should be sure that the lighting is dull so shadows do not create false illusions.

c. The nurse should ensure that the patient has appropriate shoes or slippers that fit well.

d. The nurse should request that all throw rugs be removed if they are not flat and do not have nonslip backing.

6. Several joints will adduct to a maximum of 45 degrees under normal circumstances. Which of the following joints cannot adduct?

a. shoulder

b. wrist

c. thumb

d. elbow

7. A 7-year-old boy was hit by a car this morning and broke both of his legs. He has been admitted to your surgical unit and is now in traction. What is the most appropriate nursing diagnosis for this patient?

a. impaired physical mobility

b. activity intolerance

c. risk for disuse syndrome

d. pain

8. A nursing student is learning proper body mechanics during clinical rotation. Which of the following actions by the student indicates that the student needs reinforcement teaching?

a. The nursing student maintains a narrow base of support when standing or moving.

b. The nursing student uses her/his body as a counterweight to add force to movements.

c. The nursing student incorporates leverage to prevent muscle strain and reduce energy expenditure.

d. The nursing student asks for assistance when moving a patient.

9. A nurse is planning to move a patient from his bed to a reclining chair. The patient is obese and is unable to assist with the transfer in any way. What is the best device to use for this transfer?

a. gait belt

b. sliding board

c. a hydraulic lift

d. a convertible chair

10. When planning an aerobic exercise routine for a healthy individual, the nurse instructs the patient to begin at the lowest recommended level of maximal heart rate, which is:

a. 50%

b. 60%

c. 70%

d. 80%

11. The nurse implementing a teaching plan informs the clients with risk factors associated with sedentary lifestyle that the risk factors are significantly reduced by:

a. 30 minutes of brisk walking every day.

b. 20 minutes of walking every other day.

c. 30 minutes of running or 45 minutes of brisk walking every day.

d. 30 minutes of walking every other day.

CHAPTER 43

REST AND SLEEP

OVERVIEW

This chapter discusses the roles of rest and sleep in health maintenance. It emphasizes your role in facilitating sleep for the client, particularly with nonpharmacologic sleep aids.

LEARNING OUTCOMES

After completing this chapter, the student will be able to:

- Explain the functions and the physiology of sleep
- Identify the characteristics of NREM and REM sleep
- Identify the four stages of NREM sleep
- Describe variations in sleep patterns throughout the life span
- Identify factors that affect normal sleep
- Describe common sleep disorders
- Identify the components of a sleep pattern assessment
- Develop nursing diagnoses, outcomes, and nursing interventions related to sleep problems
- Describe interventions that promote normal sleep

www.prenhall.com/kozier

Additional resources for this chapter can be found on the Student CD-ROM accompanying this textbook, and on the Companion Website at www.prenhall.com/kozier. Click on Chapter 43 to select the activities for this chapter.

CD-ROM
- Audio Glossary
- NCLEX Review

Companion Website
- Additional NCLEX Review
- Case Study: Client Who Has Difficulty Falling Asleep
- Care Plan Activity: Client with Sleep Disorder
- MediaLink Application: Diagnosing Sleep Apnea
- Links to Resources

KEY TOPICS

This study guide chapter reinforces the following terms/topics discussed in the textbook chapter:

- biorhythms
- circadian synchronization
- effleurage
- electroencephalogram (EEG)
- hypersomnia
- insomnia
- narcolepsy
- nocturnal emissions
- NREM sleep
- parasomnia
- polysomnography
- primary sleep disorders

- REM sleep
- rest
- secondary sleep disorders
- sleep
- sleep apnea
- sleep deprivation

LECTURE OUTLINE

I. Physiology of sleep
   A. Circadian rhythms
   B. Stages of sleep
      1. NREM sleep
      2. REM sleep
   C. Sleep cycles
II. Functions of sleep
III. Normal sleep patterns and requirements
   A. Newborns
   B. Infants
   C. Toddlers
   D. Preschoolers
   E. School-age children
   F. Adolescents
   G. Young Adults
   H. Middle-aged adults
   I. Elders
IV. Factors affecting sleep
   A. Illness
   B. Environment
   C. Fatigue
   D. Lifestyle
   E. Emotional stress
   F. Stimulants and alcohol
   G. Diet
   H. Smoking
   I. Motivation
   J. Medications
V. Common sleep disorders
   A. Parasomnias
   B. Primary sleep disorders
      1. Insomnia
      2. Hypersomnia
      3. Narcolepsy
      4. Sleep apnea
      5. Sleep deprivation
   C. Secondary sleep disorders
VI. Chapter highlights
VII. Review questions
VIII. Readings and references
   A. Suggested readings
   B. Related research
   C. References
   D. Selected bibliography

FOCUSED STUDY TIPS

1. Define the following:
   biorhythms
   circadian synchronization
   effleurage
   hypersomnia
   insomnia
   narcolepsy
   nocturnal emissions
   NREM sleep
   parasomnias
   REM sleep
   sleep apnea
2. What is the purpose of rest? What are the characteristics of rest?
3. Why is sleep considered a basic need? What are the characteristics of sleep?
4. What effect does exhaustion have on the duration of REM sleep?
5. What are the functions of sleep?
6. As an individual moves from young adulthood to older adulthood, several changes in the sleep–wake cycle are evident. What are these changes?
7. Assessment of a client's sleep involves several activities. What are the essential components of a sleep assessment?
8. Diagram the adult sleep cycle in the space below.
9. Identify at least five factors that affect sleep.
10. When is it appropriate to ask a client to keep a sleep diary? What information should the diary contain?
11. Which diagnostic test is used to evaluate clients with sleep problems?

CASE STUDY

Mahalia Winters is a 52-year-old client admitted to the community hospital for surgical repair of a bowel obstruction. She is admitted to your unit with the following orders:

Vital signs q2–4h
Bedrest with BRP (bathroom privileges)
Strict NPO
Lactated Ringers @ 125 cc/hr
Cefoxitin 1.0 Gm q6h IV
Benadryl 50 mg @ HS
Demerol 50–100 mg IM q4h PRN pain
To be seen by anesthesia for preoperative evaluation
Scheduled for surgery in the A.M.

1. *What factors might affect Mahalia's sleep pattern?*
2. *What information about sleep would be valuable for you to know when planning her care?*
   Mahalia has undergone a bowel resection for obstruction. Her clinical course has been rocky. Her unstable condition necessitated a 6-day stay in the intensive care unit. She has now returned to your clinical unit. The nurse from ICU reports that Mahalia has had little sleep over the past 6 days.
3. *What signs and symptoms of a sleep problem would you expect to find on physical examination?*
4. *Mahalia asks you about the wisdom of using sleeping medications. How would you respond?*

CARE PLAN CRITICAL THINKING ACTIVITIES

Based on Mahalia's history and current complaint, fill in the appropriate elements of the care plan:
Assessment and Diagnosis
Planning and Implementation
Evaluation

NCLEX TEST QUESTIONS

1. A nurse observing the cardiac monitor of a patient who is sleeping notes that the patient's heart rate has dropped compared to the rate while awake. The nurse would:
   a. notify the physician.
   b. wake up the patient.
   c. take the patient's blood pressure.
   d. observe the patient to ensure vital functions remain stable.
2. A nurse observing a patient sleeping notices that the patient's eyelids are twitching. The nurse caring for this patient recognizes the patient is in what stage of sleep?
   a. REM
   b. NREM stage 1
   c. NREM stage 2
   d. NREM stage 4
3. A patient is admitted to the hospital for pneumonia. The patient tells the nurse that since she has been ill she has gotten hardly any sleep because she is coughing all the time. The nurse knows that not getting enough sleep can affect the patient by:
   a. leading to nervousness, anxiety and mood swings.
   b. increasing her tolerance to drug therapy.
   c. decreasing the locus of control.
   d. leading to malabsorption of nutrients.
4. Before the nurse identifies sleep pattern disturbance as a nursing diagnosis for a patient, the nursing assessment should:
   a. include factors that identify the individual is at risk for or experiencing changes in sleep patterns that cause discomfort or interfere with lifestyle for a prolonged period of time.
   b. identify that the patient has had a problem with sleep pattern or is experiencing changes in sleep pattern due to a medical condition or treatments for 1 or 2 days.
   c. identify use of sleeping aids on a daily basis.
   d. include a nocturnal polysomnogram.

5. The nurse caring for clients with sleep disturbances knows that which of the following stages of sleep is characterized by decreases in temperature, blood pressure, and pulse, as well as a relaxation of muscles?
   a. stage 1
   b. stage 2
   c. stage 3
   d. stage 4
6. The nurse caring for clients with sleep disturbances knows that characteristics of NREM sleep would not include which of the following?
   a. active dreaming
   b. deep, restful sleep
   c. decrease in blood pressure
   d. slow-wave sleep
7. The patient who reports frequent episodes of falling asleep involuntarily during the daytime should be evaluated for:
   a. insomnia.
   b. narcolepsy.
   c. sleep apnea.
   d. parasomnia.
8. The patient complains of having difficulty falling asleep at night. After evaluating the following assessment data, the nurse determines the one factor that may be interfering with sleep to be that the client:
   a. smokes two packs of cigarettes per day.
   b. exercises on a treadmill 1 hour every morning.
   c. snacks on milk and turkey or a ham sandwich before bed.
   d. takes a hot shower before bed.
9. The diagnostic test used to measure the sleeping patient's brain waves is the:
   a. electroencephalogram (EEG).
   b. electrooculogram (EOG).
   c. electromyogram (EMG).
   d. electrocardiogram (ECG).
10. The patient who has been started on sleep medication should be instructed by the nurse to:
    a. continue taking the medication for at least 2 months.
    b. repeat administration of the medication if unable to fall asleep within the first hour.
    c. avoid driving or handling machinery while the drug is in his or her system.
    d. take medication at least 4 hours before retiring for the night.

CHAPTER 44

PAIN MANAGEMENT

OVERVIEW

This chapter presents current theories on pain and pain management. It stresses your role in assessing, diagnosing, planning care, intervening in, and evaluating the client's pain experience. It also underscores the importance of understanding the uniqueness of pain perception.

LEARNING OUTCOMES

After completing this chapter, the student will be able to:

- Identify types and categories of pain according to location, etiology, and duration
- Differentiate pain threshold from pain tolerance
- Describe the four processes involved in nociception, and how pain interventions can work during each process
- Describe the gate control theory and its application to nursing care
- Identify subjective and objective data to collect and analyze when assessing pain
- Identify examples of nursing diagnoses for clients with pain
- State outcome criteria by which to evaluate a client's response to interventions for pain
- Identify barriers to effective pain management
- Describe pharmacologic interventions for pain
- Define tolerance, dependence, and addiction
- Describe the World Health Organization's ladder step approach to cancer pain
- Identify rationales for using various analgesic delivery routes
- Describe nonpharmacologic pain control interventions

www.prenhall.com/kozier

Additional resources for this chapter can be found on the Student CD-ROM accompanying this textbook, and on the Companion Website at www.prenhall.com/kozier. Click on Chapter 44 to select the activities for this chapter.

CD-ROM

- Audio Glossary
- NCLEX Review

Companion Website

- Additional NCLEX Review
- Case Study: Treating a Client with Stomach Cancer
- Care Plan Activity: Treating Chronic Back Pain
- MediaLink Application: The Mayday Pain Project
- Links to Resources

KEY TOPICS

This study guide chapter reinforces the following terms/topics discussed in the textbook chapter:

- acute pain
- adjuvent analgesic
- agonist analgesic
- agonist–antagonist analgesic
- chronic pain
- cordotomy
- cutaneous pain
- deep somatic pain
- equianalgesia
- fifth vital sign
- hyperalgesia
- intractable pain
- nerve block
- neurectomy
- neuropathic pain
- nociception
- nociceptor
- nonsteroidal anti-inflammatory drugs (NSAIDs)
- pain
- pain reaction
- pain sensation
- pain threshold
- pain tolerance
- patient-controlled analgesia (PCA)
- phantom pain
- placebo
- preemptive analgesia
- radiating pain
- referred pain
- rhizotomy
- spinal cord stimulation (SCS)
- sympathectomy
- transcutaneous electrical nerve stimulation (TENS)
- visceral pain

LECTURE OUTLINE

I. The nature of pain
   A. Types of pain
   B. Concepts associated with pain
II. Physiology of pain
   A. Nociception
      1. Transduction
      2. Transmission
      3. Perception
      4. Modulation
   B. Gate control theory
   C. Responses to pain
   D. Factors affecting the pain experience
      1. Ethnic/cultural values
      2. Developmental stage
      3. Environment and support people
      4. Past pain experiences
      5. Meaning of pain
      6. Anxiety and stress
   E. Chapter highlights
   F. Review questions
   G. Readings and references
      1. Suggested readings
      2. Related research
      3. References
      4. Selected bibliography

FOCUSED STUDY TIPS

1. Define the following:
   acute pain
   chronic pain
   intractable pain
   neuropathic pain
   phantom pain
   radiating pain
   referred pain
2. List words or phrases used to describe pain.
3. Your client is experiencing significant leg pain due to a recent injury. According to gate control theory, you could affect his pain perception by ascending modulation. What is ascending modulation?
4. Numerous factors affect the pain experience. List factors that would be least likely to affect pain.
5. How often should pain assessments be performed?

6. Compare and contrast acute pain with chronic pain.
7. What is the role of opioids with pain management?
8. What is the preferred route of delivery for opioid administration?
9. Patient-controlled analgesia (PCA) may be used for acute and chronic pain. What type of client would benefit most from using PCA?
10. Your client is experiencing severe postoperative pain. You have just administered an opioid by injection but wish to supplement pain relief with nonpharmacologic pain management strategies. Which strategy can you implement independently?
11. Patrick Mooney is a 13-year-old high school freshman. During lunch period, he and another student argued and a fight ensued. Patrick has a "black eye" and an abrasion on his left cheek. The other child is without injury. As the school nurse, what independent nursing actions could you take to alleviate Patrick's pain? Provide rationales for your choices.
12. What are the collaborative nursing actions to reduce pain?

CASE STUDY

Cassandra Thomas is 24-year-old client complaining of abdominal pain. She locates her pain in the epigastric region. On a 0 to 10 scale, she rates her pain as a 6. She describes the pain as "constant throbbing" and says she feels nauseous.

1. *What additional pain history information would help you plan your care for Cassandra?*
2. *On examination, Cassandra's vital signs are BP 140/90, HR 112, RR 26, T 99.9F oral. Her skin is moist and warm to touch. She is mouth –breathing, and her oral mucosa appears pale and dry. She is lying on her side with her knees and hips flexed. She speaks only when asked a direct question. Is Cassandra's pain acute or chronic?*
3. *Develop a pain management strategy appropriate for Cassandra.*
4. *If opioids are prescribed for Cassandra, what side effects would you anticipate?*
5. *Morphine via PCA pump is prescribed for Cassandra. Identify the benefits of this method.*
6. *How would you evaluate the effectiveness of your pain management strategies?*

CARE PLAN CRITICAL THINKING ACTIVITIES

Fill in the appropriate elements of the care plan for Cassandra:
Assessment and Diagnosis
Planning and Implementation
Evaluation

NCLEX TEST QUESTIONS

1. When evaluating the effectiveness of pain control measures, the nurse asks the patient to describe the pain on a 0 to 10 scale 30 minutes after receiving pain medication. The nurse is evaluating which of the following components of pain?
   a. quality
   b. duration
   c. intensity
   d. onset
2. Which of the following statements made by a coworker is recognized by the nurse as a common misconception about pain?
   a. "Clients are unlikely to become addicted to an analgesic provided to treat pain."
   b. "Surgical clients experience pain only when they have had minor surgery."
   c. "The person who experiences the pain is the only authority about its existence and nature."
   d. "Pain is a subjective experience, and the intensity and duration of pain vary considerably among individuals."
3. The nurse assessing a client experiencing acute pain does not anticipate assessing which of the following signs or symptoms?
   a. increased pulse rate

b. skin warm and dry
c. dilated pupils
d. increased respiratory rate

4. A newly hired nurse at a pain management clinic is learning about the types of pain. The nurse understands that which type of pain is highly resistant to relief?
   a. referred
   b. neuropathic
   c. intractable
   d. phantom
5. The nurse caring for clients in acute pain understands that the amount of pain stimulation a person requires in order to feel pain is referred to as:
   a. pain threshold.
   b. pain reaction.
   c. pain tolerance.
   d. intractable pain.
6. A nurse providing care to clients in chronic pain understands that full agonist analgesics have no ceiling on the level of analgesia, their dose can be steadily increased to relieve pain, and there is no maximum daily dose limit. Which of the following drugs is not included in the full agonist category?
   a. meperidine (Demerol)
   b. propoxyphene (Darvon)
   c. morphine
   d. butorphanol tartrate (Stadol)
7. The nurse evaluating a client's understanding of preventive measures for common opioid side effects recognizes further teaching is required when the client makes which of the following statements?
   a. "I will increase my fluid intake to 8 glasses a day."
   b. "I will increase my fiber intake by eating more fresh fruits and vegetables."
   c. "I will apply cool packs to my skin if itching occurs."
   d. "I will stop taking my medication if itching occurs."
8. Which of the following actions taken by a nurse providing care to a client with an epidural catheter for the administration of analgesics is contraindicated? The nurse:
   a. applies tape over all injection ports on the epidural line.
   b. uses alcohol in the care of the catheter.
   c. administers naloxone hydrochloride to a client with respirations of 6 per minute who is difficult to arouse.
   d. gently aspirates prior to bolus medication administration of medication.
9. The nurse assessing a client receiving narcotic analgesics notes the client to be frequently drowsy and arousable but drifting off to sleep during conversation. Based on these assessment findings, the nurse takes which of the following actions?
   a. no action
   b. administers naloxone (Narcan)
   c. informs the primary health care provider
   d. assesses the client's level of pain
10. The nurse is providing information regarding nonpharmacologic pain management to clients experiencing chronic pain. The nurse explains that cutaneous stimulation is believed to create the release of endorphins that block pain stimuli transmission. In evaluating the clients' understanding of the teaching session, which of the following identified by a client is not considered cutaneous stimulation?
   a. massage
   b. application of heat or cold
   c. acupressure
   d. transcutaneous electrical nerve stimulation

CHAPTER 45

NUTRITION

OVERVIEW

This chapter discusses the importance of nutrition in the maintenance of health. It highlights your role in assessing the adequacy of nutrition, teaching nutritional content, and assisting the client to receive adequate nutrition through oral, enteral, or parenteral routes.

LEARNING OUTCOMES

After completing this chapter, the student will be able to:

- Identify essential nutrients and dietary sources of each
- Describe normal digestion, absorption, and metabolism of carbohydrates, proteins, and lipids
- Explain essential aspects of energy balance
- Discuss body weight and body mass standards
- Identify factors influencing nutrition
- Identify developmental nutritional considerations
- Evaluate a diet using the food guide pyramid
- Discuss essential components and purposes of nutritional screening and nutritional assessment
- Identify risk factors for and clinical signs of malnutrition
- Describe nursing interventions to promote optimal nutrition
- Discuss nursing interventions to treat clients with nutritional problems
- Plan, implement, and evaluate nursing care associated with nursing diagnoses related to nutritional problems

www.prenhall.com/kozier

Additional resources for this chapter can be found on the Student CD-ROM accompanying this textbook, and on the Companion Website at www.prenhall.com/kozier. Click on Chapter 45 to select the activities for this chapter.

CD-ROM
- Audio Glossary
- NCLEX Review
- Animations
  - Carbohydrates
  - Proteins
  - Lipids
  - Inserting a Nasogastric Tube
  - A & P Review
    - Cellular Metabolism
    - Organic Compounds

Companion Website
- Additional NCLEX Review
- Case Study: Client with Percutaneous Endoscopic Gastrostomy
- Care Plan Activity: Client Experiencing Loss of Appetite
- MediaLink Application: Vegetarian Nutrition
- Links to Resources

KEY TOPICS

This study guide chapter reinforces the following terms/topics discussed in the textbook chapter:

- 24-hour food recall
- anabolism
- anemia
- anorexia
- anorexia nervosa
- basal metabolic rate (BMR)
- body mass index (BMI)
- bottle mouth syndrome
- bulimia
- caloric value
- calorie (c, cal, kcal)
- catabolism
- cholesterol
- complete proteins
- demand feeding
- diet history
- disaccharides
- dysphagia
- enteral
- enzymes
- essential amino acids
- fad
- fats
- fat-soluble vitamins
- fatty acids
- food diary
- food frequency record
- gastrostomy
- glycerides
- glycogen
- glycogenesis
- ideal body weight (IBW)
- incomplete proteins
- iron deficiency anemia
- jejunostomy
- kilocalorie (Kcal)
- kilojoule (kJ)
- large calorie (Calorie, kilocalorie [Kcal]))
- lipids
- lipoproteins
- macrominerals
- malnutrition
- metabolism
- microminerals
- mid-arm circumference
- mid-arm muscle circumference (MAMC)
- minerals
- monosaccharides
- monounsaturated fatty acids
- nasoenteric tube
- nasogastric tube
- nitrogen balance
- nonessential amino acids
- nutrients
- nutrition
- nutritive value
- obese
- overnutrition
- oils
- overweight
- parenteral
- partially complete proteins
- percutaneous endoscopic gastrostomy (PEG)
- percutaneous endoscopic jejunostomy (PEJ)
- polysaccharides
- polyunsaturated fatty acids
- protein-calorie malnutrition
- pureed diet
- regurgitation
- resting energy expenditure (REE)
- saturated fatty acids
- skinfold measurement
- small calorie (c, cal)
- triglycerides
- undernutrition
- unsaturated fatty acid
- urea
- vitamin
- water-soluble vitamins

LECTURE OUTLINE

- I. Essential nutrients
  - A. Carbohydrates
    - 1. Types of carbohydrates
      - a. Sugars
      - b. Starches
      - c. Fiber
    - 2. Digestion
    - 3. Carbohydrate metabolism
      - a. Storage and conversion
  - B. Proteins
    - 1. Digestion
    - 2. Storage
    - 3. Protein metabolism
      - a. Anabolism
      - b. Catabolism
      - c. Nitrogen balance
  - C. Lipids
    - 1. Digestion
  - D. Micronutrients
- II. Energy balance
  - A. Energy intake
  - B. Energy output
- III. Body weight and body mass standards
- IV. Factors affecting nutrition
  - A. Development
  - B. Gender
  - C. Ethnicity and culture
  - D. Beliefs about food
  - E. Personal preferences
  - F. Religious practices
  - G. Lifestyle
  - H. Medications and therapy
  - I. Health
  - J. Alcohol consumption
  - K. Advertising
  - L. Psychologic factors
- V. Nutritional variations throughout the life cycle
  - A. Neonate to 1 year
  - B. Toddler
  - C. Preschooler
  - D. School-age
  - E. Adolescents
  - F. Young adult
  - G. Middle-aged adult
  - H. Elders
- VI. Standards for a healthy diet
  - A. Dietary guidelines for Americans
    - 1. The food guide pyramid
  - B. Canada's food guide to healthy eating
  - C. Recommended dietary intake
  - D. Vegetarian diets
- VII. Altered nutrition
- VIII. Chapter highlights
- IX. Review questions
- X. Readings and references
  - A. Suggested readings
  - B. Related research
  - C. References
  - D. Selected bibliography

FOCUSED STUDY TIPS

1. Define the following:
   basal metabolic rate
   body mass index
   caloric value
   enteral feedings
   metabolism
   nutrients
   parenteral feedings
2. What determines the amount of calories a person needs for weight maintenance?
3. What is the body's most basic nutrient need?
4. List foods that are considered complex carbohydrates.
5. Cholesterol is a substance that has been linked to many health hazards. What is the major source of cholesterol in the body?
6. Which vitamins are water-soluble?
7. What biochemical data may indicate poor nutritional status?
8. What are the three major functions of nutrients?
9. Evaluate your own diet for compliance with the Dietary Guidelines for Americans and the Food Guide Pyramid. How well do you comply with these recommendations?
10. What are the factors that influence an individual's eating habits?

CASE STUDY

Thad Denois is recovering from neurosurgery. The neurosurgeon orders placement of a nasogastric tube for short-term enteral feedings.

1. *Explain how you would insert a nasogastric tube.*
2. *How would you verify tube placement?*
3. *The physician orders a commercially prepared tube feeding to be administered at 50 cc/hr. What nursing actions must you take to ensure safe administration?*

CARE PLAN CRITICAL THINKING ACTIVITIES

Fill in the appropriate elements of the care plan for this client:
Assessment and Diagnosis
Planning and Implementation
Evaluation

NCLEX TEST QUESTIONS

1. During a nutritional assessment, the nurse learns a patient ingests 400 micrograms of folic acid every day. What is the benefit of this vitamin to the patient?
   a. It helps with the maturation of red blood cells.
   b. It helps synthesize cholesterol.
   c. It helps in the formation of red blood cells.
   d. It is essential for normal blood clotting.
2. The nurse is caring for a malnourished elderly male patient. Which of the following would be true about this patient's energy requirements?
   a. His diet should be low in protein.
   b. He needs supplemental insulin.
   c. He is in a state of anabolism.
   d. He is in a state of catabolism.
3. The nurse is caring for a patient recovering from an automobile accident. This patient has not eaten for more than 2 weeks and is receiving intravenous fluids for hydration. Which of the following types of nutritional disorders might this patient begin to exhibit?
   a. cachexia
   b. protein deficiency state
   c. mixed malnutrition
   d. hypermetabolism
4. During the physical assessment of a patient, the nurse suspects a poor nutritional status. Which of the following might this nurse have seen during the assessment?
   a. firm pink nails
   b. flat abdomen
   c. smooth beefy red tongue
   d. deep red tongue with surface papillae
5. The nurse is caring for a patient receiving enteral feedings. Which of the following nursing diagnoses would address the major common side effect of this feeding method?
   a. Altered skin integrity: risk due to potential for diarrhea
   b. Altered nutrition: risk for more than body requirements
   c. Altered nutrition: less than body requirements related to inability to ingest food
   d. Altered nutrition: risk for more than body requirements related to dysfunctional psychological conditioning in relationship to food
6. While preparing a feeding bag for a patient receiving nasogastric tube feedings, the nurse notes the feeding bag was first used 2 days ago. What should the nurse do with the feeding bag?
   a. Add the ordered amount of solution to the feeding bag
   b. Flush the bag with water before using
   c. Attach a 50 ml syringe to the bag
   d. Discard the bag and use a new one
7. In planning a diet for a patient who is a lacto-ovo-vegetarian, the nurse consults with the dietitian for a description of food choices. Which of the following descriptions is accurate?
   a. vegetables only
   b. dairy products, eggs, and vegetables
   c. dairy products and vegetables only
   d. vegetables and eggs only

8. The nurse teaching a group of adults about the USDA Food Pyramid emphasizes that the number of servings daily from the bread, cereal, rice, and pasta group should fall between:
   a. 8 and 10 servings.
   b. 12 and 16 servings.
   c. 6 and 11 servings.
   d. 2 and 6 servings.
9. Dietary replacement for meat that the nurse can suggest to the vegetarian patient includes:
   a. oatmeal.
   b. tofu.
   c. cheese.
   d. rice.
10. The laboratory findings that the nurse may expect to see on a patient with chronic inadequate protein intake would not include which of the following?
    a. a low hemoglobin and hematocrit
    b. a reduced lymphocyte count
    c. a decrease in creatinine
    d. an increase in albumin

CHAPTER 46

FECAL ELIMINATION

OVERVIEW

This chapter presents normal and common abnormal elimination patterns. It emphasizes your role in assessing and promoting regular fecal elimination patterns. The chapter introduces the skills of enema administration, application of an ostomy appliance, and evaluation of elimination.

LEARNING OUTCOMES

After completing this chapter, the student will be able to:

- Identify factors that influence fecal elimination and patterns of defecation
- Distinguish normal and abnormal characteristics and constituents of feces
- Describe methods used to assess the intestinal tract
- Identify common causes and effects of selected fecal elimination problems
- Identify examples of nursing diagnoses, outcomes, and interventions for clients with elimination problems
- Identify measures that maintain normal fecal elimination pattern
- Describe essentials of fecal stoma care for clients with ostomies

www.prenhall.com/kozier

Additional resources for this chapter can be found on the Student CD-ROM accompanying this textbook, and on the Companion Website at www.prenhall.com/kozier. Click on Chapter 46 to select the activities for this chapter.

CD-ROM

- Audio Glossary
- NCLEX Review
- Animations
  - The Digestive System
  - Performing an Enema
  - A & P Review
    - The Digestive System
    - The Intestinal Wall

Companion Website

- Additional NCLEX Review
- Case Study: Client Who Had Abdominal Surgery
- Care Plan Activity: Client Who Had a Stroke
- MediaLink Application: The United Ostomy Association
- Links to Resources

KEY TOPICS

This study guide chapter reinforces the following terms/topics discussed in the textbook chapter:

- bedpan
- bowel incontinence
- carminative
- cathartics
- chyme
- colostomy
- commode
- constipation
- defecation
- diarrhea
- enema
- fecal impaction
- fecal incontinence
- feces
- flatulence
- flatus
- gastrocolic reflex
- gastrostomy
- haustra
- haustral churning
- hemorrhoid
- ileostomy
- ingestion
- laxative
- mass peristalsis
- meconium
- ostomy
- peristalsis
- stoma
- stool
- suppositories

LECTURE OUTLINE

I. Physiology of defecation
  A. Large intestine
  B. Rectum and anal canal
  C. Defecation
  D. Feces
II. Factors that affect defecation
  A. Development
    1. Newborns and infants
    2. Toddlers
    3. School-age children and adolescents
    4. Older adults
  B. Diet
    1. Fluid
  C. Activity
  D. Psychologic factors
  E. Defecation habits
  F. Medications
  G. Diagnostic procedures
  H. Anesthesia and surgery
  I. Pathologic conditions
  J. Pain
III. Fecal elimination problems
  A. Constipation
    1. Fecal impaction
  B. Diarrhea
  C. Bowel incontinence
  D. Flatulence
IV. Bowel diversion ostomies
  A. Permanence
  B. Anatomic location
  C. Construction of the stoma
V. Chapter highlights
VI. Review questions
VII. Readings and references
  A. Suggested readings
  B. Related research
  C. References
  D. Selected bibliography

FOCUSED STUDY TIPS

1. Define the following:
   bowel incontinence
   diarrhea
   flatulence
   constipation
   fecal impaction
2. The large intestine plays numerous roles in digestion and defecation. What are the functions of the large intestine?

3. Your client states that he is concerned that his stool is black in color. As part of your assessment, you should inquire about use of which over-the-counter medications?
4. Your client complains of nausea. You notice that she has a distended abdomen and a small amount of liquid stool on the bed linens. For which fecal elimination problem would you would want to assess?
5. Describe how you would remove a fecal impaction.
6. To provide adequate protection against body fluids, what should the nurse wear when offering a bedpan?
7. When should medications be used to facilitate bowel functioning?
8. Your client is scheduled for a proctosigmoidoscopy. What is this procedure used for?
9. What does a guaiac test detect?
10. What is the correct position for a client receiving an enema?
11. Your bedridden, hospitalized client complains of bloating and gas. What measures can you implement independently to help decrease flatulence?
12. For what is a fecal incontinence pouch used?
13. Identify at least ten potential causes of constipation.
14. Identify at least three potential causes of diarrhea.
15. List at least five high-fiber foods.

CASE STUDY

You are assigned to care for Earl Pagano, a teenage client recovering from orthopedic surgery. During his surgery, pins were placed in his left femur and tibia to enable skeletal traction. Due to the traction, he is confined to bed. This is his third postoperative day, and he has not had a bowel movement since admission.

1. *What nursing action should you take?*
2. *Earl is at risk for constipation. Identify at least two risk factors for constipation for him.*
3. *By the sixth postoperative day, Earl has still not had a bowel movement. Earl has been eating 100% of a regular diet for 5 days. He complains of feeling bloated. His normal elimination pattern is one time per day.*

CARE PLAN CRITICAL THINKING ACTIVITIES

Fill in the appropriate elements of the care plan for Earl Pagano:
Assessment and Diagnosis
Planning and Implementation
Evaluation

NCLEX TEST QUESTIONS

1. The nurse is assessing factors related to a client's complaint of constipation. Which of the following factors is not associated with constipation?
   a. insufficient fluid intake
   b. change in daily routine
   c. insufficient activity or immobility
   d. daily iron supplements
2. The nurse is providing preoperative teaching to a client scheduled for a gastrostomy. The client demonstrates an understanding when he states that a gastrostomy is an opening:
   a. through the abdominal wall into the jejunum.
   b. through the abdominal wall into the stomach.
   c. into the ureter.
   d. into the ileum.
3. A client scheduled to undergo a sigmoidostomy expresses concern about bowel control following the surgery. The nurse's instructions to the client is based on the fact that a sigmoidostomy produces:
   a. liquid fecal drainage and cannot be regulated.
   b. a malodorous, mushy drainage and there is usually no control.
   c. a liquid fecal drainage that can be regulated.
   d. stools that are normal or formed consistency, and the discharge can be regulated.

4. A nurse developing a plan of care for a client newly admitted with prolonged diarrhea establishes which of the following as the priority nursing diagnosis for the client?
   a. risk for impaired skin integrity related to prolonged diarrhea
   b. knowledge deficit related to lack of previous experience
   c. anxiety related to lack of control of fecal elimination
   d. risk for fluid volume deficit related to prolonged diarrhea
5. A nurse is teaching a client about the various types of enemas. Which of the following enema solutions poses the greatest risk of fluid and electrolyte imbalances and water intoxication?
   a. hypertonic solutions
   b. hypotonic solutions
   c. isotonic solutions
   d. soapsuds enemas
6. A nursing assistant correctly performs the administration of an enema on an adult client when the tube is inserted:
   a. 1 to 1.5 inches.
   b. 2 to 3 inches.
   c. 3 to 4 inches.
   d. 4 to 5 inches.
7. A client who is 3 days postoperative a colostomy expresses concern that when the stoma is touched it bleeds slightly. The nurse's response is based on the knowledge that:
   a. slight bleeding when the stoma is touched is normal.
   b. bleeding may indicate infection.
   c. bleeding may indicate impaired blood circulation.
   d. the client's clotting factors may be impaired.
8. The nurse evaluating a client's understanding of peristomal skin and stoma care recognizes the need for further teaching when the client states:
   a. "I use toilet tissue to remove excess stool."
   b. "I use a towel to pat dry the area."
   c. "I peel the bag off slowly holding the skin taut."
   d. "I use alcohol to remove the sticky residue."
9. The nurse performs a guaiac test on a client's stool and the result is positive. Which of the following existing factors would not contribute to a false positive result?
   a. The client recently consumed red meat.
   b. The client recently consumed turnips.
   c. The client recently consumed red Jell-O.
   d. The client recently consumed melons.
10. A client is scheduled for a colonoscopy. The client demonstrates an understanding of the procedure when she states that a colonoscopy provides a view of the:
   a. anal canal.
   b. rectum.
   c. rectum and sigmoid colon.
   d. large intestine.

CHAPTER 47

URINARY ELIMINATION

OVERVIEW

This chapter presents normal and common abnormal urinary elimination patterns. It emphasizes your role in assessing and promoting regular urinary elimination patterns. The chapter introduces the skills of urine specimen collection; insertion, maintenance, and discontinuation of urinary catheters; and catheter irrigation.

LEARNING OUTCOMES

After completing this chapter, the student will be able to:

- Describe the process of urination, from urine formation through micturition
- Identify factors that influence urinary elimination
- Identify common causes of selected urinary problems
- Describe nursing assessment of urinary function, including subjective and objective data
- Identify normal and abnormal characteristics and constituents of urine
- Develop nursing diagnoses, desired outcomes, and interventions related to urinary elimination
- Delineate ways to prevent urinary infection
- Explain the care of clients with retention catheters or urinary diversions

KEY TOPICS

This study guide chapter reinforces the following terms/topics discussed in the textbook chapter:

- anuria
- bladder training
- blood urea nitrogen (BUN)
- creatinine clearance
- Credé's maneuver
- detrusor muscle
- dialysis
- diuresis

www.prenhall.com/kozier

Additional resources for this chapter can be found on the Student CD-ROM accompanying this textbook, and on the Companion Website at www.prenhall.com/kozier. Click on Chapter 47 to select the activities for this chapter.

CD-ROM

- Audio Glossary
- NCLEX Review
- Animations
  - Renal Function
  - Furosemide Drug
  - Catheterization
  - A & P Review

Companion Website

- Additional NCLEX Review
- Case Study: Intermittent Self-Catheterization
- Care Plan Activity: Client Who Just Had Urinary Catheter Removed
- MediaLink Application: Urinary Incontinence
- Links to Resources

- diuretics
- dysuria
- enuresis
- flaccid
- glomerulus
- habit training
- irrigation
- meatus
- micturition
- neurogenic bladder
- nocturia
- nocturnal enuresis
- nocturnal frequency
- oliguria
- polydipsia
- polyuria
- prompted voiding
- reflux
- residual urine
- suprapubic catheter
- trigone
- urgency
- urinary frequency
- urinary hesitancy
- urinary incontinence
- urinary retention
- urination
- voiding

LECTURE OUTLINE

I. Physiology of urinary elimination
  A. Kidneys
  B. Ureters
  C. Bladder
  D. Urethra
  E. Urination
II. Factors affecting voiding
  A. Developmental factors
  B. Psychosocial factors
  C. Fluid and food intake
  D. Medications
  E. Muscle tone
  F. Pathologic conditions
  G. Surgical and diagnostic procedures
III. Altered urine production
  A. Polyuria
  B. Oliguria and anuria
IV. Altered urinary elimination
  A. Frequency and nocturia
  B. Urgency
  C. Dysuria
  D. Enuresis
  E. Urinary incontinence
  F. Urinary retention
  G. Neurogenic bladder
V. Assessing
  A. Nursing history
  B. Physical assessment
  C. Assessing urine
    1. Measuring urinary output
    2. Measuring residual urine
  D. Diagnostic tests
VI. Diagnosing
VII. Planning
  A. Planning for home care
VIII. Implementing
  A. Maintaining normal urinary elimination
    1. Promoting fluid intake
    2. Maintaining normal voiding habits
    3. Assisting with toileting
  B. Preventing urinary tract infections
  C. Managing urinary incontinence
    1. Continence (bladder) training
    2. Pelvic muscle exercises
    3. Maintaining skin integrity
    4. Applying external urinary drainage devices
  D. Procedure 47–1: Applying an external urinary device
    1. Purposes
  E. Assessment
  F. Planning
    1. Delegation
    2. Equipment
  G. Implementation
    1. Preparation
    2. Performance
  H. Evaluation
  I. Managing urinary retention
  J. Urinary catheterization
  K. Procedure 47–2: Performing urinary catheterization
    1. Purposes
  L. Assessment
  M. Planning
    1. Delegation
    2. Equipment
  N. Implementation
    1. Preparation
    2. Performance

O. Evaluation
P. Nursing interventions for clients with retention catheters
   1. Fluids
   2. Dietary measures
   3. Perineal care
   4. Changing the catheter and tubing
   5. Removing retention catheters
Q. Clean intermittent self-catheterization
R. Urinary irrigations
S. Procedure 47–3: Performing bladder irrigation
   1. Purposes
T. Assessment
U. Planning
   1. Delegation
   2. Equipment
V. Implementation
   1. Performance
W. Evaluation
X. Urinary diversions
Y. Suprapubic catheter care

IX. Evaluating
X. Chapter highlights
XI. Review questions
XII. Readings and references
   A. Suggested readings
   B. Related research
   C. References
   D. Selected bibliography

FOCUSED STUDY TIPS

1. Define the following:
   dysuria
   enuresis
   neurogenic bladder
   nocturia
   oliguria
   polyuria
   urinary retention
2. What is the primary role of the kidneys?
3. Urine in the bladder stimulates stretch receptors and triggers the need to void. In the adult, the need to void is signaled after how much urine enters the bladder?
4. A 30-year-old client complains of urinary frequency. What factors would you want to assess?
5. To conduct a routine urinalysis, what type of specimen is needed?
6. What supplies are needed to collect a urine sample for a culture and sensitivity exam on an ambulatory client?
7. The physician has written an order for a urine culture from a client with an indwelling catheter. What steps should you take to collect the sample?
8. List characteristics of normal urine.
9. Describe the cystoscopy procedure.
10. Why is the use of a condom catheter for an incontinent male client preferable to insertion of a retention catheter?
11. Identify at least five factors that inhibit voiding.
12. What does a complete assessment of urinary function include?
13. Gail Chan is a 15-year-old high school student. She is seen by the family nurse practitioner (FNP) in the ambulatory clinic for a urinary tract infection. The FNP prescribes an antibiotic for the infection. During the physical examination, the FNP determines that Gail is an active, normally healthy adolescent. As part of her treatment plan, provide Gail with at least three suggestions to prevent further urinary tract problems.
14. Ethel Jackson is a 78-year-old client with urinary incontinence. Ethel lives independently at home. She reports that she has curtailed many of her social activities due to her incontinence. How you would instruct Ethel on managing her urinary incontinence?

CASE STUDY

James Saratoga is a 58-year-old client with severe urinary retention. The physician has ordered insertion of a Foley catheter for ongoing urinary drainage.

1. *Identify the precautions you must take to protect James while inserting a retention catheter.*
2. *James's condition has improved and the physician has ordered discontinuation of the Foley catheter. Describe how you would remove the catheter.*

CARE PLAN CRITICAL THINKING ACTIVITIES

Fill in the appropriate elements of the care plan for James Saratoga:
Assessment and Diagnosis
Planning and Implementation
Evaluation

NCLEX TEST QUESTIONS

1. A nurse is assessing an adult patient for renal function. She notes that in the past 24 hours, the patient has voided 850 cc of urine. What does this finding indicate?
   a. The patient's urine output is too high.
   b. The patient's urine output is too low.
   c. The patient's urine output is normal.
   d. The patient's renal function is normal.
2. The nurse catheterizes a bed-bound patient just after the patient voids 600 cc of urine. The catheterization procedure yields an additional 275 cc of urine. What is the appropriate nursing diagnosis for this patient?
   a. Functional incontinence related to inability to empty bladder as evidence by presence of residual urine
   b. Stress incontinence related to inability to relax the external urethral sphincter as evidenced by presence of residual urine
   c. Urinary retention related to immobility as evidenced by presence of residual urine
   d. Overflow incontinence related to inability to empty bladder as evidenced by presence of residual urine
3. The nurse is preparing to irrigate a urinary catheter. Which of the following nursing actions is not correct?
   a. The nurse follows sterile technique during the procedure.
   b. The nurse uses a solution of soap and tap water for the irrigation.
   c. The nurse documents the irrigant fluid as intake.
   d. The nurse applies gentle but firm pressure to the syringe to instill irrigant.
4. The nurse is teaching a patient for preparation for a cystoscopy. Which of the following teaching points is incorrect?
   a. The patient must be on a liquid diet the day of the test unless anesthesia is planned, in which case the patient must be NPO.
   b. There is a possibility that the patient will have an IV.
   c. The patient will be placed in the left lateral position for the test.
   d. The length of the procedure is usually 30 to 60 minutes.
5. The processes of filtration, reabsorption, and secretion are carried out in the working unit of the kidney which is called the:
   a. Bowman's capsule.
   b. nephron.
   c. trigone.
   d. ureters.
6. The mother of a 7-year-old boy brings the child to the clinic to be assessed for bed wetting. This condition is known as:
   a. nocturia.
   b. nocturnal enuresis.
   c. diurnal enuresis.
   d. urinary frequency.
7. The nurse assesses and reports urine output of less than 30 mL an hour as:
   a. anuria.
   b. polyuria.
   c. oliguria.
   d. dysuria.
8. When assessing the color of the patient's urine, the nurse notes the color to be dark amber. This assessment is indicative of:
   a. a large intake of coffee.
   b. a decreased fluid intake.
   c. an increased protein intake.
   d. an infection.
9. A patient complains of frequent and unexpected urine dribbling when she sneezes or laughs. The most appropriate nursing diagnosis for this condition is:
   a. stress incontinence.
   b. functional incontinence.
   c. urge incontinence.
   d. total incontinence.
10. The nurse evaluating a female client's understanding of measures to prevent urinary

tract infections recognizes that the client requires further teaching when which of the following statements is made?

a. "I will avoid taking a bubble bath."
b. "I will void at least every 6 hours."
c. "I will drink eight 8-ounce glasses of water each day."
d. "I will wear cotton underwear instead of nylon."

CHAPTER 48

OXYGENATION

OVERVIEW

This chapter provides an overview of respiration, ventilation, and the importance of adequate oxygenation. It introduces you to vital information and skills that will enable you to maintain a patent airway and to identify actual or potential hazards to optimum oxygenation.

LEARNING OUTCOMES

After completing this chapter, the student will be able to:

- Outline the structure and function of the respiratory system
- Describe the processes of breathing (ventilation) and gas exchange (respiration)
- Explain the role and function of the respiratory system in transporting oxygen and carbon dioxide to and from body tissues
- Identify factors influencing respiratory function
- Identify common manifestations of impaired respiratory function
- Identify and describe nursing measures to promote respiratory function and oxygenation
- Explain the use of therapeutic measures such as artificial airways, medications, oxygen therapy, inhalation therapy, pharyngeal suction, and chest drainage to promote respiratory function
- State outcome criteria for evaluating client responses to measures that promote adequate oxygenation

www.prenhall.com/kozier

Additional resources for this chapter can be found on the Student CD-ROM accompanying this textbook, and on the Companion Website at www.prenhall.com/kozier. Click on Chapter 48 to select the activities for this chapter.

CD-ROM
- Audio Glossary
- NCLEX Review
- Animations
  - Gas Exchange in the Lung
  - Carbon Dioxide Transport
  - Oxygen Transport
  - A & P Review
- Videos

Companion Website
- Additional NCLEX Review
- Case Study: Coping With Emphysema
- Care Plan Activity: Deep Breathing and Coughing
- MediaLink Application:
  - Learning About Lung Disease
- Links to Resources

KEY TOPICS

This study guide chapter reinforces the following terms/topics discussed in the textbook chapter:

- adventitious breath sounds
- apnea
- atelectasis
- Biot's respirations
- bradypnea
- bronchoscopy
- Cheyne-Stokes respirations
- cyanosis
- diffusion
- dyspnea
- emphysema
- erythrocytes
- eupnea
- exhalation
- expectorate
- expiration
- hematocrit
- hemoglobin
- hemothorax
- humidifiers
- hypercapnia
- hypercarbia
- hyperinflation
- hyperoxygenation
- hyperventilation
- hypoventilation
- hypoxemia
- hypoxia
- incentive spirometers
- inhalation
- inspiration
- intrapleural pressure
- intrapulmonary pressure
- Kussmaul's breathing
- laryngoscopy
- lung compliance
- lung recoil
- lung scan
- orthopnea
- oxyhemoglobin
- partial pressure
- percussion
- pneumothorax
- postural drainage
- respiratory membrane
- respiration
- sputum
- stridor
- suctioning
- surfactant
- tachypnea
- tidal volume
- torr
- ventilation
- vibration

LECTURE OUTLINE

I. Physiology of the respiratory system
  A. Structure of the respiratory system
  B. Pulmonary ventilation
  C. Alveolar gas exchange
  D. Transport of oxygen and carbon dioxide
II. Respiratory regulation
III. Factors affecting respiratory function
  A. Age
  B. Environment
  C. Lifestyle
  D. Health status
  E. Medications
  F. Stress
IV. Alterations in respiratory function
  A. Hypoxia
  B. Altered breathing patterns
  C. Obstructed airway
V. Chapter highlights
VI. Review questions
VII. Readings and references
  A. Suggested readings
  B. Related research
  C. References
  D. Selected bibliography

FOCUSED STUDY TIPS

1. Define the following:
   cardiac output
   lung compliance
   partial pressure
   respiration
   surfactant
   tidal volume
   ventilation
2. Ventilation of the lung depends on several factors, such as clear airways. What other factors must be present?
3. Oxygen must be transported from the lungs to the tissues. How does this occur?
4. List the three parts to the process of respiration.
5. Describe intrapleural pressure. What role does it serve?
6. The chart describes the client as "experiencing frequent episodes of hypoxia." What does this mean?
7. You evaluate your client's oxygen saturation by pulse oximetry. The saturation is 85%. What is your first priority?
8. When is it appropriate to suction a client?
9. How long should a suction attempt of the oropharynx or nasopharynx last?
10. When might a chest tube be needed for a client?
11. What type of medication suppresses the cough reflex?
12. What is the difference between oropharyngeal or nasopharyngeal suctioning and endoctracheal suctioning?
13. Identify the body's five cleaning mechanisms that protect the airways.
14. In the healthy individual, adequate ventilation is maintained by frequent changes of position, ambulation, and exercise. Identify four nursing interventions to maintain normal respiratory function in the ill client.
15. Identify at least two nursing goals when caring for a client with a tracheostomy.

CASE STUDY

Linda Jaia is a 42-year-old woman complaining of shortness of breath. Examination reveals the following findings:

BP	*132/85*
P	*128*
RR	*32*
T	*39.5C*
SaO_2	*91% on room air*

Fine crackles audible throughout left lung fields

1. *Identify the abnormal findings.*
2. *The physician orders the following diagnostic studies:*
   Sputum C&S (culture & sensitivity)
   Chest X-ray
   CBC
   Describe how you would carry out each of these orders.
3. *A chest X-ray confirms a diagnosis of pneumonia. The physician orders the following:*

   Deep-breathing exercises q2h
   O_2 at 5 liters per minute via nasal cannula
   Chest PT (chest physiotherapy or percussion, vibration, and postural drainage) q4h while awake
   Pulse oximetry
   Describe the deep-breathing exercises that you will teach Linda.
4. *What would be an appropriate chest physiotherapy schedule for Linda?*
5. *Briefly describe how you would utilize pulse oximetry. What is the normal range of values for this monitor?*
6. *Describe the advantages of supplying oxygen via nasal cannula.*

CARE PLAN CRITICAL THINKING ACTIVITIES

Fill in the appropriate elements of the care plan for this client:
Assessment and Diagnosis
Planning and Implementation
Evaluation

NCLEX TEST QUESTIONS

1. The nurse is assessing the smoking history of a 62-year-old man. The man states that he smoked a pack and a half of cigarettes for 32 years. How many pack years does the nurse document for this patient?
   a. 50 pack years
   b. 34 pack years
   c. 48 pack years
   d. 42 pack years
2. A nurse is preparing a patient for sputum collection. Which of the following actions is not appropriate for this procedure?
   a. The nurse should ask the patient to brush his/her teeth and rinse his/her mouth before the procedure.
   b. The nurse should instruct the patient to avoid deep coughing during the procedure.
   c. The nurse should attempt to collect the sputum first thing in the morning.
   d. The nurse should assess the patient's respiratory status prior to collecting sputum.
3. The nurse is assessing a patient's respiratory status. The patient's breathing is rapid and shallow at a rate of 28 breaths per minute. What is the appropriate term for this patient's respiratory status?
   a. tachypnea
   b. bradypnea
   c. apnea
   d. orthopnea
4. The nurse is preparing to draw blood to measure the hematocrit level of a patient. The patient asks what the test is for. What is the best response to this question?
   a. It measures the oxygen-carrying capacity of the blood.
   b. It will make a determination of the number of circulating erythrocytes in whole blood.
   c. It implies effectiveness of gas exchange in the lungs.
   d. It measures percentage by volume of red blood cells in whole blood.
5. A 6-year-old patient was brought into the emergency room after experiencing a severe crushing injury to the chest. The patient is short of breath and refuses to cough due to pain. What is the best nursing diagnosis for this patient?
   a. Altered peripheral tissue perfusion related to crushing injury as evidenced by refusal to cough
   b. Ineffective breathing pattern related to age as evidenced by medical record
   c. Difficulty breathing related to pain as evidenced by refusal to cough
   d. Ineffective airway clearance related to trauma as evidenced by inability to cough
6. A nurse is caring for a patient with the following nursing diagnosis: Ineffective breathing pattern (hypoventilation) related to acute pain as evidenced by reports of acute pain with breathing. What is an appropriate nursing intervention for this patient?
   a. Teach the patient pursed-lip breathing techniques.
   b. Avoid use of pain medications to ensure optimal respiratory function.
   c. Teach the patient diaphragmatic pursed-lip breathing.
   d. Teach the patient how to avoid splinting her incision when coughing and deep breathing.
7. The nurse caring for clients with respiratory disorders recognizes that the primary regulator of ventilation is:
   a. O_2
   b. CO_2
   c. PO_2
   d. PAO_2
8. The nurse planning care for the patient under acute stress recognizes that oxygenation:
   a. is not adversely affected by the stress.
   b. needs decrease due to lower metabolism.
   c. needs of the body tissues increase.
   d. will improve as the person adapts to stress.

9. The post–abdominal-surgical patient is noted by the nurse to have shallow respirations of 8 per minute and tachycardia. The nurse obtains an order for oxygen administration as the patient is at risk for:
   a. hypoventilation.
   b. hyperventilation.
   c. airway obstruction.
   d. orthopnea.
10. The nurse working with the patient who has chronic obstructive lung disease gives which of the following instructions for oxygen use?
    a. Keep oxygen at 5 to 6 L per nasal cannula.
    b. Turn oxygen up a liter when short of breath.
    c. Leave oxygen at the 1 to 2 L setting.
    d. Turn oxygen up to 10 L when in respiratory distress.
11. A patient with congestive heart failure (CHF) is assessed with episodes of apnea interspersed with periods of rapid, deep breaths and then slow, shallow breaths. The nurse reports this finding to the physician as:
    a. Cheyne-Stokes respirations.
    b. kussmaul respirations.
    c. eupnea.
    d. apnea.

CHAPTER 49

CIRCULATION

OVERVIEW

This chapter focuses on the role of circulation in the maintenance of health and well-being. The major structures and vessels are reviewed along with the role of blood to transport nutrients and remove wastes.

LEARNING OUTCOMES

After completing this chapter, the student will be able to:

- Outline the structure and function of the cardiovascular system
- Identify factors influencing circulatory function
- Identify major risk factors for the development of coronary heart disease
- Discuss the manifestations of cardiovascular disorders
- Identify common responses to alterations in circulatory status
- List signs of alterations in cardiovascular function
- Identify and describe nursing measures to promote circulation
- Describe the critical nature of cardiopulmonary resuscitation

KEY TOPICS

This study guide chapter reinforces the following terms/topics discussed in the textbook chapter:

- afterload
- angiography
- atria
- atrioventricular (AV) node
- atrioventricular (AV) valves
- automaticity
- blood pressure (BP)
- bundle of his
- cardiac output (CO)
- code blue
- contractility
- coronary arteries
- creatine kinase (CK)
- diastole

www.prenhall.com/kozier

Additional resources for this chapter can be found on the Student CD-ROM accompanying this textbook, and on the Companion Website at www.prenhall.com/kozier. Click on Chapter 49 to select the activities for this chapter.

CD-ROM
- Audio Glossary
- NCLEX Review
- Animations
  - Anatomy 3D
  - A & P Review
  - Circulation
  - Normal Heart Hemodynamics
  - Congenital Heart Defects

Companion Website
- Additional NCLEX Review
- Case Study: Client With Diabetes
- Care Plan Activity: Client Experiencing Pain from Walking
- MediaLink Application: Using Heart Savers Website
- Links to Resources

- echocardiogram
- electrocardiogram (ECG)
- endocardium
- epicardium
- heart failure
- hemoglobin
- hypoxia
- ischemia
- myocardial infarction (MI)
- myocardium
- pericardium
- peripheral vascular resistance (PVR)
- preload
- Purkinje fiber
- semilunar valve
- septum
- sinoatrial (SA or sinus) node
- stroke volume (SV)
- systole
- troponin
- ventricle

LECTURE OUTLINE

I. Physiology of the cardiovascular system
  A. The heart
    1. Coronary circulation
    2. Cardiac cycle
    3. Cardiac conduction system
    4. Cardiac output
      a. Heart rate
      b. Preload
      c. Contractility
      d. Afterload
  B. The blood vessels
    1. Arterial circulation
    2. Venous return
  C. Blood
II. Life span considerations
III. Factors affecting cardiovascular function
  A. Risk factors
    1. Non-modifiable
    2. Elevated serum lipids
    3. Hypertension
    4. Cigarette smoking
    5. Diabetes
    6. Obesity
    7. Sedentary lifestyle
  B. Other factors affecting cardiovascular function
    1. Heat and cold
    2. Health status
    3. Stress and coping
    4. Diet
    5. Alcohol
    6. Elevated homocysteine level
IV. Alterations in cardiovascular function
  A. Decreased cardiac output
  B. Impaired tissue perfusion
  C. Blood alterations
V. Chapter highlights
VI. Review questions
VII. Readings and references
  A. Suggested readings
  B. Related research
  C. References
  D. Selected bibliography

FOCUSED STUDY TIPS

1. Define the following:
   afterload
   bundle of his
   diastole
   Purkinje fiber
   systole
   automaticity
   contractility
   ischemia
   preload
2. Describe the structures within the heart.
3. Describe the path blood takes when moving through the heart to the general circulation.
4. How does a person's blood pressure reflect the condition of the heart?
5. What is the primary pacemaker of the heart?
6. How is cardiac output calculated?
7. What is the Frank-Starling Law of the Heart?
8. How are stroke volume and contractility related?
9. Describe the pulmonary circulation.

10. What are the layers of the blood vessels?
11. What is mean arterial pressure? Why is it important?
12. What are the functions of blood?
13. What is the primary cell within the blood?
14. List the normal heart rates for:
    adult
    early childhood
    newborn
15. Which heart disease is caused by a bacterial infection?
16. Which condition is responsible for sudden death and is often referred to as the silent killer?
17. Describe the difference between modifiable and nonmodifiable cardiac risk factors.
18. How does the body respond to a decrease in circulating oxygen?
19. How does stress effect the cardiovascular system?
20. List the signs and symptoms of a myocardial infarction.
21. What is heart failure?
22. List signs and symptoms of atherosclerosis.
23. A 45-year-old male is admitted to the hospital with sudden shortness of breath and hemoptysis. He has a history of deep vein thrombosis caused by frequent airline travel. What condition might this client be experiencing?

CASE STUDY

Arlene Smith, a 55-year-old female, is admitted to the hospital with substernal chest pain, radiating to her left jaw. After administering an electrocardiogram, the physician diagnoses this client as having a myocardial infarction.

1. *Which diagnostic blood test would validate this diagnosis?*
2. *Ms. Smith is having problems with an irregular heart beat. Which types of medications might be prescribed for this client?*
3. *Ms. Smith is prescribed bed rest. What can you do to ensure she doesn't develop pooling of blood in her lower extremities?*
4. *What is the easiest way for you to apply Ms. Smith's antiembolism stockings?*
5. *When should these stockings be removed?*
6. *During routine morning care, Ms. Smith asks you what "Code Blue" means. She states that she keeps hearing that phrase announced over the intercom. What will you tell her?*

CARE PLAN CRITICAL THINKING ACTIVITIES

Fill in the appropriate elements of the care plan for Ms. Smith:
Assessment and Diagnosis
Planning and Implementation
Evaluation

NCLEX TEST QUESTIONS

1. A client with sickle cell disease complains of chronic fatigue and shortness of breath. Upon assessment, the nurse notes skin pallor and hypotension. Based on this assessment data, the nurse should implement measures related to
   a. sickle cell crisis.
   b. anemia.
   c. pulmonary embolism.
   d. hemorrhage.
2. Which of the following measures is contraindicated in a client with cardiac dysfunction?
   a. avoiding pillows under the knees while in bed
   b. legs elevated in bed
   c. leg exercises in bed
   d. frequent position changes in bed
3. The nurse administering digitalis (digoxin) understands that the positive inotropic effects of this drug include:

a. increased contractile strength of the heart.
b. vasodilation.
c. block the sympathetic nervous system action on the heart.
d. decreased oxygen consumption.

4. The correct technique for the nurse to determine the appropriate size anti-embolic thigh-length stockings is to
   a. measure the length of both legs from the heel to the gluteal fold.
   b. measure the circumference of each calf and each thigh at the widest point.
   c. measure the length of both legs from the heel to the gluteal fold and measure the circumference of each calf and each thigh at the widest point.
   d. measure from the heel to the popliteal space and measure the circumference of each calf and each thigh at the widest point.
5. A nursing student learning anatomy and physiology of the heart correctly identifies the heart's outermost layer as the:
   a. epicardium.
   b. pericardium.
   c. endocardium.
   d. myocardium.
6. When evaluating client teaching regarding the heart, the client demonstrates an understanding of heart anatomy when which of the following are identified as the semilunar valves?
   a. pulmonic valve and the aortic valve
   b. tricuspid valve and mitral valve
   c. pulmonic valve and tricuspid valve
   d. aortic valve and mitral valve
7. A client learning about the cardiac cycle correctly identifies systole as:
   a. when the ventricles fill with blood.
   b. adding an additional volume to the ventricles.
   c. the primary pacemaker of the heart.
   d. when the heart ejects (propels) the blood into the pulmonary and systemic circulations.
8. The nursing student demonstrates an understanding of circulation when the student identifies cardiac output as the:
   a. amount of blood pumped by the ventricles in 1 minute.
   b. amount of blood ejected with each contraction.
   c. degree to which muscle fibers in the ventricle are stretched at the end of the relaxation period.
   d. resistance against which the heart must pump to eject the blood into the circulation.
9. A nurse is planning an inservice on arterial circulation. The nurse would not include which of the following as a factor in determining peripheral vascular resistance (PVR)?
   a. mean arterial pressure
   b. viscosity, or thickness, of the blood
   c. blood vessel length
   d. blood vessel diameter
10. The nurse teaching clients about oxygenation and circulation knows that oxygen binding is affected by several factors. Which of the following is not a factor affecting oxygen binding?
    a. serum sodium
    b. PCO_2
    c. pH
    d. temperature

CHAPTER 50

FLUID, ELECTROLYTE, AND ACID-BASE BALANCE

OVERVIEW

This chapter discusses the complex nature of fluid and electrolyte status in health and disease. It emphasizes your role in assessing actual and potential fluid and electrolyte imbalances. You are introduced to a variety of laboratory findings and to the regulation and maintenance of intravenous fluids, nutrition, and blood products.

LEARNING OUTCOMES

After completing this chapter, the student will be able to:

- Discuss the function, distribution, movement, and regulation of fluids and electrolytes in the body
- Describe the regulation of acid-base balance in the body, including the roles of buffers, the lungs, and the kidneys
- Identify factors affecting normal body fluid, electrolyte, and acid-base balance
- Discuss the risk factors for and the causes and effects of fluid, electrolyte, and acid-base imbalances
- Collect assessment data related to the client's fluid, electrolyte, and acid-base balances
- Identify examples of nursing diagnoses, outcomes, and interventions for clients with altered fluid, electrolyte, or acid-base balance
- Teach clients measures to maintain fluid and electrolyte balance
- Implement measures to correct imbalances of fluids and electrolytes or acids and bases such as enteral or parenteral replacements and blood transfusions
- Evaluate the effect of nursing and collaborative interventions on the client's fluid, electrolyte, or acid-base balance

www.prenhall.com/kozier

Additional resources for this chapter can be found on the Student CD-ROM accompanying this textbook, and on the Companion Website at www.prenhall.com/kozier. Click on Chapter 50 to select the activities for this chapter.

CD-ROM

- Audio Glossary
- NCLEX Review
- Animations
  - Membrane Transport
  - Filtration Pressure
  - Fluid Balance
  - Acid-Base Balance
  - Inserting A Central Venous Line

Companion Website

- Additional NCLEX Review
- Case Study: Client with Suspected Electrolyte Imbalance
- Care Plan Activity: Client with Heart Failure
- MediaLink Application: Determining Body Fluid Problems
- Links to Resources

KEY TOPICS

This study guide chapter reinforces the following terms/topics discussed in the textbook chapter:

- acid
- acidosis
- active transport
- agglutinins
- agglutinogens
- alkalosis
- anions
- antibodies
- antigens
- arterial blood gases
- bases
- buffers
- cations
- central venous catheter
- colloid
- colloid osmotic pressure
- compensation
- crystalloids
- dehydration
- diffusion
- drip factor
- edema
- electrolytes
- extracellular fluid (ECF)
- filtration
- filtration pressure
- fluid volume deficit
- fluid volume excess
- hematocrit
- hemolytic transfusion reaction
- homeostasis
- hydrostatic pressure
- hypercalcemia
- hyperchloremia
- hyperkalemia
- hypermagnesemia
- hypernatremia
- hyperphosphatemia
- hypertonic
- hypervolemia
- hypocalcemia
- hypochloremia
- hypokalemia
- hypomagnesemia
- hyponatremia
- hypophosphatemia
- hypotonic
- hypovolemia
- insensible fluid loss
- interstitial fluid
- intracellular fluid (ICF)
- intravascular fluid
- ions
- isotonic
- metabolic acidosis
- metabolic alkalosis
- milliequivalent
- obligatory losses
- osmolality
- osmosis
- osmotic pressure
- overhydration
- peripherally inserted central venous catheter (PICC)
- pH
- pitting edema
- plasma
- renin–angiotensin–aldosterone system
- respiratory acidosis
- respiratory alkalosis
- selectively permeable
- solutes
- solvent
- specific gravity
- third space syndrome
- transcellular fluid
- volume expanders

LECTURE OUTLINE

I. Body fluids and electrolytes
   A. Distribution of body fluids
   B. Composition of body fluids
   C. Movement of body fluids and electrolytes
      1. Osmosis
      2. Diffusion
      3. Filtration
      4. Active transport
   D. Regulating body fluids
      1. Fluid intake
      2. Fluid output
         a. Urine
         b. Insensible losses
         c. Feces
      3. Maintaining homeostasis
         a. Kidneys
         b. Antidiuretic hormone
         c. Renin–angiotensin–aldosterone system
         d. Atrial natriuretic factor
   E. Regulating electrolytes
      1. Sodium (Na^+)
      2. Potassium (K^+)
      3. Calcium (Ca^{++})
      4. Magnesium (Mg^{++})
      5. Chloride (Cl^-)
      6. Phosphate (PO_4^-)
      7. Bicarbonate (HCO_4^-)

II. Acid-base balance
   A. Regulation of acid-base balance
      1. Buffers
      2. Respiratory regulation
      3. Renal regulation

III. Factors affecting body fluid, electrolytes, and acid base balance
   A. Age
   B. Gender and body size
   C. Environmental temperature
   D. Lifestyle

IV. Disturbances in fluid volume, electrolyte, and acid-base balances
   A. Fluid imbalances
      1. Fluid volume deficit
         a. Third space syndrome
      2. Fluid volume excess
         a. Edema
      3. Dehydration
      4. Overhydration
   B. Electrolyte imbalances
      1. Sodium
      2. Potassium
      3. Calcium
      4. Magnesium
      5. Chloride
      6. Phosphate
   C. Acid-base imbalances
      1. Respiratory acidosis
      2. Respiratory alkalosis
      3. Metabolic acidosis
      4. Metabolic alkalosis

V. Chapter highlights

VI. Review questions

VII. Readings and references
   A. Suggested readings
   B. Related research
   C. References
   D. Selected bibliography

FOCUSED STUDY TIPS

1. Define the following:

active transport	calcium
chloride	diffusion
electrolyte	filtration
magnesium	osmosis
phosphate	potassium
sodium	

2. What is a cation?
3. What is an anion?
4. What role does active transport play?
5. List hypotonic solutions.
6. Fluid is an essential body requirement. How much fluid does the average adult who is engaged in moderate activity require per day?
7. Describe dehydration. Which types of clients are more prone to developing this fluid imbalance?
8. What occurs in the body with overhydration?

9. A note on your client's chart states, "Observe for evidence of third spacing." What does this mean?
10. How much does one liter of fluid weigh?
11. What is the Chvostek's sign?
12. What are the four routes of fluid output for a healthy adult?
13. What are the seven major factors that affect fluid and electrolyte balance?
14. How do isotonic imbalances and osmolar imbalances differ?
15. Describe the difference between dependent edema and pitting edema.
16. Identify five ways to assess a client who has or is at risk for developing fluid and electrolyte disturbances.
17. Explain the nurse's responsibilities in IV therapy.
18. What type of IV therapy equipment is used in your facility?
19. Order: Give a bolus of 500 cc of Lactated Ringer's solution over 2 hours followed by 1,000 cc over 8 hours. What is the hourly rate of infusion for the bolus? What is the hourly rate for the continued infusion?
20. Identify your own blood type.
21. Identify three key safety measures to protect the client receiving TPN.
22. Analyze the following ABG results. What is your diagnosis?

    pH 7.26 — PaO_2 80
    $PaCO_2$40 — HCO_3^-18.1
23. Analysis:

    pH 7.32 — $PaO_2$56
    $PaCO_2$64 — HCO_3–33.5
24. Analysis:

    pH 7.48 — PaO_2 60
    $PaCO_2$40 — HCO_3–30
25. Analysis:

    pH 7.5 — $PaO_2$88
    $PaCO_2$27 — HCO_3–22

CASE STUDY

Michael Sporing is a 68-year-old male admitted to the hospital with renal failure and fluid overload. His bicarbonate and potassium levels are elevated. Mr. Sporing's vital signs are as follows: T 100.3 F, P 102 and irregular, R 24 and labored, BP 158/98.

CARE PLAN CRITICAL THINKING ACTIVITIES

Fill in the appropriate elements of the care plan for Mr. Sporing:

Assessment and Diagnosis
Planning and Implementation
Evaluation

NCLEX TEST QUESTIONS

1. A nurse notices that a patient's respiratory rate has increased to 40 breaths per minute. Hyperventilation for an extended period of time can result in:
   a. excess elimination of CO_2.
   b. decrease in CO_2 elimination.
   c. metabolic alkalosis.
   d. retention of water.
2. The nurse caring for a client with ascites due to liver failure knows that the patient is at risk for isotonic dehydration because:
   a. fluid is trapped in the intraperitoneal cavity and is nonfunctional.

b. pressure from the abdominal cavity increases fluid intake.
c. water loss is greater that electrolyte loss.
d. electrolyte losses are greater than fluid losses.

3. In establishing a fluid intake plan for the patient who has just recovered from dehydration, the nurse recognizes that the suggested combined oral fluid intake for the adult is:
   a. 1,800 to 2,500 mL/day.
   b. 1,200 to –1,500 mL/day.
   c. 1,000 to –1,200 mL/day.
   d. 500 to –1,000 mL/day.
4. In the patient with pneumonia, diaphoresis is occurring on and off throughout the day. Which of the following factors will significantly increase the insensible fluid loss in the body?
   a. frequent coughing up of secretions
   b. rise in body temperature and metabolism
   c. loss of appetite and decrease in fluid intake
   d. IV fluids infusing at 50 mL/hr
5. The patient admitted through the emergency department with severe dehydration and diarrhea is also assessed with muscle cramps and tetany. Which of the following electrolyte imbalances is indicative of these symptoms?
   a. hyperkalcmia
   b. hypocalcemia
   c. hypermagnesemia
   d. hypernatremia
6. The patient who is on nasogastric suction and also has a large draining wound is at high risk for which of the following acid-base imbalances?
   a. hyponatremia
   b. hyperkalemia
   c. hypermagnesemia
   d. metabolic acidosis
7. The patient with congestive heart failure (CHF) who is in respiratory acidosis will naturally compensate for this imbalance by which of the following mechanisms?
   a. renal retention of HCO_3
   b. renal excretion of HCO_3
   c. respiratory elimination of CO_2
   d. respiratory retention of CO_2
8. The patient who is undergoing treatment for diabetic ketoacidosis will most likely compensate for this imbalance by:
   a. renal retention of HCO_3.
   b. renal excretion of HCO_3.
   c. respiratory elimination of CO_2.
   d. respiratory retention of CO_2.
9. The nurse can expect to note which of the following laboratory results for a patient with fluid volume excess?
   a. increased urine pH
   b. increased hematocrit level
   c. increased urine specific gravity
   d. decreased urine osmolality
10. The nurse assesses the patient's IV site and notes redness, tenderness, and warmth at the insertion site. Which of the following actions by the nurse is most appropriate?
   a. Discontinue the IV immediately.
   b. Apply warm compresses over the running IV site.
   c. Raise the arm while the IV is infusing.
   d. Document the findings and continue to observe.

Answer Key for NCLEX Test Questions

Chapter 1

1. (c). Nursing process: Implementation; Client Need Category: Safe, Effective Care Environment. a. Ordering medication is outside the scope of nursing practice. b.Suturing wounds on a client is outside the scope of nursing practice. d. Ordering laboratory tests without a physician's order is outside the scope of nursing practice.

2. (b). Nursing process: Implementation; Client Need Category: Safe, Effective Care Environment. a. The nurse is responsible for managing the care given to the client. c. Being accessible to physicians is not a priority. d. Delegation to licensed and unlicensed assistive personnel provides safe and effective nursing care.

3. (a). Nursing process: Evaluation; Client Need Category: Safe, Effective Care Environment. b. Standards of Hospice Care are used to evaluate professional behavior of the nurses in home care. c. Standards of Home Care are used to evaluate professional behavior in home health. d. Standards of Nurse Practitioners are used to evaluate professional behavior of advanced practice nurses.

4. (d). Nursing process: Implementation; Client Need Category: Safe, Effective Care Environment. a. Midwifery is an advanced practice role. b. Administrator is an advanced practice role. c. Clinical nurse specialist is an advanced practice role.

5. (b). Nursing process: Implementation; Client Need Category: Health Promotion and Maintenance. a. Restoring health is a form of secondary intervention. c. Care of the dying is a form of secondary intervention. d. Rehabilitation is a form of tertiary intervention.

6. (c). Nursing process: Implementation; Client Need Category: Physiological Integrity. a. Obtaining diagnostic tests reduces the likelihood the client will develop complications related to an existing condition. b. Assisting clients to recognize alterations in health helps nurses promote health and wellness. d. Rehabilitation restores a client to a state of health.

7. (b). Nursing process: Implementation; Client Need Category: Safe, Effective Care Environment. a. The physician needs to be notified that a client has a living will. c. The physician is the primary person who needs to be notified that a client has a living will. d. The family should be aware that the client has a living will.

8. (c). Nursing process: Implementation; Client Need Category: Safe, Effective Care Environment. a. The role of counselor is the process of helping a client to recognize and cope with stressful psychological or social problems. b. The nurse acts as a change agent when assisting others to make modifications to their own behaviors. d. As a teacher, the nurse helps clients learn about the health and health care procedures they need to perform to restore or maintain health.

9. (d). Nursing process: Implementation; Client Need Category: Safe, Effective Care Environment. a. The role of counselor is the process of helping a client to recognize and cope with stressful psychological or social problems. b. The nurse acts as a change agent when assisting others to make modifications in their own behaviors. c. In a client advocate role, the nurse may represent the client's needs and wishes to other health professionals.

10. (b). Nursing process: Implementation; Client Need Category: Safe, Effective Care Environment. a. The American Medical Association provides standards of clinical practice for physicians. c.The National League for Nursing provides guidelines to schools of nursing. d. The International Council of Nurses provides a network system for nurses worldwide.

Chapter 2

1. (c). Nursing process: Planning; Client Need Category: Safe, Effective Care Environment. a. The nurse needs to conduct a review of literature to become familiar with end-of-life issues. b. The nurse is a client advocate. d. The nurse is the client advocate.

2. (b). Nursing process: Planning; Client Need Category: Safe, Effective Care Environment. a. Nursing research is conducted to improve client care. c. Nursing research is conducted to improve client care. d. Nursing research is conducted to improve client care.

3. (d). Nursing process: Planning; Client Need Category: Safe, Effective Care Environment. a. It is the registered nurse's responsibility to assess the client's condition. b. It is the registered nurse's responsibility to develop the client care plan. c. It is the registered nurse's responsibility to evaluate the effectiveness of the care provided.

4. (a). Nursing process: Planning; Client Need Category: Safe, Effective Care Environment. b. The major emphasis of a doctoral degree is to prepare a researcher. c. One major emphasis of a master's degree is to prepare a nurse educator. d. One major emphasis of a master's degree is to prepare a nurse administrator.

5. (d). Nursing process: Planning; Client Need Category: Safe, Effective Care Environment. a. The major emphasis of a doctoral degree is to prepare a researcher. b. One major emphasis of a master's degree is to prepare a nurse educator. c. One major emphasis of a master's degree is to prepare a nurse administrator.

6. (d). Nursing process: Planning; Client Need Category: Safe, Effective Care Environment. a. The major emphasis of an associate degree is to prepare a bedside nurse. b. The major emphasis of a baccalaureate degree is to prepare a generalist. c. The major emphasis of a licensed vocational nurse is to prepare a technician.

7. (d). Nursing process: Planning; Client Need Category: Safe, Effective Care Environment. a. A program sponsored by the hospital on equipment is considered an inservice. b.Speaking with pharmaceutical representatives is informative but not continuing education. c. Watching videos on fire safety and body mechanics is considered an inservice.

8. (d). Nursing process: Planning; Client Need Category: Safe, Effective Care Environment. a. Longitudinal studies are considered quantitative studies. b. Interviewing subjects is best used in qualitative studies. c. In mixed methods, the researcher uses both quantitative and qualitative methods.

9. (b). Nursing process: Planning; Client Need Category: Safe, Effective Care Environment. a. Longitudinal studies are usually 1 year in length; hospice cares for clients with life expectancies 6 months or less. c. Both surveys and interviews are used in mixed methodology. d. Interviews, not surveys, are used in qualitative studies.

10. (b). Nursing process: Planning; Client Need Category: Safe, Effective Care Environment. a. A client has the right to be informed of alternative behavioral interventions. c. A client has the right to confidentiality regarding his medical history. d. A client has the right to be protected from all risks related to the study.

Chapter 3

1. (d). Nursing process: Planning; Client Need Category: Health Promotion and Maintenance. a. Freud's theory of the unconscious is a theory used in psychology. b. Darwin's theory of evolution is used in biology. c. Einstein's theory of relativity is used in mathematics.

2. (d). Nursing process: Planning; Client Need Category: Psychosocial Integrity. a. Imogene King's theory is based on systems theory and the behavioral sciences. King developed a transactional model between nurse and client. b. Roy's theory focuses on creation spirituality and on the relationship between the client and the environment. c. Dorothea Orem's theory focuses on restoring the client through self-care activities.

3. (a). Nursing Process: Planning; Client Need Category: Psychosocial Integrity. b. In Peplau's identification phase, the client recognizes the problem. c. In Peplau's exploration phase, the nurse helps clients explore solutions to problems. d. In Peplau's resolution phase, the client resolves the problem.

4. (d). Nursing Process: Planning; Client Need Category: Safe, Effective Care Environment. a. Henderson believes that clients need to express their emotions. b. Henderson believes that clients are to remain independent and not dependent on health care providers. c. Henderson believes clients should be autonomous.

5. (d). Nursing Process: Planning; Client Need Category: Psychosocial Integrity. a. Henderson's theory supports that clients have 14 fundamental needs. b. Peplau's theory was developed to assist in therapeutic communication. c. Watson's theory emphasizes human caring.

6. (c). Nursing process: Planning; Client Need Category: Health Promotion and Maintenance. a. Henderson's theory supports the concept that clients have fourteen fundamental needs. b. Rogers' theory emphasizes noncontact therapeutic touch. d.Watson's theory emphasizes human caring.

7. (d). Nursing Process: Planning; Client Need Category: Health Promotion and Maintenance. a. Henderson's theory supports that clients have fourteen fundamental needs. b. Rogers' theory emphasizes noncontact therapeutic touch. c. Watson's theory emphasizes human caring.

8. (d). Nursing Process: Planning; Client Need Category: Health Promotion and Maintenance. a. In Neuman's theory, unrealistic role expectations are examples of interpersonal stressors. b. In Neuman's theory, financial concerns are examples of extrapersonal stressors. c. In Neuman's theory, community resources are examples of extrapersonal stressors.

9. (d). Nursing Process: Planning; Client Need Category: Psychosocial Integrity. a. Roy's theory supports unity between the client and God. b. Watson's theory supports human caring. c. King's theory is based on a transactional model.

10. (c). Nursing Process: Planning; Client Need Category: Health Promotion and Maintenance. a. Roy's theory supports unity between the client and God. b. Watson's theory supports human caring. d. Orem's General Theory Model supports client self-care.

Chapter 4

1. (b). Nursing process: Implementation; Client Need Category: Safe, Effective Care Environment. a. It is the nurse's duty to inform the physician that the client does not understand the procedure. c. It is the nurse's duty to inform the physician that the client does not understand the procedure. d. It is not the family's responsibility to sign the consent form as long as the client is competent to sign the form.

2. (c). Nursing process: Planning; Client Need Category: Safe, Effective Care Environment. a. As long as the 40-year-old is competent to sign the consent form, there is no problem. b. As long as the 60-year-old is competent to sign the consent form, there is no problem. d. Eighteen years old is a legal age to sign a consent form without parents' signatures.

3. (c). Nursing process: Implementation; Client Need Category: Safe, Effective Care Environment. a. Witnessing a signature implies that the client's signature is authentic. b. Witnessing a signature implies that the client gave her consent willingly. d. Witnessing a signature implies that the client's signature is authentic.

4. (c). Nursing process: Implementation; Client Need Category: Safe, Effective Care Environment. a. The informed consent is legally binding if the blind client repeats in her own words what the nurse explained to her. b. The informed consent is legally binding if the blind client repeats in her own words what the nurse explained to her. d. The informed consent is legally binding if the blind client repeats in her own words what the nurse explained to her.

5. (d). Nursing process: Implementation; Client Need Category: Safe, Effective Care Environment. a. It is the nurse's responsibility to answer the call-light or delegate to another licensed person. b. It is the nurse's responsibility to answer the call-light or delegate to another licensed person. c. It is the nurse's responsibility to answer the call-light or delegate to another licensed person.

6. (c). Nursing process: Implementation; Client Need Category: Safe, Effective Care Environment. a. In the educator role, the nurse teaches. b. In the counselor role, the nurse listens and counsels the client. d. In the caregiver role, the nurse administers the medication.

7. (b). Nursing process: Planning; Client Need Category: Safe, Effective Care Environment. a. These are symptoms of drug addiction. c. These are symptoms of drug addiction, not schizophrenia. d. These are symptoms of drug addiction, not depression.

8. (c). Nursing process: Planning; Client Need Category: Safe, Effective Care Environment. a. As long as the client can read the form, she must sign the form willingly. b. As long as the client can read the form, she must sign the form willingly. d. As long as the client can read the form, she must sign the form willingly.

9. (d). Nursing process: Implementation; Client Need Category: Safe, Effective Care Environment. a. Failing to provide discharge instructions is a form of malpractice. b. Failing to provide discharge instructions is a form of malpractice. c. Failing to provide discharge instructions is a form of malpractice.

10. (b). Nursing process: Implementation; Client Need Category: Psychosocial Integrity. a. If the woman would like to have a translator present, it is the nurse's responsibility to provide a translator. c. If the woman would like to have a translator present, it is the nurse's responsibility to provide a translator. d. If the woman would like to have a translator present, it is the nurse's responsibility to provide a translator.

Chapter 5

1. (d). Nursing process: Implementation; Client Need Category: Safe, Effective Care Environment. a. This statement is a belief, not a value. b. This statement is a belief, not a value. c. This statement is an attitude, not a value.

2. (c). Nursing process: Planning; Client Need Category: Safe, Effective Care Environment. a. To get a job is not a professional value. b. Being autonomous is a professional value. d. Being committed to service is a professional value.

3. (b). Nursing process: Analysis; Client Need Category: Psychosocial Integrity. a. To clarify the client's values, the nurse must help the client examine possible consequences of choices. c. To to clarify the client's values, the nurse must help the client examine possible consequences of choices. d. To clarify the client's values, the nurse must help the client examine possible consequences of choices.

4. (b). Nursing process: Implementation; Client Need Category: Safe, Effective Care Environment.

a. Consequences-based theories look to the consequences of an action in judging whether that action is right or wrong. c. Relationships-based theories stress courage, generosity, commitment, and the need to nurture and maintain relationships. d. Caring-based theories are the same as relationships-based theories.

5. (b). Nursing process: Implementation; Client Need Category: Safe, Effective Care Environment. a. Autonomy means independence. c. Beneficence means "doing good." d. Justice refers to fairness.

6. (c). Nursing process: Implementation; Client Need Category: Safe, Effective Care Environment. a. Nurses are governed by the Code of Ethics for Nurses. b. Nurses are governed by the Code of Ethics for Nurses. d. The Patient's Bill of Rights protects the client's rights.

7. (b). Nursing process: Implementation; Client Need Category: Safe, Effective Care Environment. a. To enhance her ethical decisions, a nurse must be familiar with the Nursing Code of Ethics. c. To enhance her ethical decisions, a nurse must be familiar with the Nursing Code of Ethics. d. To enhance her ethical decisions, a nurse must be familiar with the Nursing Code of Ethics.

8. (d). Nursing process: Implementation; Client Need Category: Safe, Effective Care Environment. a. Abortion is an ethical problem for nurses. b. Abortion is an ethical problem for nurses. c. Abortion is an ethical problem for nurses.

9. (c). Nursing process: Implementation; Client Need Category: Safe, Effective Care Environment. a. A nurse must practice justice or fairness in regard to both clients. b. A nurse must practice justice or fairness in regard to both clients. d. A nurse must practice justice or fairness in regard to both clients.

10. (c). Nursing process: Implementation; Client Need Category: Safe, Effective Care Environment. a. Fidelity means to be faithful to agreements and promises. b. Fidelity means to be faithful to agreements and promises. d. Fidelity means to be faithful to agreements and promises.

Chapter 6

1. (b). Nursing Process: Implementation; Category of Client Need: Health Promotion and Maintenance. a. Screening is done to detect early hypertension and refer to physician. c. Screening is done to detect early hypertension. d. Screening is done to detect early hypertension.

2. (a). Nursing Process: Implementation; Category of Client Need: Health Promotion and Maintenance. b. Palliative care provides comfort for the dying. c. Immunization is not a secondary prevention. d. Rehabilitation is a tertiary prevention.

3. (d). Nursing process: Implementation; Category of Client Need: Physiological Integrity. a. Cardiac rehab is health restoration. b. Cardiac rehab is health restoration. c. Cardiac rehab is health restoration.

4. (c). Nursing Process: Implementation; Category of Client Need: Physiological Integrity. a. Outpatient colonoscopy is secondary prevention. b. Outpatient colonoscopy is secondary prevention. d. Outpatient colonoscopy is secondary prevention.

5. (c). Nursing Process: Planning; Category of Client Need:Safe, Effective Care Environment a. Worker safety is the major concern for occupational health nurses. b. Worker safety is the major concern for occupational health nurses. d. Worker safety is the major concern for occupational health nurses.

6. (d). Nursing process: Planning; Category of Client Need: Safe, Effective Care Environment. a. Acute-care hospitals provide services up to 1 month. b. Acute-care hospitals provide services up to 1 month. c. Long-term care facilities provide services for longer than 1 month.

7. (c). Nursing process: Planning; Client Need Category: Safe, Effective Care Environment. a. Extended care provides services up to 120 days. b. Extended care provides services up to 120 days. d. Extended care provides services up to 120 days.

8. (c). Nursing process: Planning; Client Need Category: Safe, Effective Care Environment. a. Psychiatric units provide rehabilitation. b. Psychiatric units provide rehabilitation. d. Psychiatric units provide rehabilitation.

9. (d). Nursing process: Implementation; Client Need Category: Safe, Effective Care Environment. a. Chiropracters are considered to be alternative health care providers. b. Chiropracters are considered to be alternative health care providers. c. Chiropracters are considered to be alternative health care providers.

10. (b). Nursing process: Planning; Client Need Category: Physiological Integrity. a. Occupational therapists provide assistance in the performance of activities of daily living. c. Occupational therapists provide assistance in the performance of activities of daily living. d. Occupational therapists provide assistance in the performance of activities of daily living.

Chapter 7

1. (d). Nursing process: Planning; Client Need Category: Safe, Effective Care Environment. a. Integrated health care is community-based. b. Integrated health care is community-based. c. Integrated health care is community-based.

2. (c). Nursing process: Implementation; Client Need Category: Health Promotion and Maintenance. a. Homeless people have benefited from an increase of advanced practice nurses. b. Homeless people have benefited from an increase of advanced practice nurses. d. Homeless people have benefited from an increase of advanced practice nurses.

3. (b). Nursing process: Implementation; Client Need Category: Health Promotion and Maintenance. a. Community participation is a principle of primary health care. c. Community participation is a principle of primary health care. d. Community participation is a principle of primary health care.

4. (d). Nursing process: Planning; Client Need Category: Safe, Effective Care Environment. a. A parish nurse serves as a personal health counselor. b. A parish nurse serves as a personal health counselor. c. A parish nurse serves as a personal health counselor.

5. (b). Nursing process: Planning; Client Need Category: Safe, Effective Care Environment. a. Effective communication is a key element for collaboration. c. Trusting other members of the health care team is a key element for collaboration. d. Effective communication is a key element for collaboration.

6. (c). Nursing process: Planning; Client Need Category: Safe, Effective Care Environment. a. Discharge planning needs to be initiated upon admission to the hospital. b. Discharge planning needs to be initiated upon admission to the hospital. d. Discharge planning needs to be initiated upon admission to the hospital.

7. (c). Nursing process: Implementation; Client Need Category: Safe, Effective Care Environment. a. To be transferred from one unit to another, the client needs to be discharged from one unit and readmitted to another. b. To be transferred, the client needs to be discharged from one unit and readmitted to another. d. To be transferred, the client needs to be discharged from one unit and readmitted to another.

8. (b). Nursing process: Assessment; Client Need Category: Safe, Effective Care Environment. a. Assessment of environmental features is done on the first home health visit. c. Assessment of environmental features is done on the first home health visit. d. Assessment of environmental features is done on the first home health visit.

9. (d). Nursing process: Planning; Client Need Category: Psychosocial Integrity. a. Plans to ensure that the client's and caregiver's needs are met before discharge are essential. b. Plans to ensure that the client's and caregiver's needs are met before discharge are essential. c. Plans to ensure that the client's and caregiver's needs are met before discharge are essential.

10. (b). Nursing process: Analysis; Client Need Category: Safe, Effective Care Environment. a. Clients receiving care in their homes are at risk for injury. c. Clients receiving care in their homes are at risk for injury. d. Clients receiving care in their homes are at risk for injury.

Chapter 8

1. (c). Nursing process: Planning; Client Need Category: Health Promotion and Maintenance. a. A goal of Healthy People 2010 is to decrease the consumption of medications. b. A goal of Healthy People 2010 is to increase exercise to 20 minutes at least three times a week. d. A goal of Healthy People 2010 is to increase the quality of life as people age.

2. (b). Nursing process: Planning; Client Need Category: Health Promotion and Maintenance. a. Forming a partnership between the individual and community is one way to link individual health and community health. c. A partnership needs to link individual health and community health. d. A partnership needs to link individual health and community health.

3. (d). Nursing process: Implementation; Client Need Category: Health Promotion and Maintenance. a. Cardiac rehab is an example of tertiary prevention. b. Dialysis treatments provide an example of secondary prevention. c. Using a nebulizer to administer treatment for COPD is an example of secondary prevention.

4. (c). Nursing process: Implementation; Client Need Category: Health Promotion and Maintenance. a. An outpatient surgical clinic does not provide health promotion activities for the public. b. Industries provide health promotion to their employees but not to the general public. d. A dental office does not provide health promotion activities for the public.

5. (d). Nursing process: Implementation; Client Need Category: Health Promotion and Maintenance. a. Rationale for a school-health promotion program is to gain knowledge about personal hygiene. b. Rationale for a school-health promotion program is to gain knowledge about personal hygiene. c. Rationale for a school-health promotion program is to gain knowledge about personal hygiene.

6. (b). Nursing process: Assessment; Client Need Category: Health Promotion and Maintenance. a. Perceived benefits of action affect the person's plan to participate in health-promoting behaviors. c. Perceived self-efficacy refers to the conviction that a person can successfully carry out the behavior necessary to achieve a desired outcome. d. Activity-related effect refers to the subjective feelings that occur before, during, and following an activity.

7. (c). Nursing process: Assessment; Client Need Category: Health Promotion and Maintenance. a. A person denies having a problem in the precontemplation stage. b. During the contemplation stage, the person acknowledges having a problem, gathers information, and verbalizes plans to change the behavior in the near future. d. In the action phase, the person integrates newly adopted behavioral patterns.

8. (c). Nursing process: Analysis; Client Need Category: Health Promotion and Maintenance. a. A NANDA wellness diagnosis begins with "readiness for enhanced." b. A NANDA wellness diagnosis begins with "readiness for enhanced." d. A NANDA wellness diagnosis begins with "readiness for enhanced."

9. (c). Nursing process: Planning; Client Need Category: Health Promotion and Maintenance. a. In health promotion care plans, the client develops his or her own plan. b. The client develops his or her own care plan. d. The client develops his or her own care plan.

10. (c). Nursing process: Planning; Client Need Category: Health Promotion and Maintenance. a. An active 18-year-old who does not smoke or drink and plays tennis daily is exhibiting health promotion behavior. b. A 40-year-old who exercises four times a week is exhibiting health promotion behavior. d. A 25-year-old serving his country in the armed services is expected to exercise daily, thus exhibiting health promotion behavior.

Chapter 9

1. (b). Nursing process: Planning; Client Need Category: Physiological Integrity. a. Home health care is being used to avoid hospitalization. c. Home health care provides secondary and tertiary prevention. d. Home health care provides intermittent care in the home.

2. (d). Nursing process: Planning; Client Need Category: Physiological Integrity. a. Consumers prefer home health care over hospitalizations. b. An increase in the aged has influenced the growth of home health care. c. The ability to provide high technologies in the home has prompted third-party reimbursers to favor home health care over hospitalizations.

3. (d). Nursing process: Planning; Client Need Category: Physiological Integrity. a. Individuals and families all benefit from home health care. b. Individuals and families are the major focus of home health care. c. Individuals and families are the major focus of home health care.

4. (a). Nursing process: Planning; Client Need Category: Safe, Effective Care Environment. b. The attending physician must call in an order to evaluate for home health services. c. A physician's order for evaluation must be in place before nurses can go to someone's home. d. A physician's order for evaluation must be in place before nurses can go to someone's home.

5. (d). Nursing process: Planning; Client Need Category: Safe, Effective Care Environment. a. Voluntary or private not-for-profit agencies are supported by donations, endowments, and charities. b. Private, proprietary agencies are for-profit organizations and are governed by either individual owners or national corporations. c. Institution-based agencies operate under a parent organization, such as a hospital, funded by the same sources as the parent.

6. (c). Nursing process: Planning; Client Need Category: Physiological Integrity. a. Durable medical equipment is covered by Medicare. b. Durable medical equipment is covered by Medicare. d. Durable medical equipment is covered by Medicare.

7. (d). Nursing process: Planning; Client Need Category: Safe, Effective Care Environment. a. The home health nurse's role as caregiver is to assess and diagnose the client's actual and potential health problems, plan care, and evaluate the outcomes. b. The home health nurse's role as case manager is to delegate duties to members of the home health team. c. The educative role of the home health nurse focuses on illness care, the prevention of problems, and the promotion of optimal wellness or well-being.

8. (b). Nursing process: Planning; Client Need Category: Safe, Effective Care Environment. a. Make sure medications are identifiable and labeled as to their usage. c. Needles are to be disposed in biohazard red box or empty can and labeled. d. To protect herself, the nurse must avoid taking any personal belongings during these visits and must have a preestablished mechanism to signal for help.

9. (d). Nursing process: Planning; Client Need Category: Psychosocial Integrity. a. Difficulty performing routine tasks for the client is a sign of caregiver overload. b. Feelings of anger and depression are signs of caregiver overload. c. Dramatic change in the home environment's appearance is a sign of caregiver overload.

10. (d). Nursing process: Implementation; Client Need Category: Safe, Effective Care Environment. a. Assessment begins when the nurse contacts the client for an initial home visit and reviews documents, such as informed consents, received from the referral agency. b. Financial papers must be signed during the initial home visit of the assessment phase. c. Assessment of a client's ability to perform self-care is made on the initial home visit.

Chapter 10

1. (c). Nursing process: Assessment; Category of Client Need: Safe, Effective Care Environment. a. Computer software is usually developed outside the hospital system and then sold to hospitals. Many software systems are not developed by nurses. b. Nurses use computers in the hospital system to assess and document a client's health conditions. d. Nurses use computers in the hospital system to assess and document a client's health conditions.

2. (d). Nursing process: Planning; Category of Client Need: Safe, Effective Care Environment. a. A hospital database contains demographic and financial information about a client. b. A computerized telephone log does not contain information about medications a client is taking. c. A hospital chart contains dosage but not side effects of medications a client is taking.

3. (c). Nursing process: Planning; Category of Client Need: Safe, Effective Care Environment. a. A pharmacy database contains information about dosage and side effects of medications. b. A business office file contains financial information about the client. d. A spreadsheet is the most efficient way to develop a staff schedule.

4. (c). Nursing process: Implementation; Category of Client Need: Safe, Effective Care Environment. a.The linkage *edu* indicates an educational institution. b. The linkage *com* indicates community or nonorganizational websites. d. The linkage *org* indicates organizations.

5. (d). Nursing process: Implementation; Category of Client Need: Safe, Effective Care Environment. a. The hospital information system is used by hospital administration. It contains information about the organizational structure and functions within the hospital. b. A computer-based patient record helps nurses enter data at the bedside. c. A management information system is used by hospital administration to contain information about the governing structure of the hospital.

6. (c). Nursing process: Planning; Category of Client Need: Safe, Effective Care Environment; Subcategory: Management of Care. a. An electronic medical record is used to help clients share in knowledge and activities that influence their health. b. A computerized patient record helps nurses enter data at the bedside. d. A spreadsheet is used to help nurses manage client scheduling.

7. (b). Nursing process: Implementation; Category of Client Need: Safe, Effective Care Environment. a. A computerized patient record helps nurses enter data at the bedside. c. Nurse educators use distance learning as a teaching strategy. d. Hospital administrators used data standardization.

8. (d). Nursing process: Planning; Category of Client Need: Safe, Effective Care Environment. a. Case management is used in home health settings. b. Nurse educators use computers to develop research grants. c. Nurses on the units use a computerized patient record to monitor the client.

9. (c). Nursing process: Planning; Category of Client Need: Safe, Effective Care Environment. a. Clients have the right to decide whom and under what circumstances their health information will be disclosed. b. Updating a client's health history is not a breach of confidentiality. d. The client retains the right to decide whom and under what circumstances their health information will be disclosed.

10. (b). Nursing process: Planning; Client Need Category: Safe, Effective Care Environment. a. Nurse educators and nurse administrators use computers to examine trends and resources available. c. Nurses in hospital systems use computers to transmit data to a hospital's main office. d. Nurse administrators use computers to reduce costs by limiting clerical services.

Chapter 11

1. (d). Nursing process: Assessment; Client Need Category: Health Promotion and Maintenance. a. Traditionally, health has been defined in terms of the presence or absence of disease. b. The World Health Organization places health in the context of environment. c. Parson's concept of health has been defined in terms of role and performance.

2. (b). Nursing process: Assessment; Client Need Category: Health Promotion and Maintenance. a. Physical wellness is the ability to carry out daily tasks and to practice positive lifestyle habits. Social wellness is the ability to interact successfully with people and within the environment. c. Social wellness is the ability to interact successfully with people and within the environment. Emotional wellness is the ability to manage stress and to express emotions appropriately. d. Intellectual wellness is the ability to learn and use information effectively for personal, family, and career development. Emotional wellness is the ability to manage stress and to express emotions appropriately.

3. (c). Nursing process: Assessment; Client Need Category: Health Promotion and Maintenance. a. In the clinical model, health is identified by the absence of signs and symptoms of disease or injury. b. In the adaptive model, health is a creative process; disease is a failure in adaptation, or maladaption. d. The agent-host-environment model is used primarily in predicting illness rather than in promoting wellness.

4. (b). Nursing process: Assessment; Client Need Category: Health Promotion and Maintenance. a. In high-level wellness, a person who implements healthy lifestyle behaviors and has the economic resources to support this lifestyle. c. In emergent high-level wellness, a person who has the knowledge to implement healthy lifestyle practices but does not implement adequate self-care practices because of family responsibilities, job demands, or other factors. d. An example of poor health in an unfavorable environment is a young child starving in a drought-stricken country.

5. (d). Nursing process: Assessment; Client Need Category: Health Promotion and Maintenance. a. Getting sunburned is an external variable. b. Working at the local petroleum industry is an external variable. c. Living in poverty is an external variable.

6. (a). Nursing process: Assessment; Client Need Category: Health Promotion and Maintenance. a. Rosenstock's health belief model intended to predict which individuals would or would not use preventive measures. b. Becker added "positive health motivation" to Rosenstock's health belief model. c. Locus of control is a concept from social learning theory that nurses can use to determine whether clients are likely to take action regarding health—that is, whether clients believe their health status is under their own or others' control.

7. (c). Nursing process: Analysis; Client Need Category: Physiological Integrity. a. Acute illness is typically characterized by severe symptoms of relatively short duration. b. Adherence is the extent to which an individual's behavior coincides with medical or health advice. d. Chronic illnesses usually have a slow onset, periods of remission, and periods of exacerbation, the latter being the time when symptoms reappear.

8. (a). Nursing process: Assessment; Client Need Category: Physiological Integrity. b. In Stage 2, the individual accepts the sick role and seeks confirmation from family and friends. c. In Stage 3, sick people seek the advice of a health professional either on their own initiative or at the urging of significant others. d. After accepting the illness and seeking treatment, the client becomes dependent on the professional for help.

9. (b). Nursing process: Assessment; Client Need Category: Health Promotion and Maintenance. a. Ill individuals become dependent on others. c. Ill individuals become less autonomous. d. Ill individuals' self-esteem is lowered.

10. (d). Nursing process: Assessment; Client Need Category: Health Promotion and Maintenance. a. Alternative/complementary therapies influence the health and well-being of elders. b. Forgetfulness influences the health and well-being of elders. c. Dementia influences the health and well-being of elders.

Chapter 12

1. (d). Nursing process: Assessment; Client Need Category: Health Promotion and Maintenance. a. When community is the client, the nurse assesses individuals and community resources, such as environmental problems. b. When community is the client, the nurse assesses individuals and community resources. c. When community is the client, the nurse assesses individuals and community resources.

2. (b). Nursing process: Assessment; Client Need Category: Psychosocial Integrity. a. In assessing holistically, a nurse must explore how a loss affects all aspects of a client's life. c. To assess holistically, a nurse must explore how a loss affects all aspects of a client's life. d. To assess holistically, the nurse must explore how a preschooler with attention deficit hyperactivity disorder affects all aspects of the mother's life.

3. (c). Nursing process: Assessment; Client Need Category: Psychosocial Integrity; Subcategory: Coping and Adaptation. a. In assessing a family, it is important to clarify family interaction patterns. b. In assessing a family, it is important to clarify family interaction patterns. d. In assessing a family, it is important to clarify family interaction patterns.

4. (c). Nursing process: Implementation; Client Need Category: Psychosocial Integrity. a. Receiving information is input. b. Providing information is output. d. Parents placing limits on their teenagers is an example of feedback.

5. (c). Nursing process: Assessment; Client Need Category: Psychosocial Integrity. a. The traditional family unit contains both parents and siblings. b. The extended family unit contains parents, siblings, grandparents, aunts, and uncles. d. A single-parent family contains only one parent as the head of the household.

6. (d). Nursing process: Assessment; Client Need Category: Psychosocial Integrity. a. Social support systems are examples of external resources. b. Religious affiliations are examples of external resources. c. Compassionate Friends Support Group is an example of an external resource.

7. (b). Nursing process: Assessment; Client Need Category: Psychosocial Integrity. a. A child who has annual dental checkups is using healthy behaviors. c. An 80-year-old who walks in the mall three times a week is using healthy behaviors. d. An unwed teenage mother is at high risk for health problems.

8. (c). Nursing process: Assessment; Client Need Category: Psychosocial Integrity. a. Alteration in comfort is an individual nursing diagnosis.
b. Readiness for effective parenting is a wellness nursing diagnosis for an individual, not a family.
d. Readiness for effective communication is a wellness nursing diagnosis for an individual, not a family.

9. (a). Nursing process: Assessment; Client Need Category: Psychosocial Integrity. b. A child exploring the environment is an example of stimulation needs, according to Richard Kalish. c. A college student learning how to hang glide is an example of stimulation needs or the need to explore, according to Richard Kalish. d. An obese woman eating chocolate after a difficult day at work is an example of a nonhealthy way of meeting her needs.

10. (d). Nursing process: Assessment; Client Need Category: Health Promotion and Maintenance. a. To assess an individual, the nurse uses developmental stages. b. To assess an individual's needs, the nurse uses Maslow's Hierarchy of Needs. c. To assess an individual's needs, the nurse uses Kalish's Hierarchy of Needs.

Chapter 13

1. (d). Nursing process: Planning; Client Need Category: Psychosocial Integrity. a. Cultural care nursing is a concept that describes the provision of nursing care across cultural boundaries and takes into account the context in which the client lives and the situations in which the client's health problems arise.
b. A nurse must practice cultural care nursing to care for a Hispanic family. c. A nurse must practice cultural care nursing to care for a Hispanic family.

2. (b). Nursing process: Planning; Client Need Category: Psychosocial Integrity. a. *Culturally competent* implies that within the delivered care the nurse understands and attends to the total context of the client's situation and uses a complex combination of knowledge, attitudes, and skills. c. *Culturally appropriate* implies that the nurse applies the underlying background knowledge that must be possessed to provide a given client with the best possible health care. d. *Culturally sensitive* implies that the nurse possesses some basic knowledge of and constructive activities toward the health traditions observed among the diverse cultural groups found in the practice setting.

3. (c). Nursing process: Planning; Client Need Category: Psychosocial Integrity. a. A subculture is usually composed of people who have a distinct identity and yet are related to a larger cultural group.
b. Diversity refers to the fact or state of being different.
d. The involuntary process of acculturation occurs when people adapt to or borrow traits from another culture, whereas assimilation is the process by which an individual develops a new cultural identity.

4. (d). Nursing process: Assessing; Client Need Category: Psychosocial Integrity. a. Race is the classification of people according to shared biological characteristics, genetic markers, or features.
b. Prejudice is a negative belief or preference that is generalized about a group and that leads to prejudgment. c. Stereotyping is assuming that all members of a culture or ethnic group are alike.

5. (a). Nursing process: Planning; Client Need Category: Psychosocial Integrity. b. An individual living outside the ethnic community of which he was a member is an example of heritage inconsistency.
c. Americanizing an individual's name is an example of heritage inconsistency. d. Denying one's heritage is an example of heritage inconsistency.

6. (c). Nursing process: Planning; Client Need Category: Psychosocial Integrity. a. Thousand-year eggs, from China, represent traditional foods that may be eaten daily to maintain physical health. b.The thunderbird, from the Hopi Nation, may be worn for spiritual protection and good luck. d.Tiger Balm, from Singapore, represents substances that are used in massage therapy as a way of restoring mental health.

7. (b). Nursing process: Assessment; Client Need Category: Psychosocial Integrity. a. Scientific health belief is based on the belief that life and life processes are controlled by physical and biochemical processes that can be manipulated by humans. c. The holistic health belief holds that the forces of nature must be maintained in balance or harmony. d. Folk medicine is defined as those beliefs and practices relating to illness prevention and healing that derive from cultural traditions rather than from modern medicine's scientific base.

8. (b). Nursing process: Planning; Client Need Category: Safe, Effective Care Environment. a. A translator converts written material from one language into another. c. It is best not to use a family member to act as an interpreter. d. An interpreter is an individual who mediates spoken communication between people speaking different languages without adding, omitting, or distorting meaning or editorializing.

9. (c). Nursing process: Implementing; Client Need Category: Safe, Effective Care Environment. a. In some European countries, touching is not appropriate.
b. In some Asian countries, touching can only be done by certain elders. d. In the Hmong culture, continuous direct eye contact is considered rude.

10. (b). Nursing process: Assessment; Client Need Category: Safe, Effective Care Environment. a. The decision to circumcise male infants is often made based on cultural and familial beliefs. c. A potential conflict includes when a Native American woman values her ample body size and may be resistant to weight control. d. An Hispanic or Asian client may be unable to obtain hospice care if the family will not permit the patient to be informed of the diagnosis or prognosis.

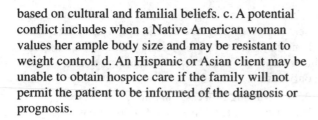

Chapter 14

1. (a). Nursing process: Implementation; Client Need Category: Physiological Integrity. b. Mind–body therapies focus on helping individuals use their minds to heal their own bodies. c. Transpersonal medicine always involves a sender, or healer, and a receiver, or person being healed. d. There is no Era IV. Era I refers to physical medicine, which focuses on the effects of "things" on the body and includes Western medical therapies.

2. (c). Nursing process: Implementation; Client Need Category: Physiological Integrity. a. Postponing surgery may increase the client's anxiety. b. Radiation is not an option to reduce anxiety. d. Biofeedback, a technique that teaches various forms of relaxation by providing a response from physiological processes, is often prescribed by physicians.

3. (d). Nursing process: Planning; Client Need Category: Physiological Integrity. a. Guided imagery is not considered a touch therapy. b. Progressive relaxation therapy is not considered a touch therapy. c. Biofeedback is not considered a touch therapy.

4. (c). Nursing process: Implementation; Client Need Category: Physiological Integrity. a. Meditation does not require the client to massage her feet. b. Progressive relaxation requires the client to tense and then relax successive muscle groups. d. Prayer is similar to meditation but is intended to be communication with God, a saint, or some other being who answers the prayer.

5. (a). Nursing process: Implementation; Client Need Category: Physiological Integrity. b. Meditation is difficult for aging clients to master. c. Hypnosis is not helpful to aging clients. d. Music therapy has a profound healing effect on the entire human body, mind, and spirit.

6. (c). Nursing process: Implementation; Client Need Category: Physiological Integrity. a. Humor and laughter help to relax a client and ease tensions. Nothing is contraindicated in the use of humor and laughter as techniques to reduce stress. b. Hypnosis can be used to control pain, alter body functions, and change lifestyle habits. d. Music therapy helps to relax a client; whereas certain oils used in aromatherapy have a reputation of bringing on menstruation.

7. (d). Nursing process: Implementation; Client Need Category: Physiological Integrity. a. Although prayer is useful to calm a person, it is not effective to stop severe nausea and vomiting. b. Although progressive relaxation is useful to calm a person, it is not effective to stop severe nausea and vomiting. c. Music therapy is useful to calm a person; however, research has shown that acupuncture is effective in relieving postoperative pain and nausea associated with pregnancy and chemotherapy.

8. (a). Nursing process: Planning; Client Need Category: Physiological Integrity. b. Therapeutic touch is a process by which practitioners believe they can transmit energy to a person who is ill or injured to potentiate the healing process. c. Intercessory prayer refers to prayer offered in favor of another. d. Herbs are defined as plants that are valued for their medicinal properties, whereas chiropractic therapy is the most widely accepted and commonly used CAM treatment in the United States.

9. (c). Nursing process: Assessment; Client Need Category: Health Promotion and Maintenance. a. Health care professionals should include questions about herbal teas and supplements when taking a patient's history. b. Health care professionals should include questions about herbal teas and supplements when taking a patient's history. d. Health care professionals should include questions about herbal teas and supplements when taking a patient's history.

10. (c). Nursing process: Planning; Client Need Category: Physiological Integrity. a. Observe for signs of vasoconstriction is a nursing action, not a nursing outcome. b. Progressive relaxation will cause the pupil size to decrease. d. Check vital signs frequently is a nursing order, not a nursing outcome.

Chapter 15

1. (d). Nursing process: Assessment; Client Need Category: Safe, Effective Care Environment. a. When unexpected situations arise, critical thinking enables the nurse to respond quickly. b. When unexpected situations arise, critical thinking enables the nurse to recognize important cues. c. When unexpected situations arise, critical thinking enables the nurse to adapt interventions to meet specific client needs.

2. (b). Nursing process: Planning; Client Need Category: Health Promotion and Maintenance. a. Developing educational strategies is part of critical thinking; implementation of these strategies requires creativity. c. Scientific method is a logical way of problem solving, which requires critical thinking, not necessarily creativity. d. Modified scientific method is a logical way of problem solving, which requires critical thinking, not necessarily creativity.

3. (b). Nursing process: Assessment; Client Need Category: Safe, Effective Care Environment. a. Inductive reasoning is a logical thought process in which generalizations are developed from specific observations. c. Deductive reasoning is a logical thought process in which generalizations are developed from the general to the specific. d. Creativity is part of critical thinking.

4. (b). Nursing process: Assessment; Client Need Category: Physiological Integrity. a. Facts are verified through investigation. c. Judgments are evaluation of facts or information that reflect values or other criteria; they constitute a type of opinion. d. Opinions are beliefs formed over time and include judgments that may fit facts or be in error.

5. (d). Nursing process: Planning; Client Need Category: Psychosocial Integrity. a. To clearly comprehend a client situation, the nurse and the client must agree on the meaning of concept terms. b. To clearly comprehend a client situation, the nurse and the client must agree on the meaning of concept terms. c. To clearly comprehend a client situation, the nurse and the client must agree on the meaning of concept terms.

6. (a). Nursing process: Implementation; Client Need Category: Physiological Integrity. b. Critical thinking requires that individuals think for themselves; critical thinkers are those who are fair-minded, assess all viewpoints with the same standards, and do not base their judgments on personal or group bias or prejudice. c. Intellectual humility means having an awareness of the limits of one's own knowledge. d. With an attitude of courage, one is willing to consider and examine one's own ideas or views.

7. (b). Nursing process: Assessment; Client Need Category: Safe, Effective Care Environment. a. One way to solve problems is trial and error, in which a number of approaches are tried until a solution is found. c. Intuition is the understanding or learning of things without the conscious use of reasoning, whereas research process is a formalized, logical, systematic approach to problem solving. d. The scientific method is useful when the researcher is working in a controlled situation.

8. (d). Nursing process: Planning; Client Need Category: Safe, Effective Care Environment. a. Research process is a formalized, logical, systematic approach to problem solving. b. Scientific method is useful when the researcher is working in a controlled situation. c. Nursing process is a systematic, rational method of planning and providing individualized nursing care.

9. (c). Nursing process: Planning; Client Need Category: Safe, Effective Care Environment. a. An appropriate scheduling decision would be to bathe the client before visiting hours. b.Taking time to feed the client may not be the best priority decision. d. A value decision would be to keep client information confidential.

10. (b). Nursing process: Planning; Client Need Category: Safe, Effective Care Environment. a. Discussing problems in a collegial way creates an environment to support critical thinking. c. Seeking information about a problem can be done in a variety of individual ways. d. Egocentricity and sociocentricity can be an obstacle to critical thinking and problem solving.

Chapter 16

1. (c). Nursing process: Assessment; Category of Client Need: Safe, Effective Care Environment. a. The purpose of the research process is to develop a scientific database. b. The purpose of the nursing process is to identify a client's health status and needs. d. The purpose of the nursing process is to identify a client's health status and needs.

2. (b). Nursing process: Assessment; Client Need Category: Safe, Effective Care Environment. a. Both medical and nursing processes begin with data gathering and analysis. c. Both processes develop a base action—either intervention or treatment. d. Both processes include an evaluative component.

3. (a). Nursing process: Assessment; Client Need Category: Safe, Effective Care Environment. b. The assessment phase involves collecting data, organizing data, validating data, and documenting data. c. The planning phase involves developing long-term goals, short-term goals, and client goals. d. The implementing phase involves implementation of strategies designed to achieve client goal.

4. (d). Nursing process: Planning; Client Need Category: Safe, Effective Care Environment. a. Organizing data is part of the assessment phase. b. Validating data is part of the assessment phase. c. Comparing patterns with norms is part of the diagnosing phase.

5. (b). Nursing process: Diagnosing; Client Need Category: Safe, Effective Care Environment. a. Assessment is done to establish a database of the client's responses to health concerns or illness and the ability to manage. c. Planning is done to develop an individualized care plan that specifies client goals/desired outcomes and related nursing interventions. d. Evaluation is done to determine whether to continue, modify, or terminate the plan of care.

6. (b). Nursing process: Assessment; Client Need Category: Physiological Integrity. a. An initial assessment is performed within a specified time after admission to a health care agency. c. An emergency assessment is done during any physiological or psychological crisis of the client. d. A time elapsed reassessment is done several months after initial assessment.

7. (c). Nursing process: Assessment; Client Need Category: Physiological Integrity. a. The first step in validating assessment data is to compare subjective and objective data to verify the client's statements with your observations. b. The first step in validating assessment data is to compare subjective and objective data to verify the client's statements with your observations. d. The first step in validating assessment data is to compare subjective and objective data to verify the client's statements with your observations.

8. (d) Nursing process: Assessment; Client Need Category: Safe, Effective Care Environment. a. A disadvantage of open-ended questions is that they take more time. b. A disadvantage of open-ended questions is that the client may only be able to give brief answers. c. A disadvantage of open-ended questions is that responses are difficult to document and require skill in recording.

9. (d). Nursing process: Evaluation; Client Need Category: Safe, Effective Care Environment. a. The assessment phase is conducted to establish a database about the client's response to health concerns or illness and the ability to manage. b. The planning phase is conducted to develop an individualized plan that specifies client goals/desired outcomes and related nursing interventions. c. The implementation phase is conducted to assist the client to meet desired goals/outcomes; promote wellness; prevent illness and disease; restore health; and facilitate coping with altered functioning.

10. (b). Nursing process: Assessment; Client Need Category: Safe, Effective Care Environment. a. Open-ended questions convey interest and trust because of the freedom they provide. c. A disadvantage of open-ended questions is that they take more time. d. Open-ended questions provide more information than necessary.

Chapter 17

1. (c). Nursing process: Diagnosis; Client Need Category: Safe, Effective Care Environment. a. The purpose of NANDA is to define a taxonomy of nursing language. b. The purpose of a nursing diagnosis is to identify a client's problem plus etiology. d. A taxonomy is a classification system or set of categories arranged on the basis of a single principle or set of principles.

2. (d). Nursing process: Diagnosis; Client Need Category: Safe, Effective Care Environment. a. The *Physician's Desk Reference* supplies information about medications. b. The Joint Commission for Accreditation of Healthcare Organizations is the accrediting body for institutions. c. The North American Nursing Diagnosis Association is an agency that provides guidelines nurses use to develop care plans.

3. (d). Nursing process: Diagnosis; Client Need Category: Physiological Integrity. a. An actual diagnosis is a client problem that is present at the time of the nursing assessment. b. A risk nursing diagnosis is a clinical judgment that a problem does not exist, but the presence of risk factors indicates that a problem is likely to develop unless a nurse intervenes. c. A wellness diagnosis is a clinical judgment about an individual, family, or community.

4. (a). Nursing process: Implementation; Client Need Category: Physiological Integrity. b. A dependent nursing intervention is when a nurse carries out a physician-prescribed therapy or treatment. c. A collaborative problem requires both medical and nursing interventions. d. Physicians prescribe orders as part of their medical interventions.

5. (a). Nursing diagnosis: Diagnosis; Client Need Category: Health Promotion and Maintenance b. Generating tentative hypotheses is part of the diagnostic process. c. Part of analyzing data is to compare data with standards or norms. d. Identifying health problems is also part of the diagnostic process.

6. (b). Nursing process: Diagnosis, Client Need Category: Safe, Effective Care Environment. a. This is an ambiguous statement. c. This statement implies that the response and probable cause are the same. d. This is an ambiguous statement.

7. (c). Nursing process: Diagnosis; Client Need Category: Safe, Effective Care Environment. a. A wellness diagnosis begins with the diagnostic label "readiness for." b. An actual problem begins with the diagnostic label "alteration of." c. The diagnostic label "impaired" is used with actual problems.

8. (a). Nursing process: Diagnosis; Client Need Category: Health Promotion and Maintenance. b. An actual problem begins with the diagnostic label of "alteration of." c. A collaborative problem begins with the diagnostic label of "potential complication." d. The diagnostic label "impaired" is used with actual problems.

9. (a). Nursing process: Diagnosis; Client Need Category: Safe, Effective Care Environment. b. Actual nursing diagnoses can be documented by using the three-part statement because the signs and symptoms have been identified. c. The three-part statement cannot be used for risk diagnoses because the client does not have signs and symptoms of the diagnosis. d. Wellness diagnoses are one-part statements.

10. (d). Nursing process: Diagnosis; Client Need Category: Health Promotion and Maintenance. a. Actual nursing diagnoses are written by using a three-part statement. b. Wellness diagnoses are written by using one-part statements. c. A potential (or risk) diagnosis is written when the health problem is likely to occur unless the nurse intervenes in a particular way. Potential problem diagnoses are written by using a two-part statement.

Chapter 18

1. (a). Nursing process: Planning; Category of Client Need: Safe, Effective Care Environment. b. The nurse begins planning for client care at the first contact. c. The nurse begins planning for client care at the first contact. d. The nurse begins planning for client care at the first contact.

2. (b). Nursing process: Planning; Category of Client Need: Safe, Effective Care Environment. a. The nurse who performs the admission assessment usually develops the initial comprehensive plan of care. c. Discharge planning is the process of anticipating and planning for needs after discharge. d. Ongoing planning occurs at the beginning of a shift as the nurse plans the care to be given that day.

3. (c). Nursing process: Planning; Category of Client Need: Safe, Effective Care Environment. a. An informal nursing care plan is a strategy for action that exists in the nurse's mind.

b. A formal nursing care plan is a written or computerized guide that organizes information about the client's care. d. An individualized care plan is tailored to meet the unique needs of a specific client–needs that are not addressed by the standardized plan.

4. (d). Nursing process: Planning; Category of Client Need: Safe, Effective Care Environment. a. Protocols are preprinted to indicate the actions commonly required for a particular group of clients. b. Policies are developed to govern the handling of frequently occurring situations. c. Procedures are developed to govern the handling of frequently occurring situations.

5. (c). Nursing process: Planning; Category of Client Need: Safe, Effective Care Environment. a. Student care plans are learning activities as well as a plan of care. b. Computerized care plans are generated by the nurse via computers. Both standardized and individualized care plans can be generated. d. A collaborative care plan describes the sequence of the care that must be given on each day during the projected length of stay for the specific type of condition. It includes medical and other treatments to be performed by other health care providers.

6. (c). Nursing process: Planning; Category of Client Need: Safe, Effective Care Environment. a. Use standardized medical or English symbols and key words rather than complete sentences to communicate ideas. b. Use standardized medical or English symbols and key words rather than complete sentences to communicate ideas. d. Ensure that the plan contains interventions for ongoing assessment of the client.

7. (d). Nursing process: Planning; Category of Client Need: Physiological Integrity. a. Loss of respiratory function is considered a high-priority problem. b. Loss of cardiac function is considered a high-priority problem. c. Decreased hygiene is considered a low-priority problem.

8. (c). Nursing process: Planning; Category of Client Need: Physiological Integrity. a. The criterion of desired performance is missing from the goal statement. b. "Restrict fluids to 1,000 ml of fluid per day" is an example of a nursing order, not a goal statement. d. "Measure hourly urine" is a nursing order, not a goal statement.

9. (b). Nursing process: Planning; Client Need Category: Physiological Integrity. a. This is a medical order, not a nursing order. c. Padding side rails during periods of restlessness and confusion is an appropriate nursing order for a client with a seizure disorder. d. Contacting home health for an evaluation must be ordered by physician, not a nurse.

10. (c). Nursing process: Planning; Client need Category: Physiological Integrity. a. Observation orders include assessments made to determine whether a complication is developing, as well as observation of the client's responses to nursing and other therapies. b. Prevention orders prescribe the care needed to prevent complications or reduce risk factors. d. Health promotion orders are appropriate when the client has no health problems or when the nurse makes a wellness nursing diagnosis.

Chapter 19

1. (c). Nursing process: Implementing; Client Need Category: Psychosocial Integrity. a. Cognitive skills include problem solving, decision making, critical thinking, and creativity. b. Cognitive skills are also referred to as intellectual skills. d. Technical skills are hands-on skills such as manipulating equipment; giving injections and bandaging; moving, lifting, and repositioning clients.

2. (d). Nursing process: Implementing; Client Need Category: Safe, Effective Care Environment. a. The process of implementing includes determining the nurse's need for assistance. b. The process of implementing includes determining the nurse's need for assistance. c. The process of implementing includes determining the nurse's need for assistance.

3. (c). Nursing process: Implementing; Client Need Category: Physiological Integrity. a. Administering Valium is a dependent nursing action. b. Referral to social services is a dependent nursing action. d. Administering lorezopam is a dependent nursing action.

4. (b). Nursing process: Implementing; Client Need Category: Physiological Integrity. a.Withholding the morphine sulfate is the first action to be taken. c. The physician is to be notified of client's respiratory rate. d. The physician is to be notified of client's respiratory rate.

5. (d). Nursing process: Evaluation; Client Need Category: Safe, Effective Care Environment. a. The purpose of collecting data during the evaluation phase is to judge the effectiveness of the nursing care. b. The purpose of collecting data during the evaluation phase is to judge the effectiveness of the nursing care. c. The purpose of collecting data during the evaluation phase is to judge the effectiveness of the nursing care.

6. (b). Nursing process: Evaluation; Client Need Category: Physiological Integrity. a. "Checking intake and output every shift" is a nursing intervention. c. "Urinary output will balance with fluid intake" is the most appropriate outcome statement. d. "Urinary output will balance with fluid intake" is the most appropriate outcome statement.

7. (c). Nursing process: Evaluation; Client Need Category: Physiological Integrity. a. Restlessness of a client with pain is objective data. b. Degree of tissue turgor of a dehydrated client is objective data. d. Relaxed facial muscles as indicators of pain relief are objective data.

8. (b). Nursing process: Evaluation; Client Need Category: Physiological Integrity. a. When writing that the goal was met, the nurse concludes that the client response is the same as the desired outcome. c. This goal was partially met—that is, either (1) a short-term goal was achieved but the long-term goal was not or (2) the desired outcome was only partially attained. d. This goal was partially met—that is, either (1) a short-term goal was achieved but the long-term goal was not or (2) the desired outcome was only partially attained.

9. (d). Nursing process: Evaluation; Client Need Category: Safe, Effective Care Environment. a. "Monitor respiratory status every 4 hours" is a nursing order. b. "Monitor level of consciousness" is a nursing order. c. "Administer prescribed expectorants" is a nursing order.

10. (d). Nursing process: Evaluation; Client Need Category: Safe, Effective Care Environment. a. Quality assurance frequently refers to evaluation of the level of care provided in a health care agency, but it may be limited to the evaluation of the performance of one nurse or more broadly involve the evaluation of the quality of the care of an agency, or even the care within a country. b. Structure evaluation focuses on the setting in which care is given. c. Process evaluation focuses on how the care was given.

Chapter 20

1. (c). Nursing process: Implementing; Client Need Category: Safe, Effective Care Environment. a. Charting is a formal, legal document that provides evidence of a client's care. b. A report is an oral, written, or computer-based communication intended to convey information to others. d. Dialoguing is an oral exchange among team members.

2. (d). Nursing process: Implementing; Client Need Category: Safe, Effective Care Environment. a. To ensure confidentiality of computerized records, never leave a computer terminal unattended. b. To ensure confidentiality of computerized records, follow agency procedures for documenting sensitive material, such as diagnosis of AIDS. c. To ensure confidentiality of computerized records, do not share your personal password with anyone, including other health team members.

3. (a). Nursing process: Evaluation; Client Need Category: Safe, Effective Care Environment. b. Client records are audited for quality assurance purposes. c. The purpose of planning care is to evaluate the effectiveness of the nursing care plan. d. Documentation helps a facility receive reimbursement from the federal government.

4. (c). Nursing process: Planning; Client Need Category: Safe, Effective Care Environment. a. The traditional client record is a source-oriented record, in which each person or department makes notations in a separate section or sections of the client's chart. b. The PIE documentation model groups information into three categories: problems, interventions, and evaluation of nursing care. d. Charting by exception is a documentation system in which only abnormal or significant findings or exceptions to norms are recorded.

5. (d). Nursing process: Planning; Client Need Category: Safe, Effective Care Environment. a. Pertinent information about the client, found on the Kardex, is name, room number, age, religion, marital status, admission date, physician's name, diagnosis, type of surgery and date, and next of kin. b. A flow sheet uses specific assessment criteria in a particular format, such as human needs or functional health patterns. c. The Kardex contains a list of diagnostic procedures ordered, such as X-rays or laboratory tests.

6. (c). Nursing process: Planning; Client Need Category: Safe, Effective Care Environment. a. Restrictions related to activities of daily living are recorded on the discharge summary. b. Behavioral modifications are part of the standard chart for long-term care facilities. d. Safety measures are to be included in the standard chart, not the discharge summaries.

7. (c). Nursing process: Assessment; Client Need Category: Safe, Effective Care Environment. a. Nurses document on nurses' notes. b. A flow sheet uses specific assessment criteria in a particular format, such as human needs or functional health patterns. d. A progress note is a chart entry made by all health professionals involved in a client's care.

8. (d). Nursing process: Implementing; Client Need Category: Safe, Effective Care Environment. a. SOAP is an acronym for subjective data, objective data, assessment, and planning. It is found in the problem-oriented medical record. b. The PIE documentation model consists of a client care assessment flow sheet and progress notes. c. Focus charting is intended to make the client and client concerns and strengths the focus of care.

9. (b). Nursing process: Implementing; Client Need Category: Safe, Effective Care Environment.
a. Accurate notations on the chart consist of facts or observations rather than opinions or interpretations.
c. Accurate notations on the chart consist of facts or observations rather than opinions or interpretations.
d. This is an opinion, not a fact or observation.

10. (c). Nursing process: Implementing; Client Need Category: Safe, Effective Care Environment. a. A change-of-shift report is a report given to all nurses on the next shift in the hospital. b. Tape-recorded reports are given to all nurses on the next shift in the hospital.
d. Nursing rounds are procedures in which two or more nurses visit selected clients at each client's bedside to obtain information that will help plan nursing care, provide clients the opportunity to discuss their care, and evaluate the nursing care the client has received.

Chapter 21

1. (b). Nursing process: Assessment; Client Need Category: Health Promotion and Maintenance.
a. Growth is physical change and increase in size.
c. Development is the capacity and skill of a person to adapt to the environment. Cultural adherence is part of developmental processes. d. Spirituality is part of developmental processes.

2. (c). Nursing process: Implementation; Client Need Category: Health Promotion and Maintenance.
a. Freud recommends making toilet training a positive experience, thereby enhancing the child's feeling of self-control. b. Freud recommends making toilet training a positive experience, thereby enhancing the child's feeling of self-control. d. Freud recommends making toilet training a positive experience, thereby enhancing the child's feeling of self-control.

3. (a). Nursing process: Assessment; Client Need Category: Health Promotion and Maintenance. b. In Erickson's stages of adult development, the young-old (65 to 74 years old) are adapting to retirement. c. In middle-old (75 to 84 years old), the adult may become increasingly dependent on others. d. In old-old (85 and over), adults need assistance with self-care.

4. (d). Nursing process: Planning; Client Need Category: Health Promotion and Maintenance.
a. According to Freud's theory of psychosexual development, the personality develops in five overlapping stages from birth to adulthood. b. Piaget's theory explores the cognitive abilities of children.
c. Peck believes an adult's identity and feelings of worth are highly dependent on that person's work role.

5. (c). Nursing process: Assessment; Client Need Category: Health Promotion and Maintenance.
a. Individuals who want to separate from their parents are in Stage 1, according to Gould. b. Individuals who still feel the need to prove themselves to their parents are in Stage 3. d. Individuals who are interested in social activities with friends and spouse are in Stage 6.

6. (b). Nursing process: Implementation; Client Need Category: Health Promotion and Maintenance.
a. According to Piaget's phases of cognitive development, a 13-year-old uses rational thinking to make decisions. c. According to Piaget's phases of cognitive development, a 13-year-old uses rational thinking to make decisions. d. According to Piaget's phases of cognitive development, a 13-year-old uses rational thinking to make decisions.

7. (a). Nursing process: Assessment; Client Need Category: Health Promotion and Maintenance.
b. *Morals* mean "relating to right and wrong," whereas *morality* refers to the requirements necessary for people to live together in society. c. *Moral behavior* is the way a person perceives those requirements and responds to them. d. *Moral development* is the pattern of change with age in moral behavior.

8. (b). Nursing process: Implementing; Client Need Category: Psychosocial Integrity. a. Kohlberg's theory was developed with males. c. Gilligan developed moral theory after interviewing women who had been abused. d. Piaget's theory is on cognitive development.

9. (a). Nursing process: Assessment; Client Need Category: Psychosocial Integrity; Subcategory: Coping and Adaptation. b. Westerhoff describes faith as a way of being and behaving that evolves from an experienced faith guided by parents and others during a person's infancy and childhood to an owned faith that is internalized in adulthood and serves as a directive for personal action. c. Gilligan is a moral theorist. d. Fowler believes that the development of faith is an interactive process between the person and the environment.

10. (b). Nursing process: Implementation; Client Need Category: Health Promotion and Maintenance. a. Erickson's theory is based on personality development. c. Peck's theory expands Erickson's theory about the older adult. d. Westerhoff is a spiritual theorist.

Chapter 22

1. (b). Nursing process: Assessment; Client Need Category: Health Promotion and Maintenance. a. At about 5 months, the mother first perceives movement by the fetus, and the first fetal heartbeat may be heard. c. At about 5 months, the mother first perceives movement by the fetus. d. At about 5 months, the mother first perceives movement by the fetus.

2. (c). Nursing process: Assessment; Client Need Category: Health Promotion and Maintenance. a. Adequate folic acid is important to prevent neural tube defects. b. Niacin is important; however, folic acid prevents neural tube defects. d. Adequate folic acid is important to prevent neural tube defects.

3. (a). Nursing process: Implementing; Client Need Category: Health Promotion and Maintenance. b. Leafy green vegetables are a folic-rich food. c. Adequate folic acid is important to prevent neural tube defects. d. Adequate folic acid is important to prevent neural tube defects.

4. (c). Nursing process: Implementing; Client Need Category: Health Promotion and Maintenance. a. Significant temperature rises due to illness, hot whirlpool baths, or saunas may result in birth defects. b. Significant temperature rises due to illness, hot whirlpool baths, or saunas may result in birth defects. d. An embryo is particularly vulnerable to damage when radiography is involved.

5. (d). Nursing process: Implementing; Client Need Category: Health Promotion and Maintenance. a. The heads of many newborn babies are misshapen because of the molding of the head that occurs during vaginal deliveries. b. The heads of many newborn babies are misshapen because of the molding of the head that occurs during vaginal deliveries. c. The heads of many newborn babies are misshapen because of the molding of the head that occurs during vaginal deliveries.

6. (b). Nursing process: Assessment; Client Need Category: Health Promotion and Maintenance. a. If the newborn is stillborn, the Apgar score would be 0. c. A normal Apgar score is 10. d. A normal Apgar score is 10.

7. (d). Nursing process: Assessment; Client Need Category: Health Promotion and Maintenance. a. Failure to thrive is a unique syndrome in which an infant falls below the fifth percentile for weight and height on a standard growth chart or is falling in percentiles on a growth chart. b. Colic is acute abdominal pain caused by periodic contractions of the intestines. c. The sudden and unexpected death of an infant may be a case of sudden infant death syndrome.

8. (c). Nursing process: Assessment; Client Need Category: Health Promotion and Maintenance. a. Colic is acute abdominal pain caused by periodic contractions of the intestines. b. Being overweight is the most common nutritional problem among children. d. Smoking is a common health problem in adolescence.

9. (a). Nursing process: Planning; Client Need Category: Health Promotion and Maintenance. b. Providing accurate information about sexual issues is a preventive measure for school age children. c. Using proper equipment when participating in sports is a preventive measure for school-age children. d. Providing opportunities for a variety of organized group activities is a preventive measure for school-age children.

10. (d). Nursing process: Assessment; Client Need Category: Health Promotion and Maintenance. a. This question is part of a developmental assessment guideline for school-age children. b. This question is part of a developmental assessment guideline for school-age children. c.This question is part of a developmental assessment guideline for school-age children.

Chapter 23

1. (a). Nursing process: Assessment; Client Need Category: Health Promotion and Maintenance. b. More young adults have been choosing to remain at home. c. Many young adults who are employed full-time receive only minimum wage and are unable to earn enough money to be totally self-supporting. d. Old-old adults may have to be removed from their homes and live in systems that provide institutional care.

2. (d). Nursing process: Assessment; Client Need Category: Health Promotion and Maintenance. a. Unintentional injuries are the leading cause of death

in the young adult. b. Unintentional injuries are the leading cause of death in the young adult.
c. Unintentional injuries are the leading cause of death in the young adult.

3. (b). Nursing process: Assessment; Client Need Category: Health Promotion and Maintenance.
a. Healthy People 2010 reports that homicide is the leading cause of death for African-Americans.
c. Healthy People 2010 reports that homicide is the leading cause of death for African-Americans.
d. Healthy People 2010 reports that homicide is the leading cause of death for African-Americans.

4. (c). Nursing process: Assessment; Client Need Category: Psychosocial Integrity. a. Middle-aged adults rely on spiritual beliefs to help them deal with illness, death, and tragedy. b. Middle-aged adults rely on spiritual beliefs to help them deal with illness, death, and tragedy. d. Older adults deal with illness, death, and tragedy easier than middle-aged adults.

5. (d). Nursing process: Assessment; Client Need Category: Health Promotion and Maintenance.
a. Motor-vehicle accidents are the most common cause of accidental death in the middle-aged group. b. Motor-vehicle accidents are the most common cause of accidental death in the middle-aged group. c. Motor-vehicle accidents are the most common cause of accidental death in the middle-aged group.

6. (d). Nursing process: Assessment; Client Need Category: Health Promotion and Maintenance. a. Older adults are the fastest-growing group in the United States today. b. Older adults are the fastest-growing group in the United States today. c. Older adults are the fastest-growing group in the United States today.

7. (b). Nursing process: Assessment; Client Need Category: Health Promotion and Maintenance. a. By age 80, all elderly people have some lens opacity that reduces visual acuity and causes glare to be a problem.
c. By age 80, all elderly people have some lens opacity that reduces visual acuity and causes glare to be a problem. d. By the age of 80, all elderly people have some lens opacity that reduces visual acuity and causes glare to be a problem.

8. (c). Nursing process: Implementing; Client Need Category: Psychosocial Integrity. a. According to activity theory, the best way to age is to stay active physically and mentally. b. According to disengagement theory, aging involves mutual withdrawal between the older person and others in the elderly person's environment. d. According to continuity theory, people maintain their values, habits, and behaviors in old age.

9. (c). Nursing process: Planning; Client Need Category: Psychosocial Integrity. a. In a nursing home, personal care assistance may be provided. b. In assisted living, personal care assistance may be provided. d. While the older adult is at day care, the caregiver has a respite from the daily care.

10. (d). Nursing process: Planning; Client Need Category: Health Promotion and Maintenance.
a. Healthy People 2010 reports that falls account for 87 percent of all fractures among adults ages 65 years and older. b. Healthy People 2010 reports that falls account for 87 percent of all fractures among adults ages 65 years and older. c. Healthy People 2010 reports that falls account for 87 percent of all fractures among adults ages 65 years and older.

Chapter 24

1. (b). Nursing process: Assessment; Client Need Category: Psychosocial Integrity. a. Leininger believes that health care personnel should work toward an understanding of care and the values, health beliefs, and lifestyles of different cultures, which will form the basis for providing culture-specific care. c. Miller believes that caring validates the humanness of both the caregiver and the cared for. d. According to Gadow and Noddings, caring may or may not involve action or verbal communication.

2. (c). Nursing process: Implementation; Client Need Category: Psychosocial Integrity. a. Physical comfort needs relate to bodily sensations and the physiologic problems associated with the medical diagnosis.
b. Psychospiritual comfort needs relate to the internal awareness of self, including esteem, self-concept, sexuality, and meaning in one's life. d. Environmental comfort needs relate to the external background of human experience.

3. (c). Nursing process: Assessment; Client Need Category: Physiological Integrity. a. The sender is a person or group who wishes to convey a message to another. b. The receiver, the third component of the communication process, is the listener, who must listen, observe, and attend. d. The second component of the communication process is the message itself—what is actually said or written, the body language that accompanies the words, and how the message is transmitted.

4. (d). Nursing process: Implementation; Client Need Category: Psychosocial Integrity. a. Gestures are culture-specific. b. The Anglo-American gesture meaning "Shoo" or "Go away" means "Come here" or "Come back" in some Asian cultures. c. Understanding gestures is important for culture-specific communication.

5. (b). Nursing process: Implementation; Client Need Category: Psychosocial Integrity. a. Intimate space is touching to 1.5 feet. c. Social space is from 4 to 12 feet in distance. d. Public space is from 12 to 15 feet in distance.

6. (c). Nursing process: Implementation; Client Need Category: Psychosocial Integrity. a. In congruent communication, the verbal and nonverbal aspects of the message match. b. In congruent communication, the verbal and nonverbal aspects of the message match. d. In congruent communication, the verbal and nonverbal aspects of the message match.

7. (b). Nursing process: Planning; Client Need Category: Safe, Effective Care Environment. a. The preinteraction phase is similar to the planning stage before an interview. c. The three stages of the introductory phase are opening the relationship, clarifying the problem, and structuring and formulating the contract. d. It is during the introductory phase that the nurse and client formulate the contract.

8. (b). Nursing process: Planning; Client Need Category: Health Promotion and Maintenance. a. The focus of a task group is the completion of a specific task. c. A self-help group is a small, voluntary organization composed of individuals who share a similar health, social, or daily living problem. d. The major purpose of teaching groups is to impart information to the participants.

9. (c). Nursing process: Analysis; Client Need Category: Psychosocial Integrity. a. Impaired verbal communication may be used as a nursing diagnosis when an individual is unable to receive, process, or transmit information or use symbols to communicate. b. School-age children who wear hearing aids are more likely to experience social isolation than those who do not wear them. d. School-age children who wear hearing aids are more likely to experience social isolation than those who do not wear them.

10. (d). Nursing process: Implementation; Client Need Category: Psychosocial Integrity. a. Stereotyping responses categorize clients and negate their uniqueness as individuals. b. Being defensive prevents the client from expressing true concerns. c. Challenging responses indicates that the nurse is failing to consider the client's feelings, making the client feel it necessary to defend a position.

Chapter 25

1. (b). Nursing process: Planning; Client Need Category: Health Promotion and Maintenance. a. One-to-one teaching is best used for individual clients. c. Teaching a group of school-age children is part of community health education. d. Client education, such as discharge planning, is done on a one-to-one basis.

2. (c). Nursing process: Planning; Client Need Category: Health Promotion and Maintenance. a. Andragogy is the art and science of teaching adults. b. Pedagogy is the art and science of teaching children. d. Geragogy is the term used to describe the process involved in stimulating and helping elderly persons to learn.

3. (b). Nursing process: Planning; Client Need Category: Health Promotion and Maintenance. a. Behavioral theorists observe responses and then manipulate the environment to bring about the intended change. c. The major attributes of humanism are its focus on the feelings and attitudes of learners, on the importance of the individual in identifying learning needs and in taking responsibility for them, and on the self-motivation of the learners to work toward self-reliance and independence. d. Feminism theory focuses on women's ways of knowing.

4. (a). Nursing process: Implementation; Client Need Category: Health Promotion and Maintenance. b. Adolescents need to know the consequences of an untreated sexually transmitted disease before they see the need for treatment, thus motivation to learn is the desire to learn. c. When the learner is actively involved in the process of learning, learning becomes more meaningful. d. Motivation to learn is important in helping adolescents learn.

5. (c). Nursing process: Planning; Client Need Category: Health Promotion and Maintenance. a. Being emotionally ready to learn helps to facilitate learning. b. Having an adequate family support system helps to facilitate learning. d. A person with low literacy skills will have a limited vocabulary and difficulty comprehending oral and written information.

6. (c). Nursing process: Analysis; Client Need Category: Health Promotion and Maintenance. a. If deficient knowledge is used as the primary concern, the nurse needs to provide the information that will change the client's behavior rather than focus on the behaviors caused by the client's lack of knowledge. b. The diagnostic statement "Risk for" can be used for deficient knowledge. d. When using the diagnostic statement "Health-seeking behavior," the client is seeking health information; the client may or may not have an altered response or dysfunction at the time but may be seeking information to improve health or prevent illness.

7. (d). Nursing process: Planning; Client Need Category: Health Promotion and Maintenance. a. State the client (learner) behavior or performance, not nurse behavior. b. Reflect an observable, measurable activity such as "Selects low-fat foods from a menu," not "Understands low-fat." c. Reflect an observable, measurable activity.

8. (b). Nursing process: Planning; Client Need Category: Health Promotion and Maintenance. a. Hands-on practice is the best method in teaching adolescents. c. Avoid handouts with many pages and a classroom lecture format with a large group. d. Hands-on practice is the best method when teaching adolescents.

9. (c). Nursing process: Planning; Client Need Category: Health Promotion and Maintenance. a. Avoid handouts with many pages and avoid classroom lecture format with a large group. b. Avoid handouts. d. Videos may be too high level for someone with low literacy skills.

10. (c). Nursing process: Planning; Client Need Category: Health Promotion and Maintenance. a. Using coloring books with children helps prepare them for treatments, surgery, or hospitalization. b. Using coloring books with children helps prepare them for treatments, surgery, or hospitalization. d. Using coloring books with children helps prepare them for treatments, surgery, or hospitalization.

Chapter 26

1. (d). Nursing Process: Evaluation; Client Need Category: Safe, Effective Care Environment. a. The word *adherence* should be substituted for *compliant* in the documentation. b. The word *adherence* should be substituted for *compliant* in the documentation. c. The word *adherence* should be substituted for *compliant* in the documentation.

2. (a). Nursing Process: Implementation; Client Need Category: Safe, Effective Care Environment. b. The manager in this situation needs to take the role of figurehead. c. The manager in this situation needs to take the role of figurehead. d. There is no such identified role in the text.

3. (c). Nursing Process: Evaluation; Client Need Category: Safe, Effective Care Environment. a. Autocratic managers make all of the decisions for the group with or without the group's input. This behavior will not contribute to a positive work environment. b. In this style, the manager allows operations and personnel to develop on their own, which leads to undefined purpose and goals for the group. d. Shared governance is a sharing of people in the formation of organizational policy. Total quality management is an example of shared governance.

4. (b). Nursing Process: Implementation; Client Need Category: Safe, Effective Care Environment. One of the greatest responsibilities of managers is their accountability for human, fiscal, and material resources. a. When controlling, the manager ensures that plans are carried out, evaluates outcomes, and evaluates staff. c. Organizing involves determining responsibilities, communicating expectations, and establishing the chain of command for authority and communication. d. Directing is the process of getting the organization's work accomplished.

5. (a). Nursing Process: Assessment; Client Need Category: Safe, Effective Care Environment. The autocratic leader (also known as authoritarian or directive) makes decisions for the group and believes that individuals are externally motivated and incapable of independent decision making. b. The democratic leader (also known as participative or consultative) encourages group discussion and decision making. c. The laissez-faire leader (also known as nondirective, permissive, or ultraliberal) presupposes the group is internally motivated and recognizes the group's need for autonomy and self-regulation. The leader assumes a hands-off approach. d. The bureaucratic leader presumes the group is externally motivated. However, the bureaucrat doesn't trust self or others to make decisions and relies instead on the organization's rules to direct the group's work efforts.

6. (c). Nursing Process: Assessment; Client Need Category: Safe, Effective Care Environment. The laissez-faire leader (also known as nondirective, permissive, or ultraliberal) presupposes the group is internally motivated and recognizes the group's need for autonomy and self-regulation. The leader assumes a hands-off approach. a. The autocratic leader (also known as authoritarian or directive) makes decisions for the group and believes that individuals are externally motivated and incapable of independent decision making. b. The democratic leader (also known as participative or consultative) encourages group discussion and decision making. d. The bureaucratic leader presumes the group is externally motivated. However, the bureaucrat does not trust self or others to make decisions and relies instead on the organization's rules to direct the group's work efforts.

7. (a). Nursing Process: Assessment; Client Need Category: Safe, Effective Care Environment. First-level managers are responsible for managing the work of nonmanagerial personnel and the day-to-day activities of a specific work group or groups. b. Middle-level managers supervise a number of first-level managers and are responsible for the activities in the departments they supervise. c. Upper-level managers are organizational executives who are primarily responsible for establishing goals and developing strategic plans. d. All managers are considered organizational managers, and this term is not used to differentiate the levels of management.

8. (b). Nursing Process: Assessment; Client Need Category: Safe, Effective Care Environment. Coercive power is based on the fear of retribution or withholding of rewards. a. Reward power is based on the incentives the leader can offer the followers for their cooperation.

c. Legitimate power is related to the authority associated with a specific person or role. d. Referent power is associated with the admiration and respect for the leader because of the leader's charisma and success.

9. (d). Nursing Process: Assessment; Client Need Category: Safe, Effective Care Environment. Planned change is an intended, purposive attempt by an individual, group, organization, or larger social system to influence its own status quo or that of another organism or a situation. a. Natural change is considered an unplanned change and occurs without any control by a person or group. b. Situational change is also referred to as natural change and is an intended, purposive attempt by an individual, group, organization, or larger social system to influence its own status quo or that of another organism or a situation. c. Overt change is a change of which a person is aware.

10. (c). Nursing Process: Assessment; Client Need Category: Safe, Effective Care Environment. Delegation is the transference of responsibility and authority for the performance of an activity to a competent individual. The delegator retains accountability for the outcome. a. Change is the process of making something different from what it was. b. Directing is the process of getting the organization's work accomplished. d. Accountability is the ability and willingness to assume responsibility for one's actions and to accept the consequences of one's behavior.

Chapter 27

1. (b). Nursing Process: Assessment; Client Need Category: Health Promotion and Maintenance. The rectal thermometer should be held in place for 3 minutes for the adult. a. One minute is not long enough for an accurate temperature measurement. c. Four minutes are not necessary. d. Five minutes are not necessary.

2. (b). Nursing Process: Assessment; Client Need Category: Health Promotion and Maintenance. Normal respirations are 12 to 20 per minute. Abnormally slow breathing is referred to as *bradypnea.* a. *Eupnea* refers to normal respirations. c. *Tachypnea* refers to rapid respirations marked by quick, shallow breaths. d. *Dyspnea* describes difficult and labored breathing.

3. (a). Nursing Process: Assessment; Client Need Category: Health Promotion and Maintenance. Normally, the apical impulse is at or just medial to the midclavicular line at the fifth intercostal space. b. Normally, the apical impulse is at or just medial to the midclavicular line at the fifth intercostal space. c. Normally, the apical impulse is at or just medial to the midclavicular line at the fifth intercostal space. d. Normally, the apical impulse is at or just medial to the midclavicular line at the fifth intercostal space.

4. (d). Nursing Process: Assessment; Client Need Category: Health Promotion and Maintenance. Phase V of Korotkoff's sounds is the pressure level when the last sound is heard. This is followed by a period of silence. The pressure at which the last sound is heard is the diastolic blood pressure in adults. a. Phase II is the period during deflation when the sounds have a muffled, whooshing, or swishing quality. b. Phase III is the period during which the blood flows freely through an increasingly open artery and the sounds become crisper and more intense. c. Phase IV is the time when the sounds become muffled and have a soft, blowing quality.

5. (c). Nursing Process: Evaluation; Client Need Category: Health Promotion and Maintenance. As age increases, the pulse rate gradually decreases. b. This is correct. c. This is correct. d. This is correct.

6. (d). Nursing Process: Assessment; Client Need Category: Physiological Integrity. a. The body responds to cooling by vasoconstriction by the shunting of blood from the extremities to the vital core organs. The observable sign of blood shunting is the blanching of peripheral nail beds; nail beds become pale or bluish in color. b. The body responds to cooling by vasoconstriction by the shunting of blood from the extremities to the vital core organs. The observable sign of blood shunting is the blanching of peripheral nail beds; nail beds become pale or bluish in color. c. The body responds to cooling by vasoconstriction by the shunting of blood from the extremities to the vital core organs. The observable sign of blood shunting is the blanching of peripheral nail beds; nail beds become pale or bluish in color.

7. (c). Nursing Process: Planning; Client Need Category: Physiological Integrity. a. Shivering causes the production of additional body heat. b. Shivering causes the production of additional body heat. d. Shivering causes the production of additional body heat.

8. (a). Nursing Process: Assessment; Client Need Category: Safe, Effective Care Environment. b. Oral temperatures require that the patient be alert, able to follow directions, and cooperative. The oral route is inappropriate for very young children and patients who are confused, are comatose, or are being observed for seizures. c. Oral temperatures require that the patient be alert, able to follow directions, and cooperative. The oral route is inappropriate for very young children and patients who are confused, are comatose, or are being observed for seizures. d. Oral temperatures require that the patient be alert, able to follow directions, and cooperative. The oral route is inappropriate for very young children and patients who are confused, are comatose, or are being observed for seizures.

9. (c). Nursing Process: Implementation; Client Need Category: Safe, Effective Care Environment. a. Oral temperature measurement should not be done on very young children. b. Because of the risk of rectal perforation, the rectal route is avoided with neonates. d. This statement is not accurate.

10. (a). Nursing Process: Assessment; Client Need Category: Physiological Integrity. b. When lung pressure decreases, the pressure in the lung becomes lower than the atmospheric pressure and air flows from the higher pressure to the lower one. c. When lung pressure decreases, the pressure in the lung becomes lower than the atmospheric pressure and air flows from the higher pressure to the lower one. d. When lung pressure decreases, the pressure in the lung becomes lower than the atmospheric pressure and air flows from the higher pressure to the lower one.

11. (d). Nursing Process: Assessment; Client Need Category: Physiological Integrity. a. Fever, which reflects an increased rate of metabolism, increases respiratory rate by about four breaths per minute for every 1F of temperature elevation. b. Fever, which reflects an increased rate of metabolism, increases respiratory rate by about four breaths per minute for every 1F of temperature elevation. c. Fever, which reflects an increased rate of metabolism, increases respiratory rate by about four breaths per minute for every 1F of temperature elevation.

12. (b). Nursing Process: Assessment; Client Need Category: Physiological Integrity. a. Orthopnea is the inability to breathe adequately while lying down. c. Orthopnea is the inability to breathe adequately while lying down. d. Orthopnea is the inability to breathe adequately while lying down.

13. (b). Nursing Process: Assessment; Client Need Category: Physiological Integrity. a. Doppler ultrasound stethoscopes are used when peripheral pulses are not palpable. c. Doppler ultrasound stethoscopes are used when peripheral pulses are not palpable. d. Doppler ultrasound stethoscopes are used when peripheral pulses are not palpable.

14. (d). Nursing Process: Assessment; Client Need Category: Physiological Integrity. a. A pulse volume documented as 1+ means the pulse is thready, weak, and easily obliterated. b. A pulse volume documented as 1+ means the pulse is thready, weak, and easily obliterated. c. A pulse volume documented as 1+ means the pulse is thready, weak, and easily obliterated.

Chapter 28

1. (c). Nursing Process: Implementation; Client Need Category: Psychosocial Integrity. a. Patients are sometimes reluctant or uncomfortable about answering personal questions. The nurse should assure the patient that the information is confidential and tell her why the questions are asked. b. Patients are sometimes reluctant or uncomfortable about answering personal questions. The nurse should assure the patient that the information is confidential and tell her why the questions are asked. d. Patients are sometimes reluctant or uncomfortable about answering personal questions. The nurse should assure the patient that the information is confidential and tell her why the questions are asked.

2. (d). Nursing Process: Implementation; Client Need Category: Psychosocial Integrity. a. This technique is used to bring the patient back to the point at which the conversation wandered. b. This technique provides feedback to validate or deny an observation. c. This technique is used to obtain very specific information.

3. (c). Nursing Process: Assessment; Client Need Category: Psychosocial Integrity. a. The first element of a health history is the reason for seeking health care. The primary concern provides the nurse with the aspect of a patient's condition or problem with which the patient is most concerned. b. The first element of a health history is the reason for seeking health care. The primary concern provides the nurse with the aspect of a patient's condition or problem with which the patient is most concerned. d. The first element of a health history is the reason for seeking health care. The primary concern provides the nurse with the aspect of a patient's condition or problem with which the patient is most concerned.

4. (d). Nursing Process: Implementation; Client Need Category: Physiological Integrity. a. The lithotomy position is the appropriate position for examining a patient's pelvis and vagina. b. The lithotomy position is the appropriate position for examining a patient's pelvis and vagina. c. The lithotomy position is the appropriate position for examining a patient's pelvis and vagina.

5. (a). Nursing Process: Assessment; Client Need Category: Health Promotion and Maintenance. Perform light palpation first to detect areas of tenderness and/or muscle guarding. b. In some practice settings, palpation is limited to light abdominal palpation to assess tenderness. c. Percussion of each of the four quadrants is performed to determine the amount of tympany and dullness. d. Palpation above the pubic symphysis is performed to assess for bladder distention.

6. (a). Nursing Process: Assessment; Client Need Category: Health Promotion and Maintenance. A fissure, seen in athlete's foot, is a linear crack that extends into the dermis. b. An erosion is a moist, shallow depression caused by wearing away of the epidermis. c. An excoriation is a linear or hollowed-out crusted area exposing dermis. d. An ulcer is a deep, irregularly shaped area of skin loss that extends into the dermis or below.

7. (c). Nursing Process: Assessment; Client Need Category: Health Promotion and Maintenance. Inflammation of the oral mucosa is referred to as *stomatitis.* a. Gingivitis is characterized by red, swollen, bleeding gum lines. b. Glossitis describes inflammation of the tongue. d. Parotitis describes inflammation of the parotid salivary gland.

8. (a). Nursing Process: Assessment; Client Need Category: Physiological Integrity. The nurse observes the time elapsed until return of original color and vein filling. Original color normally returns in 10 seconds, veins fill in about 15 seconds. b. This is incorrect. c. This is incorrect. d. This is incorrect.

9. (b). Nursing Process: Assessment; Client Need Category: Health Promotion and Maintenance. A palpable liver below the costal margin indicates an enlarged liver; the findings should be reported to the primary health care provider. a. The finding is abnormal. c. This is not correct. d. This is not correct.

10. (c). Nursing Process: Assessment; Client Need Category: Health Promotion and Maintenance. Motor or expressive aphasia involves loss of the power to express oneself by writing, making signs, or speaking. a. Sensory aphasia is the loss of the ability to comprehend written or spoken words. b. Auditory aphasia is the loss of ability to understand the symbolic content associated with sounds. d. Visual aphasia is the loss of ability to understand printed or written figures.

Chapter 29

1. (b). Nursing Process: Assessment; Client Need Category: Safe, Effective Care Environment. a. Nosocomial infections are classified as infections that are associated with the delivery of health care services in a health care facility. a. Not all nosocomial infections are iatrogenic (due to any aspect of medical therapy), nor are all nosocomial infections preventable. c. Not all nosocomial infections are iatrogenic (due to any aspect of medical therapy), nor are all nosocomial infections preventable. d. Not all nosocomial infections are iatrogenic (due to any aspect of medical therapy), nor are all nosocomial infections preventable.

2. (b). Nursing Process: Implementation; Client Need Category: Safe, Effective Care Environment. Handwashing is considered to be one of the most effective infection control measures and is the single most important means of preventing the spread of infection. a. Wearing disposable gloves when in contact with potentially infectious organisms is an effective measure of preventing the spread of infection; however, handwashing is the most important means of preventing the spread of infection. c. Avoiding contact with persons with known infections is not feasible. d. Wearing a mask is helpful to protect against airborne organisms; however, handwashing is the most important means of preventing the spread of infection.

3. (b). Nursing Process: Implementation; Client Need Category: Safe, Effective Care Environment. Droplet precautions are used for clients known or suspected to have serious illnesses transmitted by particle droplets larger than 5 microns. a. Airborne precautions are used for clients known or suspected to have serious illnesses transmitted by airborne droplet nuclei smaller than 5 microns. c. Vehicle route generally indicates infection from a vector, such as a tick. d. Direct precautions are used for clients known or suspected to have serious illnesses easily transmitted by direct client contact or by contact with items in the client's environment.

4. (c). Nursing Process: Planning; Client Need Category: Safe, Effective Care Environment. Gender is not a factor in supporting defenses of a susceptible host. a. Maintaining the intactness of the skin and mucous membranes retains one barrier against microorganisms entering the body. b. A balanced diet enhances the health of all body tissues, helps keep the skin intact, and promotes the skin's ability to repel microorganisms. d. Adequate rest and sleep are essential to health and to renewing energy.

5. (c). Nursing Process: Implementation; Client Need Category: Safe, Effective Care Environment. a. Touching the sterile drape has not contaminated the tip of the catheter. b. Touching the sterile drape has not contaminated the tip of the catheter. d. Touching the sterile drape has not contaminated the tip of the catheter.

6. (d). Nursing Process: Assessment; Client Need Category: Safe, Effective Care Environment. a. The nurse should check with the physician because the patient has a single lumen tube that generally requires intermittent suction, not continuous suction. b. The nurse should check with the physician because the patient has a single lumen tube that generally requires intermittent suction, not continuous suction. c. The nurse should check with the physician because the patient has a single lumen tube that generally requires intermittent suction, not continuous suction.

7. (b). Nursing Process: Planning; Client Need Category: Health Promotion and Maintenance. a. Health education is a major focus of preventive care. c. Health education is a major focus of preventive care. The goal of health education is to foster health-promoting and health-protective behaviors. d. Health education is a major focus of preventive care. The goal of health education is to foster health-promoting and health-protective behaviors.

8. (a). Nursing Process: Analysis; Client Need Category: Physiological Integrity. The client is at risk of being invaded by an opportunistic or pathogenic microorganism from endogenous or exogenous sources due to the broken skin. Inadequate primary defenses include broken skin, traumatized tissue, decreased ciliary action, stasis of body fluids, and so on. b. The data do not support a diagnosis of impaired physical mobility. c. Though the client may be anxious about the impaired skin integrity, it is not the priority. d. Inadequate secondary defenses include leucopenia, immunosuppression, decreased hemoglobin, suppressed inflammatory response, and others.

9. (b). Nursing Process: Implementation; Client Need Category; Safe, Effective Care Environment. The 1 inch (2.5 cm) around the edge of the sterile field is considered contaminated. a. The 1 inch (2.5 cm) around the edge of the sterile field is considered contaminated. c. The 1 inch (2.5 cm) around the edge of the sterile field is considered contaminated. d. The 1 inch (2.5 cm) around the edge of the sterile field is considered contaminated.

10. (d). Nursing Process: Implementation; Client Need Category: Safe, Effective Care Environment. Although transporting clients with infections outside their own rooms is avoided unless absolutely necessary, diagnostic testing and treatments should not be delayed. a. Securely covering a draining wound is an appropriate precaution. b. Placing a surgical mask on a client with an airborne infection is an appropriate precaution. c. Notifying personnel at the receiving area of any infection risk is an appropriate precaution.

Chapter 30

1. (b). Nursing Process: Planning; Client Need Category: Health Promotion and Maintenance. a. Health education is a major focus of preventive care. c. Health education is a major focus of preventive care. The goal of health education is to foster health-promoting and health-protective behaviors. d. Health education is a major focus of preventive care. The goal of health education is to foster health-promoting and health-protective behaviors.

2. (d). Nursing Process: Planning; Client Need Category: Safe, Effective Care Environment. Tricycle safety should be included in accident prevention programs for parents of toddlers since the newborn and infant have not reached that developmental stage yet. a. Emphasis should be on common accidents during infancy, which include burns, suffocation or choking, automobile accidents, falls, and poisoning. b. Emphasis should be on common accidents during infancy, which include burns, suffocation or choking, automobile accidents, falls, and poisoning. c. Emphasis should be on common accidents during infancy, which include burns, suffocation or choking, automobile accidents, falls, and poisoning.

3. (c). Nursing Process: Evaluation; Client Need Category: Safe, Effective Care Environment. Teaching children to cross the street safely and to obey traffic signals is appropriate for the preschooler, not the toddler. a. Toddlers should be taught to swim to avoid drowning. b. Obtaining a low bed when the child begins to climb is an appropriate safety measure for the toddler. d. Teaching not to run or ride a tricycle into the street is appropriate for the toddler.

4. (a). Nursing Process: Planning; Client Need Category: Safe, Effective Care Environment. Teaching preschoolers to avoid hazards such as busy streets, swimming pools, and other potentially dangerous areas is appropriate. b. Teaching about fireworks, gunpowder, and firearms is appropriate for the school-age child. c. Teaching about the effects of drugs and alcohol is appropriate for the school-age child. d. Teaching the use of light or reflective clothing when walking or cycling at night is appropriate for the school-age child.

5. (c). Nursing Process: Planning; Client Need Category: Safe, Effective Care Environment. School-age children should be taught appropriate safety measures for contact sports and activities in which children aim at a target. a. Toddlers should not be engaged in contact sports. b. Preschoolers should not be engaged in contact sports. d. Adolescents require further emphasis on sport safety; however, this teaching should begin with the school-age child.

6. (d). Nursing Process: Planning; Client Need Category: Psychosocial Integrity. Laceration of radial arteries with a sharp object is not included in the most common methods of adolescent suicide. a. Suicide by firearms, drugs, and automobile exhaust gases are the most common methods for adolescents. b. Suicide by firearms, drugs, and automobile exhaust gases are the most common methods for adolescents. c. Suicide by firearms, drugs, and automobile exhaust gases are the most common methods for adolescents.

7. (d). Nursing Process: Implementation; Client Need Category: Health Promotion and Maintenance. Motor vehicle accidents are by far the leading cause of mortality for the young adult. a. Other causes of accidental death for young adults include drowning, fires, burns, and firearms. b. Other causes of accidental death for young adults include drowning, fires, burns, and firearms. c. Other causes of accidental death for young adults include drowning, fires, burns, and firearms.

8. (a). Nursing Process: Planning; Client Need Category: Health Promotion and Maintenance. Falls are the leading cause of accidents among older adults. They are also a major cause of hospital and nursing home admissions. b. Fires are a hazard for the elderly person with a failing memory. c. Motor vehicle accidents occur because accommodation of the eye to light is impaired and peripheral vision is impaired. d. Firearms are not a major cause of accidents in the older adult population.

9. (c). Nursing Process: Planning; Client Need Category: Safe, Effective Care Environment. Restraints should be released at least every 2 to 4 hours, with range-of-motion exercises and skin care. a. The restraint should be assessed every 30 minutes. b. Restraints should be released at least every 2 to 4 hours, with range-of-motion exercises and skin care. d. Restraints should be released at least every 2 to 4 hours, with range-of-motion exercises and skin care.

10. (c). Nursing Process: Assessment; Client Need Category: Physiological Integrity. The symptoms described are classic complaints of carbon monoxide poisoning. a. Though food poisoning may be suspected, the symptoms are indicative of carbon monoxide poisoning. b. Though medication overdose may be suspected, a thorough history of client's medications is warranted, and the symptoms are indicative of carbon monoxide poisoning. d. Though ingestion of a toxic substance may be suspected, the symptoms are indicative of carbon monoxide poisoning.

Chapter 31

1. (c). Nursing Process: Diagnosis; Client Need Category: Physiological Integrity. a. Since the diaper dermatitis is present, the diagnosis is "actual," not "risk." b. Since the diaper dermatitis is present, the diagnosis is "actual," not "risk," plus the more appropriate diagnosis is "impaired skin integrity." d. The better diagnosis is impaired skin integrity, and there is no evidence of a knowledge deficit.

2. (d). Nursing Process: Implementation; Client Need Category: Safe, Effective Care Environment. a. Alkaline soaps may cause irritation and drying of skin and should be avoided. b. Sitz baths are used to soothe hemorrhoids and perineal wounds and are not indicated for pruritis. c. Changing laundry detergent can irritate the skin and is only indicated if it has been determined that the current laundry detergent is the causative factor.

3. (c). Nursing Process: Implementation; Client Need Category: Safe, Effective Care Environment. a. This action is correct as warm soaking will soften the beard. b. This action is appropriate as there is a potential for blood exposure. d.This is the correct angle for shaving a patient to prevent irritation and skin breakdown.

4. (a). Nursing Process: Evaluation; Client Need Category: Physiological Integrity. The goals for clients with oral hygiene or oral problems are to maintain or improve oral hygiene practices and to maintain or restore the integrity of the oral tissues. b. Adequate skin turgor does not assess oral hygiene. c. Moist and pink conjunctiva does not assess oral hygiene. d. Adequate saliva formation does not indicate oral mucosa integrity is intact.

5. (c). Nursing Process: Evaluation; Client Need Category: Physiological Integrity. a. This is a positive sign of wound healing. Red tissue indicates the presence of healthy granulation tissue. b. Deep wounds should heal from the "inside out"; a decreasing depth is a positive sign of healing. d. Yellow tissue indicates the presence of fibrous debris or viscous exudate. Black tissue indicates necrosis and/or eschar and is a poor sign of wound healing.

6. (c). Nursing Process: Implementation; Client Need Category: Physiological Integrity. The water for a bath should feel comfortably warm to the client. People vary in their sensitivity to heat; generally, the temperature should be 110° to 115°F. Most clients will verify a suitable temperature. a. This temperature is too cool. b. This temperature is too cool. d. This temperature is too hot.

7. (c). Nursing Process: Implementation; Client Need Category: Physiological Integrity. Hydrogen peroxide is not recommended for use in oral care because it irritates healthy oral mucosa and may alter the microflora of the mouth. a. Depending on the health of the client's mouth, oral care may be needed every 2 to 8 hours. b. If commercially prepared applicators of lemon juice and oil are not available, a gauze square wrapped around a tongue blade and dipped into lemon juice and oil may be used. d. Normal saline solution is recommended for oral hygiene for the dependent client.

8. (d). Nursing Process: Evaluation; Client Need Category: Physiological Integrity. The eyes should be wiped from the inner to outer canthus to prevent debris from being washed into the nasolacrimal duct. a. This is correct technique. b. This is correct technique. c. This is correct technique.

9. (b). Nursing Process: Evaluation; Client Need Category: Physiological Integrity. Hot water is not used for cleaning dentures because heat will change the shape of some dentures. a. Placing a washcloth in the bowl of the sink prevents damage if the dentures are dropped. c. A toothbrush or special stiff-bristled brush may be used to clean dentures. d. Dentures may be soaked in 5 to 10 ml of white vinegar and warm water.

10. (d). Nursing Process: Evaluation; Client Need Category: Physiological Integrity. Lotion will moisten skin and soften calluses. The client should be encouraged to use lotion or creams. a. Feet should be washed daily and dried well, especially between the toes. b. Filing rather than cutting toenails is appropriate to avoid skin injury. c. The client should wear clean socks daily.

Chapter 32

1. (a). Nursing Process: Assessment; Client Need Category: Physiological Integrity. Normal platelet count is 150,000–400,000 × $10^3/mL^3$. b. The normal white blood cell count is 5–10 × $10^3/mL^3$. c. The normal red blood cell count is 4.7–6.1 × $10^6/mL^3$ in the male. d. The normal hematocrit for the male is 42%–52%.
2. (a). Nursing Process: Assessment; Client Need Category: Physiological Integrity. The normal hemoglobin level for an adult male is 14–18 g/dL. b. This is the normal hemoglobin level for an adult female. c. This is the normal hematocrit level for an adult male. d. This is the normal hematocrit level for an adult female.
3. (a). Nursing Process: Assessment; Client Need Category: Physiological Integrity. Normal serum potassium level is 3.5–5.0 mEq/L. Serious cardiac complications may result from hypokalemia. b. Normal sodium level is 135–145 mEq/L. c. Normal chloride level is 95–105 mEq/L. d. Normal magnesium level is 1.5–2.5 mEq/L.
4. (b). Nursing Process: Assessment; Client Need Category: Physiological Integrity. The peak level identifies the highest concentration of the drug in the blood serum. a. The trough level represents the lowest concentration of the drug in the blood serum. c. The therapeutic level is the level determined to be the most effective. d. A subtherapeutic level represents a drug level that is ineffective.
5. (c). Nursing Process: Implementation; Client Need Category: Physiological Integrity. At the start of the collection period, the nurse should have the client void and discard the urine. a. This is correct. b. This is correct. d. This is correct.
6. (b). Nursing Process: Implementation; Client Need Category: Physiological Integrity. The nurse assists the client to assume a position that allows easy access to the intercostal spaces. This is usually a sitting position with arms elevated above the head or the client leaning forward over a pillow. a. This does not allow for easy access to the intercostal spaces. c. This does not allow for easy access to the intercostal spaces. d. This does not allow for easy access to the intercostal spaces.
7. (a). Nursing Process: Planning; Client Need Category: Physiological Integrity. The posterior superior iliac crest is the preferred site. The client is placed in the prone position or on the side. b. The sternum and the anterior or posterior iliac spine are commonly used sites, but the posterior superior iliac crest is the preferred site. c. The sternum and the anterior or posterior iliac spine are commonly used sites, but the posterior superior iliac crest is the preferred site. d. The sternum and the anterior or posterior iliac spine are commonly used sites, but the posterior superior iliac crest is the preferred site.
8. (c). Nursing Process: Implementation; Client Need Category: Physiological Integrity. The client is instructed to void just before the procedure to reduce the possibility of puncturing the urinary bladder. a. This is appropriate. b. This is appropriate. d. This is appropriate.
9. (b). Nursing Process: Implementation; Client Need Category: Physiological Integrity. Severe abdominal pain experienced after a liver biopsy may indicate bile peritonitis. The primary health care provider should be informed. a. Relief of pain is important; however, the client may be experiencing bile peritonitis and immediate intervention is necessary. c. Repositioning in bed may be appropriate after complications related to the procedure are ruled out. d. Relaxation techniques may be appropriate after complications related to the procedure are ruled out.
10. (c). Nursing Process: Implementation; Client Need Category: Physiological Integrity. Normally about 1500 mL is the maximum amount of fluid drained out at one time in order to avoid hypovolemic shock. a. More may be withdrawn. b. More may be withdrawn. d. This is more than the normal maximum amount.

Chapter 33

1. (d). Nursing Process: Implementation; Client Need Category: Physiological Integrity. The correct technique for the Z-track method is to pull skin to the side, insert the needle at a 90-degree angle, inject the medication, remove the needle, and release the skin. This prevents seepage of the medication into the subcutaneous tissues. a. This is incorrect. b. This is incorrect. c. This is incorrect.
2. (a). Nursing Process: Assessment; Client Need Category: Physiological Integrity. Drugs may produce a response by stimulating enzyme activity or hormone production, which is called a syngeristic effect. b. Drug interaction with a cellular receptor to produce a response is known as agonist. c. Distribution is the transportation of a drug from its site of absorption to its site of action. d. Biotransformation is a process by which a drug is converted to a less active form.
3. (b). Nursing Process: Assessment; Client Need Category: Physiological Integrity. Drug toxicity results from overdosage, ingestion of a drug intended for

external use, and buildup of the drug in the blood because of impaired metabolism or excretion. Respiratory depression due to the cumulative effect of morphine sulfate in the body is an example of a toxic effect. a. A side effect of a drug is one that is unintended and is usually predictable and may be either harmless or potentially harmful. c. A drug allergy is an immunological reaction to a drug. d. An anaphylactic reaction is a severe allergic reaction to a drug.

4. (b). Nursing Process: Planning; Client Need Category: Psychosocial Integrity. Drug dependence is a person's reliance on or need to take a drug or substance. The dependence may be either physiologic or psychologic. a. Drug abuse is inappropriate intake of a substance, either continually or periodically. c. Drug habituation denotes a mild form of psychologic dependence. The individual develops the habit of taking the substance and feels better after taking it. d. Drug interaction occurs when the administration of one drug before, at the same time as, or after another drug alters the effect of one or both drugs.

5. (c). Nursing Process: Planning; Client Need Category: Physiological Integrity. A severe drug reaction is called anaphylactic reaction. The earliest symptoms of anaphylactic reaction are acute shortness of breath, acute hypotension, and tachycardia. a. Drug toxicity results from overdosage, ingestion of a drug intended for external use, and buildup of the drug in the blood because of impaired metabolism or excretion. b. A drug allergy is an immunologic reaction to a drug. d. Drug tolerance exists in a person who has unusually low physiologic activity in response to a drug.

6. (b). Nursing Process: Planning; Client Need Category: Physiological Integrity. Factors affecting medication action include increased, not decreased, adipose tissue. a. Decreased gastric acid production and blood flow in the older adult are factors affecting medication action. c. Decreased total body fluid proportionate to the body mass can increase the possibility of drug toxicity. d. Older adults may also experience a decreased number of protein-binding sites and changes in the blood-brain barrier.

7. (c). Nursing Process: Implementation; Client Need Category: Physiological Integrity. 1 gr is equivalent to 60 mg, therefore, if 60 mg = 1 gr, then × mg = ¼ gr (0.25 gr):

$$x = \frac{(60 \times 0.25)}{1}$$

$$x = 15 \text{ mg}$$

a. This is incorrect. b. This is incorrect. d. This is incorrect.

8. (a). Nursing Process: Implementation; Client Need Category: Physiological Integrity. Abbreviations used to identify the eye are OD (right eye), OS (left eye), and OU (both eyes). The order is for one drop in each eye twice a day. b. Abbreviations used to identify the eye are OD (right eye), OS (left eye), and OU (both eyes). The order is for one drop in each eye twice a day. c. Abbreviations used to identify the eye are OD (right eye), OS (left eye), and OU (both eyes). The order is for one drop in each eye twice a day. d. Abbreviations used to identify the eye are OD (right eye), OS (left eye), and OU (both eyes). The order is for one drop in each eye twice a day.

9. (b). Nursing Process: Evaluation; Client Need Category: Physiological Integrity. The client should be instructed to close the eyelids but not to squeeze them shut. Squeezing can injure the eye and push out the medication. a. This is appropriate technique. c. This is appropriate technique. d. This is appropriate technique.

10. (d). Nursing Process: Implementation; Client Need Category: Physiological Integrity. The correct insertion of a suppository in an adult is to insert the suppository 10 cm (4 inches) beyond the internal sphincter. a. This is correct technique. b. This is correct technique. c. This is correct technique.

Chapter 34

1. (b). Nursing Process: Assessment; Client Need Category: Physiological Integrity. a. Suntan is an example of hyperpigmentation. c. Albinism is a congenital lack of pigmentation that may be total or partial. d. Erythema is a generalized area of redness that blanches when palpated.

2. (a). Nursing Process: Assessment; Client Need Category: Physiological Integrity. b. Stage 3 pressure ulcers are full-thickness ulcerations involving subcutaneous fat and extending to the fascia. c. Stage 4 pressure ulcers are full-thickness ulcers that penetrate deep fascia and muscle and may expose bone and supporting structures. d. The nurse's scope of practice includes full assessment of pressure ulcers, including staging.

3. (d). Nursing Process: Assessment; Client Need Category: Physiological Integrity. a. This type of exudate is documented as purulent. b. This type of exudate is documented as serous. c. This type of exudate is documented as sanguinous.

4. (d). Nursing Process: Implementation; Client Need Category: Safe, Effective Care Environment. a. Alkaline soaps may cause irritation and drying of skin and should be avoided. b. Sitz baths are used to soothe hemorrhoids and perineal wounds and are not indicated for pruritis. c. Changing laundry detergent can irritate the skin and is only indicated if it has been determined that the current laundry detergent is the causative factor.

5. (b). Nursing Process: Implementation; Client Need Category: Safe, Effective Care Environment. a. This action is correct as the nurse needs to verify the medical order and check the current progress notes to determine the condition of the wound. c. The nurse will need a pair of clean gloves to remove and discard the old dressing and a pair of sterile gloves to put on the new sterile dressing. d. Cleansing the wound is important to loosen necrotic debris. The physician may order normal saline, a wound-cleaning solution, or an antibacterial solution for this purpose.

6. (d). Nursing Process: Implementation; Client Need Category: Safe, Effective Care Environment. Dirty or infected wounds include old, accidental wounds containing dead tissue and wounds with evidence of a clinical infection, such as purulent drainage. a. Clean wounds are uninfected wounds in which minimal inflammation is encountered and the respiratory, alimentary, genital, and urinary tracts are not entered. b. Clean-contaminated wounds are surgical wounds in which the respiratory, alimentary, genital, or urinary tract has been entered. Such wounds show no evidence of infection. c. Contaminated wounds are open, fresh, accidental wounds and surgical wounds involving a major break in sterile technique or a large amount of spillage from the gastrointestinal tract.

7. (b). Nursing Process: Assessment; Client Need Category: Physiological Integrity. A stage 2 ulcer is superficial and presents clinically as an abrasion, blister, or shallow crater. a. A stage 1 ulcer is nonblanchable erythema of intact skin; this is the heralding lesion of skin ulceration. c. Clean wounds are unifected wounds in which minimal inflammation is encountered and the respiratory, alimentary, genital, and urinary tracts are not entered. d. Contaminated wounds are open, fresh, accidental wounds and surgical wounds involving a major break in sterile technique or a large amount of spillage from the gastrointestinal tract.

8. (b). Nursing Process: Assessment; Client Need Category: Physiological Integrity. A stage 4 ulcer is full-thickness loss with extensive destruction, tissue necrosis, or damage to muscle, bone, or supporting structures. a. A stage 3 ulcer is full-thickness skin loss involving damage or necrosis or subcutaneous tissue that may extend down to, but not through, underlying fascia. c. Clean wounds are uninfected wounds in which minimal inflammation is encountered and the respiratory, alimentary, genital, and urinary tracts are not entered. d. Contaminated wounds are open, fresh, accidental wounds and surgical wounds involving a major break in sterile technique or a large amount of spillage from the gastrointestinal tract.

9. (b). Nursing Process: Assessment; Client Need Category: Physiological Integrity. A serosanguineous drainge is clean and blood-tinged drainage commonly seen in surgical incisions. a. Serous drainage consists cheifly of serum (the clear portion of the blood). c. Purulent drainage is thicker than serous exudate because of the presence of pus. d. Purosanguineous drainage consists of pus and blood and is often seen in a new wound that is infected.

10. (c). Nursing Process: Implementation; Client Need Category: Physiological Integrity. Pain and swelling at the surgical site may indicate infection. a. Itching and tingling around the surgical incision may be experienced and do not indicate infection. b. Serous drainage is a normal occurrence for surgical wounds. d. Sloughing off of scab formation is a normal occurrence.

11. (b). Nursing Process: Assessment; Client Need Category: Physiological Integrity. Secondary intention healing occurs when the edges cannot or should not be approximated. a. Primary intention healing occurs where the tissue surfaces have been approximated (closed). c. There are only two types of healing: primary and secondary. d. Open reduction is not a wound healing stage.

12. (c). Nursing Process: Assessment; Client Need Category: Physiological Integrity. Dehiscence is the partial or toal rupturing of a sutured wound. a. Superficial separation is not a complication of wound healing. b. Hemorrhage is persistent bleeding. d. Evisceration is the protrusion of the internal viscera through an incision.

13. (c). Nursing Process: Planning; Client Need Category: Physiological Integrity. Hydrocolloid dressings, transparent adhesive, polyurethane foam, and hydrogel are appopirate interventions for a stage 2 ulcer. a. Gauze dressings are appropriate for stage 3 and stage 4 ulcers. b. Dry gauze is appropriate for stage 3 and stage 4 ulcers. d. Wet-to-dry gauze dressings may be considered appropriate for stage 3 and stage 4 ulcers.

Chapter 35

1. (d). Nursing Process: Implementation; Client Need Category: Psychosocial Integrity. a. A patient's primary concern is the aspect of the health problem about which he or she is most distressed. Nurses obtain this data by asking "What about your problem bothers you most?" b. A patient's primary concern is the aspect of the health problem about which he or she is most distressed. Nurses obtain this data by asking "What about your problem bothers you most?" c. A patient's primary concern is the aspect of the health problem about which he or she is most distressed. Nurses obtain this data by asking "What about your problem bothers you most?"

2. (d). Nursing Process: Implementation; Client Need Category: Psychosocial Integrity. a. This intervention is not associated with the identified nursing diagnosis. b. This intervention is not associated with the identified nursing diagnosis. c. This intervention is not associated with the identified nursing diagnosis.

3. (b). Nursing Process: Implementation; Client Need Category: Physiological Integrity. Airway patency is the immediate priority for the client in the immediate postoperative period. a. Pain management is an important priority, but patent airway is the main priority. c. Wound care may or may not be necessary; however, maintaining a patent airway is the priority. d. Assessment of neurological status is important; however, maintaining a patent airway is the priority.

4. (c). Nursing Process: Implementation; Client Need Category: Physiological Integrity. Pain and swelling at the surgical site may indicate infection and should be reported immediately. a. Itching and tingling around the surgical incision are normal. b. Serous drainage is normal. d. Sloughing off of scab formation is normal.

5. (c). Nursing Process: Assessment; Client Need Category: Physiological Integrity. Wound dehiscence is the separation of a suture line before the incision heals. a. Superficial separation is not correct terminology. b. Hemorrhage is internal or external bleeding. d. Evisceration is extrusion of internal organs and tissues through the incision.

6. (b). Nursing Process: Implementation; Client Need Category: Physiological Integrity. Conscious sedation is described as minimal depression of the level of consciousness in which the client will retain the ability to consciously maintain a patent airway and respond to verbal and physical stimuli. a. Epidural anesthesia is an injection of an anesthetic agent into the epidural space. c. Regional anesthesia is the temporary interruption of the transmission of nerve impulses to and from a specific area or region of the body. d. General anesthesia is the loss of all sensation and consciousness.

7. (d). Nursing Process: Assessment; Client Need Category: Physiological Integrity. Clinical signs of hypovolemia are tachycardia, decreased urine output, and decreased blood pressure. a. Clinical signs of pulmonary embolism include sudden chest pain, shortness of breath, cyanosis, and shock. b. Clinical signs of atelectasis include tachycardia, tachypnea, diaphoresis, anxiety, and decreased chest wall movement. c. Hyopvolemic shock is manifested by rapid weak pulse, dyspnea, tachypnea, restlessness and anxiety, urine outpus less than 30 mL/hr, decreased blood pressure, cool and clammy skin, thirst, and pallor.

8. (b). Nursing Process: Implementation; Client Need Category: Physiological Integrity. The clinical signs of pulmonary embolism include sudden chest pain, shortness of breath, cyanosis, and shock (low blood pressure and tachycardia). a. Pneumonia is manifested by elevated temperature, cough, expectoration of blood-tinged or purulent sputum, dyspnea, chest pain. c. Atelectasis is manifested by tachycardia , tachypnea, diaphoresis, anxiety, and decreased chest wall movement. d. Hyopvolemic shock is manifested by rapid weak pulse, dyspnea, tachypnea, restlessness and anxiety, urine outpus less than 30 mL/hr, decreased blood pressure, cool and clammy skin, thirst, and pallor.

9. (a). Nursing Process: Implementation; Client Need Category: Physiological Integrity. If difficulty withdrawing the solution is encountered, inject 20 mL of air and aspirate again, and/or reposition the client or the nasogastric tube. Injecting 60 mL of air may cause abdominal distention, pain, and stress on the suture line. b. If difficulty withdrawing the solution is encountered, reposition the client or the nasogastric tube. c. Forceful withdrawal could damage the gastric mucosa. d. If aspirating difficulty continues, reattach the tube in intermittent low suction, and notify the physician.

10. (c). Nursing Process: Evaluation; Client Need Category: Physiological Integrity. The forceps tips should be kept lower than the handles at all times to prevent their contamination by fluid traveling up to the handle and the wrist and back to the tips. a. A sterile cotton ball or swab should be used for each stroke. b. This is proper drain care. d. This is proper dressing placement, depending on the client's usual position. Layers of dressings are placed for best absorption of drainage, which flows by gravity.

Chapter 36

1. (b). Nursing Process: Implementation; Client Need Category: Safe, Effective Care Environment. a. Habituation is a form of learning that occurs when a stimulus that originally produced a response is presented so often that the individual stops responding to it. c. Sensitization, a form of nonassociative learning, has the opposite effect of habituation. It arouses human interest and helps to determine dangerous stimuli. d. Children who experience pain in a visit to the clinic may be conditioned to view physicians and nurses with fear. This is called classical conditioning and is a normal behavior.

2. (d). Nursing Process: Assessment; Client Need Category: Physiological Integrity. a. Myopia (nearsightedness) occurs from the elongation of the eyeball and causes objects that are at a distance to be out of focus. b. Diplopia is double vision, or seeing two images of a single object. c. Glaucoma is a condition of increased intraocular pressure that can lead to blindness. A person with glaucoma can see only straight ahead (tunnel vision).

3. (a). Nursing Process: Assessment; Client Need Category: Physiological Integrity. b. Sensorineural hearing loss occurs when there is a disorder of the inner ear, damage to the hair cells of the cochlea, or pathology in the acoustic nerve or the brain. c. Mixed hearing loss is a combination of conductive and sensorineural loss in the same ear. d. The patient is experiencing conductive hearing loss, which can result from obstruction of the external canal.

4. (b). Nursing Process: Assessment; Client Need Category: Physiological Integrity. In the semicomatose state of awareness, the client can be aroused by extreme or repeated stimuli. a. In coma, the client will not respond to verbal stimuli. c. The client is said to be somnolent when demonstrating extreme drowsiness but will respond to stimuli. d. The client is described as disoriented when not oriented to time, person, or place.

5. (a). Nursing Process: Assessment; Client Need Category: Physiological Integrity. a. Sensory deprivation is a decrease or lack of meaningful stimuli and is indicated by excessive yawning, decreased attention span, impaired memory, hallucinations, apathy, crying, and periodic disorientation. b. Sensory overload generally occurs when a person is unable to process or manage the amount or intensity of sensory stimuli. c. Sensory deficit is impaired reception, perception, or both of one or more of the senses. d. Sensory awareness is not a category of sensory alterations.

6. (b). Nursing Process: Planning; Client Need Category: Safe, Effective Care Environment. Unfamiliar environments can add to the blind individual's confusion, and the diversity and unfamiliarity of the hospital environment can create sensory overload. a. Blind individuals often have highly structured home environments and do not necessarily experience an increase in injuries. c. In general, blind individuals are not necessarily at higher risk for injuries. d. Blind individuals, if given the opportunity, can adapt to new environments.

7. (c). Nursing Process: Evaluation; Client Need Category: Physiological Integrity. Strong chemicals, such as ammonia, used in confined spaces may affect the client before they are smelled. a. Because a gas leak can go undetected, clients need to keep gas stoves and heaters in good working order. b. Food poisoning is a concern with clients who have difficulty detecting spoiled meat or dairy products. These clients need to carefully inspect food for freshness and expiration date. d. Food poisoning is a concern with clients who have difficulty detecting spoiled meat or dairy products. These clients need to carefully inspect food for freshness and expiration.

8. (d). Nursing Process: Planning; Client Need Category: Safe, Effective Care Environment. The visually impaired client is assisted with ambulation by standing to his or her side, walking about 1 foot ahead, and allowing him or her to grasp your arm. a. In the health care setting, the client should be oriented to the arrangement of room furnishings. b. The pathways should be clear, and furniture should not be rearranged without orienting the client. c. Self-care articles should be within the client's reach and the client should be oriented to their location.

9. (d). Nursing Process: Planning; Client Need Category: Safe, Effective Care Environment. Sometimes the number of visitors and the length of visits must be restricted for the client experiencing sensory overload. a. Measures to prevent sensory overload include minimizing unnecessary light, noise, and distraction. b. Measures to prevent sensory overload include providing the client with a private room. c. Measures to prevent sensory overload include reducing noxious odors. Wounds should be kept clean and covered, and a room deodorizer should be used when indicated.

10. (d). Nursing Process: Evaluation; Client Need Category: Safe, Effective Care Environment. You should speak at a moderate rate and in a normal tone of voice. Shouting does not make your voice more distinct, and in some instances it makes understanding more difficult. a. Before initiating conversation, convey your presence by moving to a position where you can be seen or where you can gently touch the person. b. Address the person directly. Do not turn away in the middle of a remark or story. c. Always speak as clearly and accurately as possible.

Chapter 37

1. (a). Nursing Process: Assessment; Client Need Category: Psychosocial. b. Gender identity is a sense of oneself as either male or female. c. Personality is the total character and encompasses the whole of an individual and cannot be labeled good or bad. d. Role performance is the way an individual participates in society.

2. (d). Nursing Process: Assessment; Client Need Category: Psychosocial Integrity. a. This behavior is associated with adequate self-esteem. b. This behavior is associated with adequate self-esteem. c. This behavior is associated with adequate self-esteem.

3. (d). Nursing Process: Assessment; Client Need Category: Psychosocial Integrity. a. Four factors that influence perception include sensory function, self-concept, learning, and needs. b. Four factors that influence perception include sensory function, self-concept, learning, and needs. c. Four factors that influence perception include sensory function, self-concept, learning, and needs.

4. (b). Nursing Process: Assessment; Client Need Category: Psychosocial Integrity. a. The client has a need that is unmet. If this need goes unmet it will narrow the client's perceptual field and he will focus his attention on the unmet need. c. The client has a need that is unmet. If this need goes unmet, it will narrow the client's perceptual field and he will focus his attention on the unmet need. d. The client has a need that is unmet. If this need goes unmet, it will narrow the client's perceptual field and he will focus his attention on the unmet need.

5. (d). Nursing Process: Implementation; Client Need Category: Psychosocial Integrity. a. Being able to predict a stressful event and/or the belief that one can exert some control over stressful situations lessens the severity of the reaction. b. Being able to predict a stressful event and/or the belief that one can exert some control over stressful situations lessens the severity of the reaction. c. Being able to predict a stressful event and/or the belief that one can exert some control over stressful situations lessens the severity of the reaction.

6. (c). Nursing Process: Assessment; Client Need Category: Psychosocial Integrity. a. Elevated blood pressure is a physical indicator that a client may be having difficulty coping with stress. b. Irritability is an emotional indicator that a client may be having difficulty coping with stress. d. Upset stomach is a physical indicator that a client may be having difficulty coping with stress.

7. (b). Nursing Process: Assessment; Client Need Category: Psychosocial Integrity. Behaviors associated with low self-esteem include avoidance of eye contact and the inability to accept positive remarks about self. a. The behaviors do not demonstrate a high sense of self-worth. c. Though the client may have experienced unmet physiological needs, the behaviors indicate low self-esteem. d. The behaviors do not indicate mental incapacitation.

8. (a). Nursing Process: Assessment; Client Need Category: Health Promotion and Maintenance. The early adulthood stage of Erikson's psychosocial development is Intimacy vs. Isolation. b. Generativity vs. Stagnation is the psychosocial developmental stage for middle-age adults. c. Industry vs. Inferiority is the psychosocial developmental stage for early school years. d. Identity vs. Role Confusion is the psychosocial developmental stage for adolescence.

9. (c). Nursing Process: Assessment; Client Need Category: Psychosocial Integrity. People undergoing role strain are frustrated because they feel or are made to feel inadequate or unsuited to a role. a. Role development involves socialization into a particular role. b. Role ambiguity occurs when expectations are unclear and people do not know what to do or how to do it and are unable to predict the reactions of others to their behavior. d. Role conflicts arise from opposing or incompatible expectations.

10. (a). Nursing Process: Assessment; Client Need Category: Psychosocial. Repeated failures, unrealistic expectations, inability to cope with life stressors, and abusive relationships are self-esteem stressors. b. Hospitalization is considered a role stressor. c. Loss of body parts is considered a body-image stressor. d. Sexuality concerns are considered identity stressors.

Chapter 38

1. (c). Nursing Process: Assessment; Client Need Category: Psychosocial. a. These behaviors are associated with the sexual development of adolescents. b. These behaviors are associated with school-age sexual development. d. These behaviors are associated with the sexual development of adolescents.

2. (a). Nursing Process: Implementation; Client Need Category: Health Promotion and Maintenance. Providing the client with factual information regarding sexual functioning after a hysterectomy may assist the client to maintain a healthy sexual self-concept. b. This does not assist the client. c. This does not assist the client. d. A fertility specialist is not necessary.

3. (c). Nursing Process: Planning; Client Need Category: Health Promotion and Maintenance. Gender identity is the belief or awareness that individuals have of being male or female. a. Sexual identity consists of gender, gender-identity, gender-role behavior, and sexual orientation. b. Biologic sex refers to an individual's chromosomal makeup, external and internal genitalia, secondary sex characteristics, and hormonal states. d. Sexual orientation is the preference of a person for one sex or the other.

4. (d). Nursing Process: Evaluation; Client Need Category: Health Promotion and Maintenance. There is no physiologic basis for abstinence during menses. a. Alcohol is a relaxant and central nervous system depressant. Chronic alcoholism is associated with impotence. b. This is correct. c. This is correct.

5. (c). Nursing Process: Implementation; Client Need Category: Health Promotion and Maintenance. Nursing strategies for inappropriate sexual behavior include informing the client that he is expected to keep himself covered when staff are in the room. a. The nurse must provide client care; refusing to enter the client's room is inappropriate. b. Though reporting the client's behavior may be appropriate, communicating expectations to the client is the priority. d. The client's inappropriate behavior should not be ignored.

6. (a). Nursing Process: Evaluation; Client Need Category: Health Promotion and Maintenance. The best time for a testicular self-examination is after a warm bath or shower when the scrotal sac is relaxed. b. This is correct. c. This is correct. d. This is correct.

7. (d). Nursing Process: Assessment; Client Need Category: Health Promotion and Maintenance. Clinical signs of candidiasis are red and excoriated vulva; intense itching of vaginal and vulvar tissues; and thick, white, cheesy, or curdlike discharge. a. Gonorrhea may be asymptomatic, or vaginal discharge, pain, and urinary frequency may be present. b. Syphilis presents as a chancre on the cervix or other genital areas, which heals in 4 to 6 weeks. c. Trichomoniasis presents as itching and redness of the vulva and skin inside the thighs, as well as copious watery, frothy vaginal discharge.

8. (c). Nursing Process: Assessment; Client Need Category: Health Promotion and Maintenance. Dyspareunia describes pain experienced by a woman during intercourse as a result of inadequate lubrication, scarring, vaginal infection, or hormonal imbalance. a. Orgasmic dysfunction is the inability of a woman to achieve orgasm. b. Vaginismus is the irregular and involuntary contraction of the muscles around the outer third of the vagina when coitus is attempted. d. Vulvodynia is a chronic vulvar discomfort or pain in the female genitalia.

9. (c). Nursing Process: Planning; Client Need Category: Health Promotion and Maintenance. Physiologic factors include neurologic disorders and prolonged use of drugs such as alcohol. a. Psychologic factors include fatigue, anger, or stress. b. Psychologic factors include boredom associated with partner. d. Psychologic factors include doubts about ability to perform or about one's masculinity.

10. (b). Nursing Process: Evaluation; Client Need Category: Health Promotion and Maintenance, The 4- to 5-year-old preschooler normally asks questions about "where babies come from." These questions should be answered honestly and simply. a. The 4- to 5-year-old preschooler normally asks questions about "where babies come from." c. The 4- to 5-year-old preschooler normally asks questions about "where babies come from." These questions should be answered honestly and simply. d. Books and other materials regarding the birth cycle are appropriate for the school-age child.

Chapter 39

1. (d). Nursing Process: Evaluation; Client Need Category: Psychosocial Integrity. a. The priest's action is a religious practice influenced by his culture. b. Culture shock is used to refer to the difficulties that people experience in adjusting to life in a foreign country. c. Territoriality refers to a person's perceptions of space in relationship to other people.

2. (a). Nursing Process: Implementation; Client Need Category: Psychosocial Integrity. b. The nurse could offer to pin the medal to the patient's gown, in support of the patient's needs for spirituality. c. The nurse could offer to pin the medal to the patient's gown, in support of the patient's needs for spirituality. d. Although it may make sense in theory, a better suggestion would be to pin the medal to the patient's gown.

3. (a). Nursing Process: Implementation; Client Need Category: Psychosocial Integrity. b. Those of the Islamic faith need to have the body positioned to face Mecca. c. Non-Islamic health care providers must wear gloves when preparing the body of someone of the Islamic faith. d. The sacrament of holy unction is provided to the sick for those of the Eastern Orthodox faith.

4. (a). Nursing Process: Implementation; Client Need Category: Psychosocial Integrity. b. This would violate the patient's wishes and hinder any chances of transcultural reciprocity. c. This would violate the patient's wishes and hinder any chances of transcultural reciprocity. d. This would violate the patient's wishes and hinder any chances of transcultural reciprocity.

5. (b). Nursing Process: Assessment; Client Need Category: Psychosocial Integrity. Members of the Jehovah's Witness faith may refuse blood transfusions as they believe this is mandated by scripture. a. The Christian Scientist religion does not oppose blood transfusions. c. The Mormon religion does not oppose blood transfusions. d. The Episcopalian religion does not oppose blood transfusions.

6. (a). Nursing Process: Planning; Client Need Category: Psychosocial Integrity. Orthodox Jews may not eat shellfish or pork. b. Mormons may not drink caffeinated or alcoholic beverages. c. Older Catholics may choose not to eat meat on Fridays because of previous Catholic religious doctrine. d. Devout Muslims eat no food and avoid beverages during daylight hours during the month of Ramadan.

7. (b). Nursing Process: Assessment; Client Need Category: Psychological Integrity. Many Jewish people require kosher food (food that is prepared according to Jewish law). a. Catholics do not require kosher foods. c. Baptists do not require kosher foods. d. Jehovah's Witnesses do not require kosher foods.

8. (c). Nursing Process: Implementation; Client Need Category: Psychosocial Integrity. Native Americans practice various ceremonies, including the sprinkling of cornmeal around the sick. a. The nurse should support the client's specific religious practices. b. The nurse should support the client's specific religious practices. d. This is inappropriate and does not recognize the importance of the client's religious practices.

9. (b). During times of spiritual distress, the nurse can best assist the client by listening carefully to the client's communication. a. Respect and trust are important attributes; however, a willingness to listen is the most therapeutic during spiritual distress. c. Love and belonging are psychosocials need of the individual. d. Self-disclosure is not appropriate in this case.

10. (a). Nursing Process: Implementation; Client Need Category: Psychosocial Integrity. Clients may choose to participate in prayer with family, friends, or clergy. In such situations, the nurse's major responsibility is to ensure a quiet environment and privacy. b. The client should be encouraged to express fears, anxiety, and concerns. c. This is not appropriate at this time. d. Nursing care may need to be adjusted to accommodate periods for prayer.

Chapter 40

1. (a). Nursing Process: Assessment; Client Need Category: Safe, Effective Care Environment. b. This patient was complaining about the change, desiring stability. c. This patient was complaining about the change, seeking stability. d. There is not enough evidence to support the idea that the patient's behavior was unstable.

2. (d). Nursing Process: Assessment; Client Need Category: Safe, Effective Care Environment. a. The global system consists of water, air, earth, flora, and fauna. b. The societal system consists of culture, ethics, religion, beliefs, values, and race. c. The community system consists of place of worship, workplace, school, business, government, and health care facilities.

3. (d). Nursing Process: Assessment; Client Need Category: Health Promotion and Maintenance. a. These are parasympathetic effects on breathing and circulation. b. These are parasympathetic effects on breathing and circulation. c. These are parasympathetic effects on breathing and circulation.

4. (c). Nursing Process: Evaluation; Client Need Category: Health Promotion and Maintenance. a. This is a stimulus or a situation that disrupts internal equilibrium. b. Stress is a constraining force or tension that individuals feel when confronted by a threatening situation. This patient is experiencing stress; however, the discussion about employment would be the stressor. d. Adaptation is adjusting to changes in the environment.

5. (d). Nursing Process: Assessment; Client Need Category: Health Promotion and Maintenance. a. The alarm stage is when the body is called to action in response to a stressor. b. This is when the body participates in the fight-or-flight response to adapt to the stressor. c. This is when the body's ability to adapt is exceeded or exhausted.

6. (a). Nursing Process: Assessment; Client Need Category: Psychosocial Integrity. b. This level is characterized by highly distractable behavior with severe learning impairment. c. This level is characterized by a narrowed perceptual field and difficulty concentrating. d. This level heightens awareness and facilitates learning.

7. (c). Nursing Process: Evaluation; Client Need Category: Psychosocial Integrity. a. There is no such thing as a maturational response to stress. Maturational crises, however, are stressful events that occur in the process of normal growth and development. b. There is no such thing as a situational response to stress. A situational crisis, however, occurs as a result of a traumatic event. d. A defense mechanism is an unconscious psychological response that allays painful or stressful feelings.

8. (c). Nursing Process: Assessment; Client Need Category: Psychosocial Integrity. a. This nurse is experiencing burnout. b. This nurse is experiencing burnout. d. This nurse is experiencing burnout.

9. (d). Nursing Process: Evaluation; Client Need Category: Health Promotion and Maintenance. a. The health crisis was an opportunity for growth. b. Although it might have been a stressor for the patient, it was an opportunity for growth. c. The health crisis was an opportunity for growth.

10. (c). Nursing Process: Assessment; Client Need Category: Psychosocial Integrity. Physiologic indicators of stress include decreased peristalsis of the intestines, resulting in possible constipation and flatus. a. Physiologic indicators of stress include increased heart rate. b. Physiologic indicators of stress include increased diaphoresis. d. Physiologic indicators of stress include decreased urinary output.

Chapter 41

1. (c). Nursing Process: Assessment; Client Need Category: Psychosocial Integrity. a. The injury has impacted the nurse's ability to perform her role as a nurse, which will influence her ability to maintain the role. b. There is no evidence that this nurse is at risk for altered sexuality. d. The injury has impacted the nurse's ability to perform her role as a nurse, which will influence her ability to maintain the role.

2. (c). Nursing Process: Evaluation; Client Need Category: Psychosocial Integrity. a. This is the immediate response after a death characterized by shock, numbness, and disbelief. b. This is when grieving individuals begin to adapt to the loss. Individuals may experience anger toward the deceased, anger toward God, and feelings of resentment toward others who still have their loved ones. d. This process begins months after the death and may last a few years. During this time, periods of depression are interspersed with period of well-being. Sadness decreases and aspects of ordinary life are resumed.

3. (d). Nursing Process: Implementation; Client Need Category: Psychosocial Integrity. a. The nurse should use nonverbal gestures of support such as staying with the patient. b. Recognize the patient may at first deny the diagnosis but do not attempt to alter the patient's coping pattern. c. Do not rush the patient through this stage. Provide the patient with time to integrate the information.

4. (c). Nursing Process: Assessment; Client Need Category: Psychosocial Integrity. a. This patient is faced with unresolved grief. b. This patient is faced with unresolved grief. d. This patient is faced with unresolved grief.

5. (b). Nursing Process: Implementation; Client Need Category: Psychosocial Integrity. a. This would be appropriate for the birth of new child. c. This would be appropriate in the diagnosis of a physical illness. d. This would be appropriate in the birth of a new infant.

6. (a). Nursing Process: Assessment; Client Need Category: Psychosocial Integrity. An anticipatory loss is experienced before the loss actually occurs. b. A perceived loss is experienced by one person but cannot be verified by others. c. An actual loss can be identified by others and can arise either in response to or in anticipation of a situation. d. Bereavement is the subjective response experienced by the surviving loved ones after the death of a person with whom they have shared a significant relationship.

7. (a). Nursing Process: Implementation; Client Need Category: Psychosocial Integrity. In order to facilitate the grieving process, the nurse can offer the client appropriate information regarding how to access community resources such as clergy, support groups, and counseling services. b. The client must go through the grieving process. c. Discussing relationships with other men is inappropriate at this time. d. The immediate need is for the client to express her grief regarding the loss of her husband.

8. (c). Nursing Process: Assessment; Client Need Category: Psychosocial Integrity. With open awareness, the client and people around know about the impending death and feel comfortable discussing it, even though it is difficult. This awareness provides the client an opportunity to finalize affairs and even participate in planning funeral arrangements. a. In closed awareness, the client and family are unaware of impending death. b. With mutual pretense, the client, family, and health personnel know that the prognosis is terminal but do not talk about it and make an effort not to raise the subject. d. Conscious awareness is not a type of awareness dealing with death.

9. (b). Nursing Process: Implementation; Client Need Category: Psychosocial Integrity. Children from 5 to 9 years old understand that death is final. a. Children from infancy to 5 years old do not understand the concept of death. c. Children from 9 to 12 years old understand that death is the inevitable end of life. d. Children from infancy to 5 years old believe that death is reversible, a temporary departure, or sleep.

10. (a). Nursing Process: Assessment; Client Need Category: Psychosocial Integrity. In denial, the client refuses to believe that loss is happening. b. With anger, the client may direct anger at the nurse or staff about matters that normally would not bother them. c. With bargaining, the client seeks to bargain to avoid loss. d. With depression, the client grieves over what has happened and what cannot be.

Chapter 42

1. (a). Nursing Process: Assessment; Client Need Category: Physiological Integrity. b. *Pronation* is the term used for turning the palm of the hand downward or backward. c. *Inversion* is the term used for turning the sole of the foot inward. d. *Eversion* is the term used for turning the sole of the foot outward.

2. (b). Nursing Process: Implementation; Client Need Category: Physiological Integrity. a. This type of exercise is isokinetic. c. This is an isometric exercise. d. Flexibility is a separate component of fitness from strength.

3. (a). Nursing Process: Implementation; Client Need Category: Physiological Integrity. b. This statement is true. c. This statement is true. d. This statement is true.

4. (b). Nursing Process: Evaluation; Client Need Category: Physiological Integrity. a. The valsalva maneuver may strain cardiac capacity in debilitated patients and should be avoided. c. Orthostatic hypotension is a precipitous drop in blood pressure associated with standing in clients on bed rest. d. This is a necessary action to promote circulation to pressure areas.

5. (b). Nursing Process: Assessment; Client Need Category: Safe, Effective Care Environment. a. Assessment of the stairs is an extremely important function of the home care nurse when caring for patients with mobility dysfunction. c. This is an essential safety factor in ensuring that the patient will not fall when attempting to ambulate. d. Throw rugs are a danger to patients with impaired mobility.

6. (d). Nursing Process: Assessment; Client Need Category: Physiological Integrity. a. The shoulder can adduct to 45 degrees. b. The wrist can adduct to 45 degrees. c. The thumb can adduct to 45 degrees.

7. (c). Nursing Process: Diagnosis; Client Need Category: Safe, Effective Care Environment. a. Since the patient has been in traction for less than 24 hours, this is not the best nursing diagnosis at this time. b. Since the patient has been in traction for less than 24 hours, this is not the best nursing diagnosis at this time. d. Although pain will be an issue to be addressed in the care plan, this question is asking about nursing care for an immobile client.

8. (a). Nursing Process: Implementation; Client Need Category: Safe, Effective Care Environment. b. This is a correct protective measure and use of body mechanics. c. This is a correct action in the use of proper body mechanics. d. If a nurse is unsure about her/his ability to safely move a patient, requesting assistance is appropriate.

9. (c). Nursing Process: Implementation; Client Need Category: Safe, Effective Care Environment. a. This is an appropriate device for patients who are able to stand and maintain their own weight. b. This device is appropriate for bed-to-bed or bed-to-gurney transfers. d. Convertible chairs are used for positioning, not transferring.

10. (b). Nursing Process: Planning; Client Need Category: Physiological Integrity. The target heart rate is 60% to 85% of the maximum. At least 60% of the maximum heart rate is the recommended intensity. a. This is too low. c. This is too high. d. This is too high.

11. (a). Walking is encouraged for 30 minutes cumulative per day, preferably all days of the week. b. The duration and frequency are not sufficient. c. Walking, biking, and swimming are recommended for beginners and older adults. d. The frequency is not sufficient.

Chapter 43

1. (d). Nursing Process: Assessment; Client Need Category: Physiological Integrity. a. It is not abnormal for a person's pulse rate to drop during sleep. b. It is not abnormal for a person's pulse rate to drop during sleep. c. It is not abnormal for a person's pulse rate to drop during sleep.

2. (a). Nursing Process: Assessment; Client Need Category: Physiological Integrity. b. This stage lasts only a few moments and is characterized by a decrease in temperature and respiratory, pulse, and metabolic rates. c. In this stage, the person becomes more relaxed but continues to be easily awakened. d. This stage of sleep relaxes and physically restores the body.

3. (a). Nursing Process: Assessment; Client Need Category: Psychosocial Integrity. b. Prolonged loss of sleep often leads to nervousness, disorientation, and mood swings. c. Prolonged loss of sleep often leads to nervousness, disorientation, and mood swings. d. Prolonged loss of sleep often leads to nervousness, disorientation, and mood swings.

4. (a). Nursing Process: Planning; Client Need Category: Physiological Integrity. b. A sleep pattern disturbance is a condition in which an individual is at risk for or experiencing changes in sleep patterns that cause discomfort or interfere with lifestyle for a long time. c. A sleep pattern disturbance is a condition in which an individual is at risk for or experiencing changes in sleep patterns that cause discomfort or interfere with lifestyle for a long time. d. A sleep pattern disturbance is a condition in which an individual is at risk for or experiencing changes in sleep patterns that cause discomfort or interfere with lifestyle for a long time.

5. (c). Nursing Process: Assessment; Client Need Category: Physiological Integrity. In stage 3, the muscles are totally relaxed, blood pressure lowers, body temperature lowers, and pulse lowers. a. In stage 1, there is a floating sensation and the individual is relaxed and drowsy. b. In stage 2, the individual is lightly asleep. d. In stage 4, the individual is in the deepest sleep stage, rarely moves, and is difficult to arouse.

6. (a). Nursing Process: Assessment; Client Need Category: Physiological Integrity. Active dreaming is a characteristic of REM sleep. b. Deep, restful sleep is a characteristic of NREM sleep. c. Decreased blood pressure is a characteristic of NREM sleep. d. NREM sleep is also referred to as slow-wave sleep because the brain waves of a sleeper are slower than the alpha and beta waves of a person who is awake or alert.

7. (b). Nursing Process: Assessment; Client Need Category: Physiological Integrity. Narcolepsy is a sudden wave of overwhelming sleepiness that occurs during the day. a. Insomnia is the inability to obtain an adequate amount or quality of sleep. c. Sleep apnea is the periodic cessation of breathing during sleep. d. Parasomnia is behavior that may interfere with sleep, such as sleepwalking.

8. (a). Nursing Process: Assessment; Client Need Category: Physiological Integrity. Nicotine has a stimulating effect on the body, and smokers often have more difficulty falling asleep than nonsmokers. b. Exercising in the morning does not promote difficulty falling asleep at night. c. Many people have rituals before bedtime, such as eating a snack. d. Many people find taking a hot bath or shower before bedtime relaxes them.

9. (a). Nursing Process: Assessment; Client Need Category: Physiological Integrity. The electroencephalogram (EEG) is used to record brain waves. b. The electrooculogram (EOG) is used to record eye movement. c. The electromyogram (EMG) is used to record the chin muscle movement. d. The electrocardiogram (ECG) is used to assess cardiac activity.

10. (c). Nursing Process: Implementation; Client Need Category: Physiological Integrity. Some medication effects can last many hours beyond the time that the client's perception of daytime drowsiness and impaired psychomotor skills have disappeared. Clients need to be cautioned about such effects and about driving or handling machinery while the drug is in their system. a. Medication should be continued as prescribed by the physician. b. Medication should not be repeated. d. Sleep medications vary in their onset and duration of action; however, 4 hours before bedtime is too early to take the medication.

Chapter 44

1. (c). Nursing Process: Evaluation; Client Need Category: Physiological Integrity. Using a pain scale rates the client's intensity of pain. a. Descriptive adjectives, such as "piercing like a knife," help people communicate the quality of pain. b. Duration is determined by asking clients how long they have had their pain. d. Onset is determined by asking the client when the pain started.

2. (b). Nursing Process: Assessment; Client Need Category: Physiological Integrity. Even after minor surgery, clients can experience intense pain. a. This statement is true. c. This statement is true. d. This statement is true.

3. (b). Nursing Process: Assessment; Client Need Category: Physiological Integrity. Acute pain results in sympathetic nervous system responses, including diaphoresis. Chronic pain results in parasympathetic nervous system responses, such as dry, warm skin. a. Increased pulse rate is a response to acute pain. c. Dilated pupils are a response to acute pain. d. Increased respiratory rate is a response to acute pain.

4. (c). Nursing Process: Assessment; Client Need Category: Physiological Integrity. Intractable pain is pain that is highly resistant to relief. a. Referred pain is pain felt in a part of the body that is considerably removed from the tissues causing pain. b. Neuropathic pain is the result of a disturbance of the peripheral or central nervous system that results in pain that may or may not be associated with an ongoing tissue-damaging process. d. Phantom pain is a painful sensation perceived in a body part that is missing.

5. (a). Nursing Process: Assessment; Client Need Category: Physiological Integrity. An individual's pain threshold is the amount of pain stimulation a person requires in order to feel pain. b. Pain reaction includes the autonomic nervous system and behavioral responses to pain. c. Pain tolerance is the maximum amount and duration of pain that an individual is willing to endure. d. Intractable pain is pain that is highly resistant to relief.

6. (d). Nursing Process: Assessment; Client Need Category: Physiological Integrity. Butophanol tartrate (Stadol) is a mixed agonist–antagonist analgesic drug that has a ceiling dose level. a. Meperidine (Demerol) is a full agonist analgesic. b. Propoxyphene (Darvon) is a full agonist analgesic. c. Morphine is a full agonist analgesic.

7. (d). Nursing Process: Evaluation; Client Need Category: Physiological Integrity. Pruritus is a common opioid side effect. Cool packs, lotion, and diversional activity are recommended. Diphenhydramine hydrochloride (Benadryl) may also be administered. A tolerance develops to pruritus; therefore, discontinuing the drug is not necessary. a. This is an appropriate preventive measure. b. This is an appropriate preventive measure. c. This is an appropriate preventive measure.

8. (b). Nursing Process: Implementation; Client Need Category: Safe, Effective Care Environment. Alcohol is contraindicated in any care of the catheter or insertion site as it can be neurotoxic. a. To avoid injection of substances intended for IV administration into the epidural catheter, apply tape over all injection ports. c. Narcan is administered for respiratory depression. d. The nurse gently aspirates prior to bolus medication administration of medication to determine that the catheter has not migrated into the subarachnoid space.

9. (c). Nursing Process: Implementation; Client Need Category: Physiological Integrity. The client's signs and symptoms indicate a need for the opioid dose to be decreased. a. This is not correct. b. The data do not suggest the need for naloxone (Narcan). d. Though assessing the client's level of pain is important, the immediate priority is to have the medication dosage reduced.

10. (d). Transcutaneous electrical nerve stimulation is a method of applying low-voltage electrical stimulation directly over identified pain areas, at an acupressure point, along peripheral nerve areas that innervate the pain area, or along the spinal column. a. This is a type of cutaneous stimulation. b. This is a type of cutaneous stimulation. c. This is a type of cutaneous stimulation.

Chapter 45

1. (a). Nursing Process: Evaluation; Client Need Category: Health Promotion and Maintenance. b. Actions of folic acid include the general metabolism of nutrients, especially amino acids, maturation of red blood cells, and prevention of certain birth defects and heart disease. Pantothenic acid helps synthesize cholesterol. c. Actions of folic acid include the general metabolism of nutrients, especially amino acids, maturation of red blood cells, and prevention of certain birth defects and heart disease. Riboflavin helps in the formation of red blood cells. d. Actions of folic acid include the general metabolism of nutrients, especially amino acids, maturation of red blood cells, and prevention of certain birth defects and heart disease. Vitamin K is essential for normal blood clotting.

2. (d). Nursing Process: Evaluation; Client Need Category: Health Promotion and Maintenance. a. Dietary protein intake is essential for the body to receive the essential amino acids. b. There is no evidence to support this patient needs supplemental insulin. c. In anabolism, body substances are synthesized. This patient is malnourished and, therefore, is in a state of catabolism.

3. (b). Nursing Process: Evaluation; Client Need Category: Health Promotion and Maintenance. a. Cachexia develops from a gradual but prolonged period of having insufficient food. The result is a syndrome of emaciation, tissue wasting, severe underweight, and occasional diarrhea. c. This is when a person who is cachectic experiences an acute stress. d. There is no such disorder identified in the text.

4. (c). Nursing Process: Assessment; Client Need Category: Health Promotion and Maintenance. a. This is an indication of good nutritional status as seen upon examination of the patient's nails. b. This is an indication of good nutritional status as seen upon examination of the patient's abdomen. d. This is an indication of good nutritional status as seen upon examination of the patient's tongue.

5. (a). Nursing Process: Planning; Client Need Category: Physiological Integrity. b. A patient receiving tube feedings is not usually at risk for receiving more nutrition than the body requires. c. This nursing diagnosis would be addressed by the enteral (tube) feeding and would not address a possible side effect of the feeding method. d. There is no evidence to support this patient has a dysfunctional relationship with food.

6. (d). Nursing Process: Implementation; Client Need Category: Physiologic Integrity. a. Reusing equipment for more than 24 hours increases the risk of contamination and related complications. The nurse should discard this bag and use a new one. b. Reusing equipment for more than 24 hours increases the risk of contamination and related complications. The nurse should discard this bag and use a new one. c. There is no reason to attach a 50 ml syringe to the bag. Reusing equipment for more than 24 hours increases the risk of contamination and related complications. The nurse should discard this bag and use a new one.

7. (b). Nursing Process: Planning; Client Need Category: Physiological Integrity. The lacto-ovo-vegetarian uses vegetables, dairy products, and eggs but avoids eating flesh. a. The vegan is a strict vegetarian and avoids all food of animal origin. c. The lacto-vegetarian uses vegetables and dairy products but avoids eating flesh and eggs. d. The ovo-vegetarian uses eggs but avoids dairy products and flesh.

8. (c). Nursing Process: Implementation; Client Need Category: Physiological Integrity. The number of servings daily from the bread, cereal, rice, and pasta group is 6 to 11 servings. a. This is incorrect. b. This is incorrect. d. This is incorrect.

9. (c). Nursing Process: Implementation; Client Need Category: Physiological Integrity. A recommendation of 4 to 6 servings of complementary protein should be made to the vegetarian. Proteins include eggs, peanut butter, peas, beans, nuts, and cheese. a. A recommendation of 4 to 6 servings of complementary protein should be made to the vegetarian. Proteins include eggs, peanut butter, peas, beans, nuts, and cheese. b. A recommendation of 4 to 6 servings of complementary protein should be recommended to the vegetarian. Proteins include eggs, peanut butter, peas, beans, nuts, and cheese. d. A recommendation of 4 to 6 servings of complementary protein should be made to the vegetarian. Proteins include eggs, peanut butter, peas, beans, nuts, and cheese.

10. (d). Nursing Process: Assessment; Client Need Category: Physiological Integrity. Albumin accounts for over 50% of the total serum proteins. A low serum albumin level is a useful indicator of prolonged protein depletion. a. A low hemoglobin may be evidence of iron deficiency anemia. b. Certain nutrient deficiencies and forms of protein-calorie malnutrition can depress the immune system. c. Creatinine reflects a person's total muscle mass.

Chapter 46

1. (d). Nursing Process: Assessment; Client Need Category: Physiological Integrity. Iron may lead to diarrhea because of irritation of the intestinal mucosa. a. Insufficient fluid intake may lead to constipation. b. A change in daily routine may lead to constipation. c. Insufficient activity or immobility may lead to constipation.

2. (b). Nursing Process: Evaluation; Client Need Category: Physiological Integrity. A gastrostomy is an opening through the abdominal wall into the stomach. a. A jejunostomy is an opening through the abdominal wall into the jejunum. c. A ureterostomy is an opening into the ureter. d. An ileostomy is an opening into the ileum.

3. (d). Nursing Process: Implementation; Client Need Category: Physiological Integrity. Stools from a sigmoidostomy are of normal or formed consistency, and the frequency of the discharge can be regulated. a. An ileostomy produces liquid fecal drainage. The drainage is constant and cannot be regulated. b. A transverse colostomy produces a malodorous, mushy drainage because some of the liquid has been reabsorbed. There is usually no control. c. Liquid fecal drainage cannot be regulated.

4. (d). Nursing Process: Analysis; Client Need Category: Physiological Integrity. Prolonged diarrhea can lead to profound fluid and electrolyte disturbances. This is the priority. a. Skin integrity is an important diagnosis; however, fluid volume is the priority. b. Knowledge deficit is an important diagnosis; however, fluid volume is the priority. c. Anxiety is an important diagnosis; however, fluid volume is the priority.

5. (b). Nursing Process: Implementation; Client Need Category: Physiological Integrity. Hypotonic solutions such as tap water may lead to fluid and electrolyte imbalance and water intoxication. a. Hypertonic solutions may lead to sodium retention. c. Isotonic solutions may possibly lead to sodium retention. d. Soapsuds enemas irritate the mucosa.

6. (c). Nursing Process: Evaluation; Client Need Category: Physiological Integrity. Because the anal canal is about 1 to 2 inches long in the adult, insertion of the tube 3 to 4 inches places the tip of the tube beyond the anal sphincter into the rectum. a. This is appropriate for the infant. b. This is appropriate for the child. d. This is too far.

7. (a). Nursing Process: Implementation; Client Need Category: Physiological Integrity. Slight bleeding initially when the stoma is touched is normal, but other bleeding should be reported. b. The data do not suggest infection. c. The data do not suggest impaired circulation. d. The data do not suggest impaired clotting factors.

8. (d). Nursing Process: Evaluation; Client Need Category: Physiological Integrity. The site should be cleansed with warm water, and a mild soap may be used. Alcohol is avoided since it may cause skin irritation and burning. a. This is appropriate. b. This is appropriate. c. This is appropriate.

9. (c). Nursing Process: Assessment; Client Need Category: Physiological Integrity. Consuming red Jell-O is not a contributing factor to a false positive guaiac test. a. False positives can occur if the client has recently ingested red meat. b. False positives can occur if the client has recently ingested turnips. d. False positives can occur if the client has recently ingested melons.

10. (d). Nursing Process: Evaluation; Client Need Category: Physiological Integrity. A colonoscopy provides a view of the large intestine. a. An anoscopy provides a view of the anal canal. b. A proctoscopy provides a view of the rectum. c. A proctosigmoidoscopy provides a view of the rectum and sigmoid colon.

Chapter 47

1. (b). Nursing Process: Assessment; Client Need Category: Physiological Integrity. a. An adult normally voids between 1,200 and 1,500 mL of urine a day. c. An adult normally voids between 1,200 and 1,500 mL of urine a day. d. An adult normally voids between 1,200 and 1,500 mL of urine a day.

2. (c). Nursing Process: Diagnosis; Client Need Category: Physiological Integrity. a. Functional incontinence is the involuntary, unpredictable loss of urine. b. Stress incontinence is defined as the loss of urine of less than 50 mL that occurs when there is sudden increase in intra-abdominal pressure. d. Overflow incontinence is a chronic retention, also known as "paradoxical incontinence"; patients are unable to void until the intra-abdominal pressure increases to such a degree that urine is involuntarily voided.

3. (b). Nursing Process: Implementation; Client Need Category: Safe, Effective Care Environment. a. Sterile technique is vital to prevent contamination with microorganisms. c. The irrigant is considered intake as it may be absorbed once it enters the bladder. d. A syringe is used for the procedure, and gentle but firm pressure is necessary to achieve irrigation.

4. (c). Nursing Process: Implementation; Client Need Category: Safe, Effective Care Environment. a. This teaching point is correct. b. An IV may be necessary to administer medications and fluids. d. This is the appropriate length of time, although if tissue removal is anticipated, the procedure could take longer.

5. (b). Nursing Process: Assessment; Client Need Category: Physiological Integrity. The nephrons are the functional units of the kidneys that filter the blood and remove metabolic wastes. a. Bowman's capsule surrounds the glomerulus of the nephron. c. The trigone is a triangular area marked by the ureter openings at the posterior corners and the opening of the urethra at the anterior inferior corner. d. The ureters connect the kidney to the bladder.

6. (b). Nursing Process: Assessment; Client Need Category: Physiological Integrity. Nocturnal enuresis, or bed-wetting, is the involuntary passing of urine during sleep. a. Nocturia, or nocturnal frequency, is frequent urination during the night. c. Diurnal enuresis is the involuntary passing of urine that occurs during the day. d. Urinary frequency is voiding at frequent intervals—that is, more often than usual.

7. (c). Nursing Process: Assessment; Client Need Category: Physiological Integrity. Oliguria is low urine output, usually less than 500 mL a day or 30 mL an hour. a. Anuria refers to a lack of urine production, with no effective urinary output. b. Polyuria refers to the production of abnormally large amounts of urine by the kidneys. d. Dysuria means voiding that is either painful or difficult.

8. (b). Nursing Process: Assessment; Client Need Category: Physiological Integrity. Dark amber urine, or concentrated urine, is indicative of decreased fluid intake. a. Coffee does not affect urine color. c. Increased protein intake is not reflected in the urine color. d. Infection is indicated by cloudy urine, malodorous urine, or blood present in the urine.

9. (a). Nursing Process: Analysis; Client Need Category: Physiological Integrity. Stress incontinence is the state in which one experiences a loss of urine of less than 50 mL occuring with increased abdominal pressure such as sneezing, coughing, laughing, or lifting. b. Functional incontinence is a state in which one experiences an involuntary, unpredictable passage of urine. c. Urge incontinence is the state in which an individual experiences involuntary passage of urine occuring soon after a strong sense of urgency to void. d. Total incontinence is the state in which one experiences a continuous and unpredictable loss of urine.

10. (b). Nursing Process: Evaluation; Client Need Category: Physiological Integrity. The client should practice frequent voiding every 2 to 4 hours to flush bacteria out of the urethra and prevent organisms from ascending into the bladder. a. Avoiding bubble baths, harsh soap, and powder in the perineal area is recommended to prevent urinary tract infections. c. The client is encouraged to drink eight 8-ounce glasses of water each day to flush bacteria out of the urinary system. d. The client is encouraged to wear cotton rather than nylon underwear to avoid accumulation of perineal moisture.

Chapter 48

1. (c). Nursing Process: Assessment; Client Need Category: Physiological Integrity. a. Pack years are calculated by multiplying how many years a person has smoked by how many packs per day. $1.5 \times 32 = 48.2$. b. Pack years are calculated by multiplying how many years a person has smoked by how many packs per day. $1.5 \times 32 = 48.4$. d. Pack years are calculated by multiplying how many years a person has smoked by how many packs per day. $1.5 \times 32 = 48$.

2. (b). Nursing Process: Intervention; Client Need Category: Safe and Effective Care Environment. a. Cleansing the mouth reduces possible contamination by oral flora and is indicated prior to sputum collection. c. Bronchial secretions accumulate during sleep and are easier to expectorate first thing in the morning. d. This action is necessary to assess the consequences of active coughing and ensure that the patient is not in respiratory distress.

3. (a). Nursing Process: Assessment; Client Need Category: Physiological Integrity. b. Bradypnea is characterized as abnormally slow breathing. c. Apnea is defined as the cessation of breathing. d. Orthopnea is a respiratory alteration in which a patient must sit or stand in order to breath comfortably.

4. (d). Nursing Process: Intervention; Client Need Category: Physiological Integrity. a. This describes the function of hemoglobin. b. This is a red blood cell count. c. This is a test of arterial blood gases.

5. (d). Nursing Process: Diagnosis; Client Need Category: Physiological Integrity. a. Altered tissue perfusion implies interruption in arterial flow or exchange problems. b. The source of this nursing diagnosis is neuromuscular; the patient's age is not a causative factor in his symptomology. c. Difficulty breathing is not an official NANDA diagnosis.

6. (c). Nursing Process: Implementation; Client Need Category: Physiological Integrity. a. This is a technique to provide a means of controlling respiration, to increase tidal volume, and to prevent air trapping by maintaining patency of the small airways. b. Pain relief is essential to ensure that the patient will ventilate fully and attempt to cough. d. Splinting the incision with a pillow or another device will decrease pain and decrease the overall incision injury during coughing.

7. (b). Nursing Process: Assessment; Client Need Category: Physiological Integrity. A chemosensitive center in the medulla oblongata is highly responsive to increases in blood CO_2, or hydrogen ion concentration, making CO_2 the primary regulator of ventilation. a. This is incorrect. c. This is incorrect. d. This is incorrect.

8. (c). Nursing Process: Planning; Client Need Category: Physiological Integrity. Acute stress increases the oxygen needs of the body tissues. a. This is incorrect. b. This is incorrect since metabolism increases. d. This is incorrect.

9. (a). Nursing Process: Implementation; Client Need Category: Physiological Integrity. Hypoventilation is inadequate alveolar ventilation. Hypoventilation may result from airway obstruction or the side effects of some drugs, such as those used for anesthesia. b. Hyperventilation is an increased movement of air into and out of the lungs. c. Airway obstruction results from a foreign object or secretions blocking the upper airway. d. Orthopnea is the inability to breathe except in an upright or standing position.

10. (c). Nursing Process: Implementation; Client Need Category: Physiological Integrity. Low-flow oxygen systems are essential for clients with chronic obstructive pulmonary disease (COPD). People with COPD may have a chronically high carbon dioxide level, and their stimulus to breathe is hypoxemia. High flows of oxygen can potentially relieve this hypoxemia, removing the stimulus to breathe. a. This is too much oxygen. b. This is inappropriate instructions. d. This is too much oxygen.

11. (a). Nursing Process: Implementation; Client Need Category: Physiological Integrity. Cheyne-Stokes respirations are marked rhythmic waxing and waning of respirations from very deep to very shallow breathing and temporary apnea. b. Kussmaul breathing is a type of hyperventilation by which the body attempts to compensate metabolic acidosis by blowing off the carbon dioxide through deep and rapid breathing. c. Eupnea is normal, quiet, rhythmic, and effortless respirations. d. Apnea is the cessation of breathing.

Chapter 49

1. (b). Nursing Process: Implementation; Client Need Category: Physiological Integrity. Signs of anemia may include chronic fatigue, shortness of breath, pallor, and hypotension. a. Sickle cell crisis is a result of vascular occlusion and the data do not suggest this. c. The data do not suggest pulmonary embolism. d. The data do not suggest hemorrhage.

2. (b). Nursing Process: Planning; Client Need Category: Physiological Integrity. Care should be taken to avoid elevating legs in clients with cardiac dysfunction as it will increase preload and may stress the dysfunctional heart. a. Avoiding pillows under the knees is appropriate to improve blood flow to the lower extremities. c. Leg exercises in bed are appropriate to prevent venous stasis. d. Frequent position changes in bed are appropriate to avoid venous stasis and pressure areas.

3. (a). Nursing Process: Implementation; Client Need Category: Physiological Integrity. Digitalis is a positive inotropic drug used to increase the contractile strength of the heart. b. Digoxin does not have vasodilation effects. c. Beta-blocking agents block the sympathetic nervous system action on the heart. d. Beta-blocking agents decrease oxygen consumption.

4. (c). Nursing Process: Implementation; Client Need Category: Safe, Effective Care Environment. The length of both legs from the heel to the gluteal fold and the circumference of each calf and each thigh at the widest point are measured to determine the appropriate size for thigh-high stockings. a. This does not include all of the measurements. b. This does not include all of the measurements. d. This is not correct.

5. (a). Nursing Process: Evaluation; Client Need Category: Physiological Integrity. The epicardium is the heart's outermost layer. b. The double layer of fibroserous membrane that encloses the heart is the pericardium. c. The endocardium lines the inside of the heart's chambers and great vessels. d. The myocardium comprises the cardiac muscle cells that form the bulk of the heart and contract with each beat.

6. (a). Nursing Process: Evaluation; Client Need Category: Health Promotion and Maintenance. The ventricles are separated from the great vessels (the pulmonary arteries and aorta) by the semilunar valves (named for their crescent moon shape), the pulmonic valve on the right, and the aortic valve on the left. b. The tricuspid valve and mitral valve are the atrioventricular valves when separating the atria and ventricles. c. This is incorrect. d. This is incorrect.

7. (d). Nursing Process: Evaluation; Client Need Category: Health Promotion and Maintenance. Systole is when the heart ejects (propels) the blood into the pulmonary and systemic circulations. a. Diastole is when the ventricles fill with blood. b. At the end of the diastolic phase the atria contract, adding an additional volume to the ventricles. This volume is sometimes called "atrial kick". c. The sinoatrial (SA) node is the primary pacemaker of the heart.

8. (a). Cardiac output is the amount of blood pumped by the ventricles in 1 minute and is calculated by multiplying the stroke volume (amount of blood ejected with each contraction) times the heart rate (SV × HR = CO). b. Stroke volume is the amount of blood ejected with each contraction. c. Preload is the degree to which muscle fibers in the ventricle are stretched at the end of the relaxation period. d. Afterload is the resistance against which the heart must pump to eject the blood into the circulation.

9. (a). Nursing Process: Planning; Client Need Category: Physiological Integrity. Peripheral vascular resistance (PVR) impedes or opposes blood flow to the tissues. PVR is determined by the viscosity, or thickness, of the blood, blood vessel length, and blood vessel diameter. Mean arterial pressure is the pressure that maintains blood flow to the tissues throughout the cardiac cycle. b. PVR is determined by the viscosity, or thickness, of the blood, blood vessel length, and blood vessel diameter. c. PVR is determined by the viscosity, or thickness, of the blood, blood vessel length, and blood vessel diameter. d. PVR is determined by the viscosity, or thickness, of the blood; blood vessel length; and blood vessel diameter.

10. (a). Nursing Process: Assessment; Client Need Category: Physiological Integrity. Sodium does not affect oxygen binding. Oxygen binding is affected by several factors, including the PO_2, temperature, pH, and PCO_2. b. Up to a certain point (about 70 mm Hg), the higher the PO_2, the greater the affinity of hemoglobin for oxygen and the more saturated the hemoglobin molecules. The relationship to temperature, pH, and PCO2 are the opposite: at higher temperatures, greater hydrogen ion concentrations (lower pH), and higher PCO2 levels, the affinity for oxygen decreases, and hemoglobin releases its oxygen molecules. c. See rationale for answer b. d. See rationale for answer b.

Chapter 50

1. (a). Nursing Process: Assessment; Client Need Category: Physiological Integrity. b. Hyperventilation results in excess excretion of CO_2 (respiratory alkalosis). c. Hyperventilation results in excess excretion of CO_2 (respiratory alkalosis). d. Hyperventilation results in excess excretion of CO_2 (respiratory alkalosis).

2. (a). Nursing Process: Assessment; Client Need Category: Physiological Integrity. b. Third spacing is a form of edema that results from a fluid shift from plasma to the interstitium, where it becomes trapped and nonfunctional, causing fluid volume deficit. c. Third spacing is a form of edema that results from a fluid shift from plasma to the interstitium, where it becomes trapped and nonfunctional, causing fluid volume deficit. d. Third spacing is a form of edema that results from a fluid shift from plasma to the interstitium, where it becomes trapped and nonfunctional, causing fluid volume deficit.

3. (a). Nursing Process: Planning; Client Need Category: Physiological Integrity. The average adult needs about 2,500 mL of oral fluid intake per day. b. This is an insufficient amount. c. This is an insufficient amount. d. This is an insufficient amount.

4. (b). Nursing Process: Assessment; Client Need Category: Physiological Integrity. Fever and exercise increase metabolic activity and heat production, thereby increasing fluid losses through the skin. a. Secretions are measurable and are not considered insensible fluid loss. c. Loss of appetite and decreased fluid intake may lead to dehydration. d. IV intake is measurable and does not increase insensible fluid loss.

5. (b). Nursing Process: Assessment; Client Need Category: Physiological Integrity. Clinical manifestations of hypocalcemia include muscle cramps, tetany, cardiac dysrhythmias, and positive Trousseau's and Chvostek's signs. a. Clinical manifestations of hyperkalemia do not include tetany. c. Clinical manifestations of hypermagnesemia do not include muscle cramps. d. Clinical manifestations of hypernatremia do not include muscle cramps or tetany.

6. (a). Nursing Process: Assessment; Client Need Category: Physiological Integrity. Gastrointestinal fluid loss such as nasogastric suction leads to loss of sodium. b. Nasogastric suction can lead to hypokalemia. c. Nasogastric suction can lead to hypomagnesemia. d. Nasogastric suction can lead to metabolic alkalosis.

7. (a). Nursing Process: Assessment; Client Need Category: Physiological Integrity. When respiratory acidosis occurs, the kidneys retain bicarbonate to restore the normal carbonic acid to bicarbonate ratio. However, the kidneys are relatively slow to respond to changes in acid-base balance, so this compensatory response may require hours to days to restore the normal pH. b. This is incorrect. c. This is incorrect. d. This is incorrect.

8. (c). Nursing Process: Assessment; Client Need Category: Physiological Integrity. The client with diabetic ketoacidosis experiences metabolic acidosis. Metabolic acidosis stimulates the respiratory center, and the rate and depth of respirations increase. Carbon dioxide is eliminated and carbonic acid levels fall, minimizing the change in pH. a. This is incorrect. b. This is incorrect. d. This is incorrect.

9. (d). Nursing Process: Assessment; Client Need Category: Physiological Integrity. A decreased urine osmolality reflects a fluid volume excess. a. Urine pH increases with metabolic alkalosis. b. Hematocrit increases with severe dehydration. c. Specific gravity is abnormally low in very dilute urine with few solutes, such as with fluid excess.

10. (a). Nursing Process: Implementation; Client Need Category: Physiological Integrity. Redness, tenderness, and warmth at the IV insertion site indicate phlebitis and that the IV should be discontinued immediately. A warm compress may then be applied. b. The warm compress is applied after removing the IV. c. This is inappropriate since the IV should be discontinued immediately. d. This is inappropriate since the IV should be discontinued immediately.